Botany:

A Functional Approach

Botany:

A Functional Approach

WALTER H. MULLER

Associate Professor of Botany
University of California, Santa Barbara

Selected Illustrations by
ISABELLE HALLER

THE MACMILLAN COMPANY, NEW YORK

COLLIER-MACMILLAN LIMITED, LONDON

Fourth Printing, 1967

Library of Congress catalog card number: 63-14864

The Macmillan Company, New York
Collier-Macmillan Canada, Ltd., Toronto, Ontario

Printed in the United States of America

Dedication

To the instructors who stimulated me, the colleagues who encouraged me, and the students who challenged me.

Preface

THIS textbook is intended for use in a one-semester general botany course on the college level. For many years I have been convinced of the need for such a text because of the greater and greater separation of introductory one-year botany courses into two distinct parts: (1) a more functional and general approach during one semester, and (2) a survey of the plant kingdom during the other semester. Several recent texts have dealt exclusively with the latter type of course. I have tried to produce a book which covers the basic principles necessary for an understanding of plant structure and function and indicates how and why plants are so extremely important to humans and other animals.

Since I feel that a course in botany lends itself more readily to the teaching of biological concepts of general educational value than do other biology courses, and since I hope and expect the text to be used in general botany courses taken by both science and non-science students (as in my own course), this book is a departure from the classical general botany text in describing in more detail such items as conservation, dust bowls, plant distributions, food chains, plant and animal diseases, and energy transformations, and relating them to the growth of populations and their food problems. The non-science student is made aware of the worldwide problem of increasing populations and its significance, and the science student also receives a sound technical basis for further training in plant sciences. The population problem is more important, and less acknowledged, than the atomic warfare problem, and it can more readily be discussed clearly and logically in a botany course, where emphasis can be placed upon the function of plants as the basis of all life—the suppliers of food and oxygen.

Throughout the text, the student is exposed to basic facts and their applications to plant and thus animal life, but the emphasis is upon an understanding rather than a memorizing of such material. Certain information must be memorized, of course, just as one memorizes the multiplication table, but then one applies such basic information to the solving of new and different problems; one does not attempt to memorize multiplication problems. The questions at the end of most chapters include the "recall" type and, more important, the "problem type." The student should be encouraged to solve the latter type especially. The former usually can be answered by judicious use of the index but are necessary to emphasize more strongly certain principles discussed in the respective chapters. Tracing atoms through different cells and tissues as they participate in various processes is one of the best ways of correlating the many plant activities and structures which must of necessity be considered separately. Several such questions have been inserted in certain chapters. In other questions, also, more than one phase of botany is covered. For example, genetics problems involving compensation points require that the student be familiar with genetics, respiration, and photosynthesis.

The angiosperm (flowering plant) is used as the type plant in most discussions concerning photosynthesis, respiration, translocation, transpiration, genetics, and the like, just as one might use the human for major emphasis in a general zoology or biology text. The plant kingdom section of the book is purposely fairly brief. The main groups are included, and individuals have been carefully selected so that relationships and evolutionary advances can be clearly indicated. However, enough material has been presented so that this text could serve as the basis for a more thorough study of the plant kingdom than is usual in a one-semester botany course. The emphasis has been placed on those features which enable plants to exploit diverse environments, those which tend to indicate possible relationships, and those which are considered to be evolutionary advances. No attempt has been made to survey the plant kingdom completely. Discussions of plant and animal diseases, decay, and economic uses of fungi (for example, antibiotics, cheese, and so forth) are blended with the discussions of the position of such plants with relation to others, since I feel that a student would be more interested in such matters after first discovering what the organisms themselves are like.

Modern, up-to-date information has been included with regard to photosynthesis, growth regulators, flowering, chromosome duplication, gene function, and cell structure. Certain of these have been treated in somewhat more detail than is usually found in a general botany text, but the great advances in research in these fields in recent years have made this necessary. The student should be aware that living organisms and their cells are complex with regard to both structure and function. A disservice is done to the student if material is so watered down as to imply a simplicity which does not really exist. Some of these topics are still in such a state of flux that future data may likely cause revisions and modifications of our present concepts. I would like to emphasize, however, that the material on metabolism in general has been simplified in order not to impose too great a technical burden upon the students who select botany as their first science course; these make up by far the greater number in most general botany courses. Some students and instructors will feel that the text is too over-simplified, while others will claim (or complain!) that too much detail and technical discussion is included. This is the nature of human individualism, and I, as author, must assume full responsibility for all arbitrary decisions of omission or commission. I hope that I will have more frequently included too much rather than too little. An instructor can always select certain pages of a text for assignments and omit others. The book would be extremely detrimental to teaching if the better students were not stimulated to additional reading and further investigation of the literature; the teacher can set no higher goal than that of stimulating a student to greater efforts.

Basic structure is presented first, so that the functioning of various cells and tissues can be understood more readily. In all cases an attempt has been made to indicate the correlation between structure and function. But the functional approach to plant distributions is emphasized—compensation points, transpiration rates, rainfall, soil types, temperature, and light intensity are all involved. The importance of food chains and population problems is covered.

Genetics is handled in considerable detail because of the tremendous importance of inheritance to an understanding of evolution and of plant and animal breeding.

Brief summaries are presented at the end of each chapter to capture salient points but not to repeat the content of that chapter. The student should not attempt to utilize these summaries as substitutes for the actual text. They should be used as "recall phrases" which bring to mind material covered in the text—a prod to remembering.

I am indebted to Isabelle Haller (wife of one of my colleagues) for creating most of the excellent pictorial illustrations. A deliberate attempt has been made to project a three-dimensional aspect to as many of the drawings as feasible. Too frequently the concept of depth is lost in diagrams and in examining prepared slides. It is hoped that the drawings in this text will assist in emphasizing the idea that all cells and tissues have depth. Extensive use has also been made of longitudinal sections for this reason. Extraneous detail has been omitted whenever possible; for example, many tissues and regions are shown in outline rather than as composed of numerous cells. Individual cells are, of course, shown when each is discussed.

I would also like to express appreciation to Jeanne Meyers, who typed a portion of the manuscript and who proofread with me through many weary hours. And I am particularly indebted to my wife, Veronica C. Muller, for typing and retyping the manuscript, for proofreading, and for continually putting up with the many difficulties I created during the writing of this text.

I wish to thank my many friends, colleagues, and students who have, knowingly and unknowingly, stimulated me toward writing this text. I wish to thank in particular Dr. Katherine Muller (no relative, unfortunately), Dr. William Purves, and Dr. James Sandoval, who read, criticized, discussed, and suggested changes in various portions of the manuscript. Many thanks to Dr. C. H. Muller (also no relative), who interested me in new perspectives in botany; to Dr. M. F. Moseley, whose morphology course was the template for the plant kingdom portions of the text; and to the late Dr. D. G. Clark for encouraging me to enter the teaching profession.

WALTER H. MULLER

Goleta, California

Table of Contents

Life and
Plants

1.1 Why study plants?

Those parts of the earth in which are found the greatest numbers
and kinds of animals, including humans, are also those areas in which
plants are most easily cultivated. In fact, the presence of plants makes
possible the very existence of animals, and the earth should really be
thought of as an area suitable for plant life and therefore for animal
life. Since animals are surrounded by and dependent upon plants, the
factors which influence plant processes, plant structure, and plant distribution affect the animal world as well. Even though a plant scientist
may be concerned with one of these facets of plant growth for itself
alone, all humans are concerned directly or indirectly with similar
problems. The beauty of a flower garden, the value of a vegetable
patch, the simplicity of a green lawn—all are possible only as a result
of investigations by many individuals and by their interest in plant
growth and development.

Man's entire existence is closely correlated with plant growth and
his increasing understanding of such growth. The development of
modern agricultural practices, storage facilities, and rapid means of
transportation has allowed man to build and live in towns and cities.
But this is a recent change: early man lived only where he could hunt
and gather plants. Farming, as such, did not exist; nor did domestic
animals. The growing of plants specifically as a food supply became
only gradually a part of man's life and has been practiced for possibly
8,000 or 10,000 years. This development, and the use of tools, led to
a more stable existence and the beginnings of village life. Knowledge

at this stage was a hit-or-miss affair, with no investigations to solve specific problems. Certain plants had food value and could grow in certain areas, but why? The tremendous advances of civilization resulted when the question of *"why"* became important and people attempted to find the answer.

Thousands of years passed before man came to realize that all life on this earth is dependent upon green plants. The food we eat, the shelter, the clothing, and the very air we breathe—all come to us through these organisms. We eat cattle that eat grass; fish that eat seaweed; or corn, wheat, beans, etc. The basic food for all organisms is produced by green plants. In this process of food manufacture, oxygen gas is liberated. This oxygen, which we obtain from air as we breathe, is essential to life. The only source of food and oxygen are plants; no animal alone can supply these.

Shelter, in the form of wood for houses, and clothing, in the form of cotton fibers, are obvious examples of uses of plant materials. But we must not forget coal, furniture, paper products, medicinals (including the famous antibiotics), chemicals and dyes of various sorts, etc. The materials obtainable from plants and their products are almost infinite in number. Probably nothing that we use has not involved plants either directly or indirectly. (Note: Even the manufacture of steel and plastics requires heat.)

To these tangible beneficial aspects of the plant world must also be added the importance of beauty and the relaxation derived therefrom. Gardening is probably the fascinating hobby of more people than all other hobbies combined; almost everyone has tried to grow something at one time or another. The enjoyment and relaxation obtained from watching a plant develop from a seed or a cutting is one way of putting aside the worries and cares that appear to be so burdensome at times. Gardening is also a big business and an important part of our economy.

Living things surround us on all sides; yet "life" is the most amazing and interesting and unknown factor in our very existence. The study of any living organism is certain to increase our understanding of the world around us and to make our days more interesting and enjoyable.

1.2 What is botany?

A dictionary might merely indicate that botany is the science of plant life and thus add two more unknown words (i.e., science and life) to the definition. **Botany** is the study, or investigation, of plant structure, function, and classification, just as **Zoology** is a similar study of animals. Within this study are many specialties which have developed as knowledge concerning plants has increased.

MORPHOLOGY

This is the study of plant form, structure, and development. If this concerns the external appearance and life histories, the investigator is termed a **morphologist.** If the emphasis is upon internal structural development, this study is called **anatomy;** whereas **cytology** concerns itself with the smallest units of structure, the cells. The concept of evolution is dependent upon such morphological investigations.

PHYSIOLOGY

This term refers to the study of processes that take place within a plant. A **physiologist** is interested in the source of materials that plants use, the influence of the environment upon plant processes, the products of plant activities, and the sequence of events that result in the growth and development of plants.

TAXONOMY

This refers to the identification and classification of plants. The **taxonomist** uses reproductive parts (e.g., flowers and cones) as far as possible in his work, since these are more stable and less influenced by environmental conditions than are the vegetative structures. Each plant is designated by a scientific name that is used throughout the world in accordance with a series of internationally accepted rules. In classifying plants every attempt is made to indicate relationships among the various groups.

GENETICS

This is the study of inheritance and variation. The **geneticist** is interested in how characteristics are transmitted from parents to **progeny** (offspring) and the mechanisms which control such a process. Plant breeding is dependent upon the information obtained from such studies.

Various other subdivisions of botany can be listed which include aspects of more than one of the above or which are even more specialized than has been indicated. **Phycology** is the study of **algae** (singular, **alga**), extremely simple forms of green plants. **Mycology** is the study of simple non-green plants, the **fungi** (singular, **fungus**). **Bacteriology** deals with the bacteria. **Plant pathology** is concerned with plant diseases and their control. **Plant ecology** involves a study of plant

3

communities and the influences of environment upon such communities or upon individual plants. These are just a few of the many specialized disciplines in botany.

As more and more knowledge accumulates, a greater tendency toward specialization is inevitable. However, the introduction to any field of study begins on the general level. Only after a general understanding of plant structure and function is obtained is it possible to delve more deeply into one of the specialized aspects of botany.

1.3 Science, life, and plants

Previous mention was made that botany could be considered as the science of plant life. To understand exactly what this statement means, we must know the meanings of the three words used in the definition (i.e., science, plant, and life). (The discovery of unknown words in the definition of an unknown term can be one of the most frustrating of experiences.)

SCIENCE

The methods whereby data are accumulated and the organizing of these data in an attempt to discover general relationships that may exist are both incorporated in the term **science.** The **scientific method** is merely a method of common sense which entails several general features:

1. Observations. A scientist carefully examines a situation or problem and accumulates factual material, or **data** (singular, **datum**).

2. Hypothesis. He then attempts an explanation of the inter-relations among the data. Such an explanation, while in the tentative stage, is an hypothesis.

3. Experimentation. The scientist next plans experiments which will test the validity of his hypothesis by comparing actual results under controlled conditions with predictions based upon his explanation. Experiments are designed so that there is but one variable; all other factors must remain constant. (See Section 10.8 for a discussion of limiting and retarding factors.) A **control** group, set up at the same time as the treated group, is one in which there are no variables; all factors are kept constant. This is an extremely important part of any experiment, because it will indicate whether or not the variable factor is bringing about a response in the treated group. In other words, if the treated group responds differently from the control group, then we can say that the one variable factor in the former group elicited the response. Of course, because of the individual variations found in any living organisms, groups of similar plants must be used in the investigation.

4. Revision and further experimentation. The results obtained in step 3 may confirm the original hypothesis or may result in a modification (revision) or in the discarding of the hypothesis. If a revision is made, further experiments are designed as before in order to test the modified hypothesis.

Hypotheses may be revised many times, as more and more information is obtained. If the results of a series of experiments by various individuals over a period of years substantiates the ideas put forth in the hypothesis, this explanation is on a firmer foundation and may be termed a **theory** or a **conceptual scheme.** If no exceptions are found, the theory may eventually become a scientific law or principle.

The results of investigations and the hypotheses resulting from them are published in various scientific journals (e.g., *The American Journal of Botany, Plant Physiology, Journal of Bacteriology*) in order to disseminate this information to all who are interested. Others can then repeat the experiments and verify or refute the hypothesis. Probably the most important standard of science is **repeatability.** If the hypothesis is sound, the experimental results will not vary significantly on repetition, and it can be verified by competent critics.

The scientist approaches problems critically and objectively and records observations accurately. He must be willing to revise his ideas if acceptable data disagree with his preconceptions. But the data must be examined carefully and critically before they are accepted. The scientist continually asks: Why, where, how?

Increased knowledge about living things has shown that these complex organisms are governed by basic principles of chemistry and physics. Such a **mechanistic** viewpoint allows for greater ease in investigations than does the **vitalistic** approach, which assumes that "vital forces" are necessary for the activities which we associate with life. **Biologists** (individuals, both botanists and zoologists, who study living things) attempt to explain the "why" of living activities by physical and chemical principles rather than on the basis of a purpose. Activities occur because certain mechanisms are present and not "in order to" achieve a result. For example, the cactus plant grows readily in the desert because it happens to have certain structural features which result in low water losses and thus a low water requirement; it does not (or did not) develop such structures in order to grow in the desert. Explanations based upon a goal or purpose are **teleological** and not scientific and should be rejected.

5

LIFE

Certain characteristics are associated with at least the more complex living organisms:

1. Cellular structure. All living creatures are composed of one or more discrete, tiny masses of living material **(protoplasm)** enclosed by a membrane. Each of these tiny structures is a **cell.**

2. Assimilation. The production of protoplasm from non-living material (i.e., food and minerals) is termed assimilation.

3. Growth. The increase in size that results from assimilation is growth.

4. Reproduction. The production of like individuals, including the possibility of genetic changes, is entailed in reproduction. (See Chapter 17 for a discussion of genetics and Section 27.11 for a discussion of mutations.) All cells come from pre-existing cells. (See, however, Chapter 30 concerning the origin of life.)

5. Respiration. This is a complex series of chemical reactions which makes energy available for the work being done by each cell as it assimilates, grows, and reproduces.

6. Responsiveness. The capacity to respond to a stimulus is also a characteristic of life.

"Life" is actually rather difficult to define. The characteristics which have been mentioned apply to the great majority of living things, but one famous (or infamous) example of an organism exhibits but few of these. A **virus** is considered to be alive mainly because it reproduces and undergoes genetic changes. Assimilation undoubtedly occurs, since virus particles increase in number, but the source of energy may be their own respiration or a parasitizing of the host-cell respiratory mechanism. The virus is invisible when an ordinary microscope is used, but examination with an electron microscope at a magnification of approximately 50,000 diameters seems to show a definite structure, even though it is not cellular. Various types of evidence demonstrate that viruses are nucleo-proteins (nucleic acid surrounded by protein), and certain of them have been purified as a crystalline material. Possibly this is the stage between what we are sure is definitely living and what we are sure is certainly non-living. (See Chapter 30 with regard to the origin of life.)

PLANT

6

Since botany refers to a study of plants, we must know what differentiates a plant from an animal. Certain general characteristics are to be found in the former and not in the latter.

1. Food manufacture. Most plants can synthesize complex food from simple substances if **chlorophyll,** a green pigment, and light are present. Animals require ready-made food in the form of plants or other animals which in turn have eaten plants. The fungi, however, are non-green plants which cannot make their own food but obtain it from external sources.

[handwritten margin note: FOOD = CHLOROPHYLL + LIGHT]

2. Cell walls. Most plants have rigid cell walls of **cellulose,** a carbohydrate material. This results in the stiff and sturdy framework and lack of motility of plants. Animal cells in general are flexible, since they lack cell walls. Here again we find exceptions, in that many of the simplest types of plants are motile and some do not have cellulose walls.

3. Unlimited growth. Most plants have unlimited growth, as the **embryonic** tissue (i.e., tissue consisting of actively dividing cells) remains active throughout life, whereas growth in animals is limited, the mature individual attaining a certain maximum size and characteristic form. In the latter there is no further growth, while a plant grows until it dies.

No single criterion separates all plants from all animals. This should not be surprising, since they are but the two main branches of a single family tree and have common ancestors in those dim ages when life first originated. The more complex the organism, the more readily it is recognized as a plant or an animal, because the relationship is so distant. The simple plants and animals, however, are usually more closely related and thus more difficult to distinguish one from another. For example, *Euglena* is a one-celled organism that is flexible, motile by means of a flagellum, and in some species capable of ingesting solid food particles by means of a small gullet. These characteristics are obviously animal-like. However, *Euglena* has chlorophyll and can manufacture its own food, a definite plant-like characteristic. Then what is this organism? It is studied as an animal by zoologists and as a plant by botanists. The important thing is that *Euglena* is studied, not what we call it. Remember that classifications are the result of man-made rules and regulations and that man cannot insist upon an organism *being* a plant or an animal—he can merely insist upon *calling* it a plant or an animal. Plant classification will be discussed more thoroughly in Chapter 18.

1.4 Kinds of plants

Now that the terms "botany" and "plant" have been discussed, mention should be made of the great variety of organisms that botanists study. There are well over 300,000 distinct kinds of plants, which range in size from the microscopic bacteria to the gigantic seaweeds and California redwoods. The former may be small spheres with a diameter of 0.5 micron (about 1/50,000 of an inch), while the latter range up to 350 feet in length or height and hundreds of tons in weight.

The familiar plants are trees, shrubs, flowering annuals, crop plants, ferns, and grasses. Some of the less well-known plants include bacteria, fungi (toadstools, mushrooms), mosses, algae (pond scum), rusts (on roses for example), and mildews. Not only do the sizes vary tremendously, but so do the rates of growth and types of nutrition. Some bacteria can reproduce within 20 or 30 minutes, while other plants may grow for 7 to 10 or more years before producing seeds. Oxygen is required for most, but others (yeast, certain bacteria) grow readily in the absence of oxygen; in fact, some bacteria will not grow in the presence of oxygen. The nutritional aspects vary from those plants which produce their own food to those which require an external supply of food.

These immense differences between plants constitute one of the most fascinating aspects of botany. This is almost as fascinating as the fact that all life depends upon the diverse plants found on and in this earth.

Subsequent chapters will discuss plant structure and function, the manner in which plants influence human affairs, erosion, solved and unsolved problems of plant growth, population problems, and the ways in which humans might make better use of the plants which surround them.

Summary

1. Plants are studied because they provide food and oxygen for animals, many useful products for humans, and because of the interest people have in living things.

2. Botany is the study of plant structure, function, and classification. Many specialized areas exist within this broad framework of study.

3. The scientific method is basically one of common sense and consists of observations, hypotheses, experimentation using control and treated groups, and revisions of hypotheses. The scientist is concerned with factual material and a mechanistic approach.

4. The characteristics of most living organisms are cellular structure, assimilation, growth, reproduction, respiration, and responsiveness.

5. Plants are generally differentiated from animals by their ability to manufacture food, the presence of cell walls, and their unlimited type of growth.

1. List ten items that you use or consume during the day, and explain how each is dependent upon plants. Be explicit as to whether plants are involved directly or indirectly.
2. List three specialties in the study of plants, and indicate how they differ.
3. Describe an experiment that would enable you to determine the effect of temperature on the rate at which seeds germinate or sprout.
4. Discuss the difficulties involved in defining life.
5. Discuss the difficulties involved in distinguishing plants from animals.
6. List ten careers in which a knowledge of plants would be essential.
7. Of what importance are scientific journals or periodicals?

SUGGESTED READINGS

Anderson, E. *Plants, Man and Life*. London: Andrew Melrose, 1954.

Campbell, N. *What Is Science?* New York: Dover, 1952.

Editors of *Scientific American*. *Plant Life*. New York: Simon and Schuster, 1957.

Peattie, D. C. *Green Laurels*. New York: Garden City Publ. Co., 1938.

Reed, H. S. *A Short History of the Plant Sciences*. Waltham, Mass.: Chronica Botanica, 1942.

Teale, E. W. (ed.) *Green Treasury*. New York: Dodd, Mead, 1952.

Cellular Structure

ONE of the characteristics of living organisms is that they are composed of one or more cells and that all these cells come from pre-existing cells. However, this concept did not arrive on the scientific scene because of a burst of brilliancy on the part of any one individual. Various observations and investigations over many years gradually resulted in a greater understanding of the structure and development of plants and animals.

2.1 The cell theory

Robert Hooke (1665) examined thin sections of cork and accurately described the cells, or boxes, of which it was composed. Though he observed only the walls of dead cells, he was aware of the three dimensional aspect of these structures and the fact that they were distinct from one another. He also estimated that more than one billion cells were contained in a cubic inch of cork. Hooke first used the term "cell" and compared the appearance of cork to that of a honeycomb, but he did not stipulate the universal occurrence of cells, though he did observe living plant cells filled with liquid.

Subsequent investigations added to the developing concept of cellular structure, and Dutrochet (1824) presented one of the first clear statements of the idea that all living things are composed of cells. He further indicated that growth results from both the increased size of cells and the addition of new little cells. The cell was considered to be the primary unit, and the function of the organism was a result of a summation of the functions of individual cells. Dutrochet did not discover the existence of a nucleus within the cell, but this information was added a few years later by the observations of Brown (1833) who first observed the nucleus in hairs and epidermal cells of orchids.

With additional investigations concerning the structure of organisms and the functioning of their component parts, plus the recognition of protozoa as single-celled animals (von Siebold, 1845), many biologists right-header

protozoa as single-celled animals (von Siebold, 1845), many biologists were led to the modern concept of cellular structure: that multicellular organisms are subdivided into functional units called cells, which are variously modified and specialized, thus resulting in a division of labor. In the case of a unicellular organism, of course, the functions of the cell are the functions of the organism. This idea of structure emphasizes the coordination among cells and tissues in the explanation of the behavior of organisms. The mere summation of the activities of individual cells is not sufficient to explain the functioning of multicellular plants and animals.

That the more complex plants and animals contain many different kinds of cells is not common knowledge. In order to understand the uses and functions of plants—how they grow, reproduce, synthesize materials—we must understand clearly the structures that are involved, because function and structure are so intimately tied together. For example, supporting or strengthening cells have thicker walls than conducting cells, while the latter are usually elongated. The possibility of a terrestrial existence depends upon the structure of land plants. The structure of the individual cells which comprise a tissue affects the efficient functioning of that tissue. Thus, we should start with a generalized cell, discuss its basic structure and function, and then undertake the more difficult task of studying the correlation of various cells functioning as tissues and organs.

2.2 The generalized cell

The size of individual cells varies greatly, from microscopic ones on the order of 0.5 micron to macroscopic units up to 10 cm. (about 4 inches). The number of cells in a plant is astronomical. Remember Hooke's estimate? A single leaf on a tree may have more than 40,000,000 cells. Count the number of leaves on a tree, multiply by 40 million, multiply by about twenty to include cells in the roots and stems, and you will have a general idea of the number of cells that are involved in the growth of a tree. Each cell consists of living and non-living material, the latter being produced by the former as the cell is developing. In some cells the protoplasm dies and disintegrates after the cells have matured. This occurs in cork cells and explains why Hooke thought of cells as little empty boxes.

CELL WALL

The outer boundary of plant cells consists of a non-living structure, secreted by the living part of the cell and termed the cell wall. It is a strong, porous, rather rigid but somewhat elastic wall and results in the cell being shaped more or less like a box with at least six sides. (See

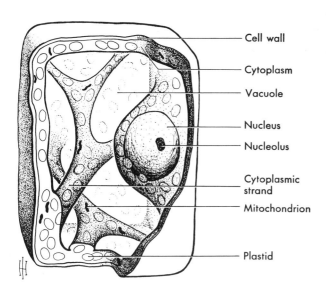

	Cell wall
	Cytoplasm
	Vacuole
	Nucleus
	Nucleolus
	Cytoplasmic strand
	Mitochondrion
	Plastid

Figure 2-1. General features of a plant cell.

Figure 2-1 for all structures pertaining to the general plant cell.) The shape varies as the cell differentiates, but the young or immature cells are basically alike. In multicellular plants the walls form a continuous structure much like the walls, floors, and ceilings in a large building. Much like layers of plaster on the walls of a room, cell walls are laminated, even though such layers may not be visible unless special staining techniques are used. The inter-connected cell walls provide strength and support to the entire plant body.

Middle lamella. As the cell wall develops, it is composed of granules which increase in size and number until they coalesce and form a thin layer called the **middle lamella,** or **intercellular layer.** This layer is composed largely of **pectic substances,** mainly calcium pectate, which are viscous and gelatinous and function as the cementing material which holds the cells together. Commercial preparations of pectins are prepared from various fruits and are added to jellies to insure the "jelling" of these materials.

Primary wall. The protoplast secretes an additional layer against the middle lamella. This second layer consists mainly of intertwined molecules of cellulose, a complex carbohydrate formed from simple glucose (sugar) molecules, and is rather plastic and capable of extension as the cell grows. In many cells no further layers are produced. The primary wall becomes more rigid as additional cellulose molecules are added after the cell has attained its mature size.

Secondary wall. In those cells with relatively thick walls, a secondary wall, usually of three layers, is present. These layers are basically cellulose, but additional materials may also be present, such as **lignin,** a complex material which is responsible for hardness and decay-

Figure 2-2. Pits and plasmodesmata. **A:** Several views of a simple pit. **B:** Several views of a bordered pit in which the cell wall arches over the thin area. **C:** Plasmodesmata extending through the pit area from the cytoplasm of one cell to the cytoplasm of a neighboring cell.

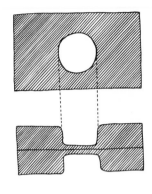

resisting qualities of many woods, and **suberin,** a waxy material found in cork cells. **Cutin,** another waxy material, is usually found as a layer on the outer wall of the cells forming the exterior surfaces of land plants.

Pits and plasmodesmata (Figure 2-2). The walls of cells vary greatly in thickness, with supporting cells having relatively thick walls and with cells which are actively synthesizing materials having rather thin walls. Most cells also have thin areas in the primary walls (no secondary wall layers), and such **pits** greatly facilitate the movement of dissolved materials from one cell to another. With special staining techniques and high magnification, many of these pits are seen to have exceedingly small pores through which delicate strands of cytoplasm **(plasmodesmata)** connect the protoplast of one cell with that of the adjacent cell. Such plasmodesmata aid in the movement of materials and may possibly transmit stimuli.

The cell walls are quite porous and are freely penetrated by water and various dissolved materials. Whether or not a substance enters or leaves a cell depends upon the solubility of that material and the characteristics of the surface layer of the protoplast and not upon qualities possessed by the cell wall. The cellulose component of the wall is quite useful commercially: wood pulp is used to manufacture paper; rayon is produced from cellulose; so are explosives, cellophane, buttons, and many other materials. Since cellulose comprises approximately 80 per cent of the dry weight of wood, forests are the source of many valuable articles in addition to lumber for buildings.

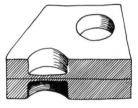

[A]

PROTOPLASM

The living material which produces and is surrounded by the non-living cell wall is commonly termed the **protoplast** or **protoplasm.** All of the various complex functions of life are carried on in this small amount of viscous, colorless, transparent material. Its consistency varies from time to time from that of raw egg-white to that of semi-solid

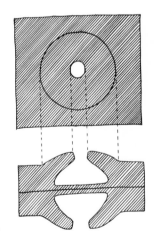

[C]

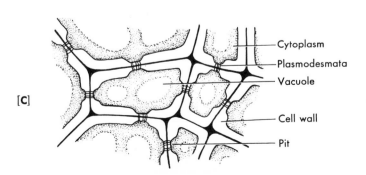

- Cytoplasm
- Plasmodesmata
- Vacuole
- Cell wall
- Pit

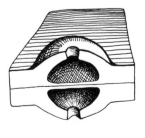

[B]

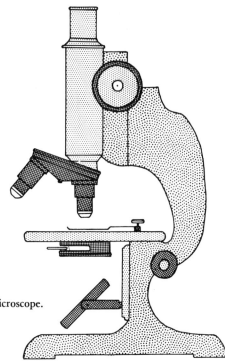

Figure 2-3. Typical student microscope.

gelatin. It is not homogeneous, for various definite structures can be observed quite readily even with low magnification. Though these structures are important (and will be discussed), the submicroscopic structure is equally important. Recent evidence indicates that large, complex protein molecules form the basic framework, much like a brush pile, and that other materials (e.g., water, fats, oils) are scattered among the proteins. One should remember that even though a chemist can determine the composition of protoplasm, listing all of the elements involved, this does not explain "life" or how protoplasm functions. The problem is similar to a jeweler describing a watch in terms of gold, silver, steel, and jewels—unless these are placed in the correct order or structure, no watch can be said to exist. The placement and inter-relationships of the component parts is all-important. Protoplasm is, of course, more complicated than a watch, especially in view of the fact that its composition is not constant but variable.

Nucleus. In observing a cell with the use of a microscope (see Figure 2-3), the most obvious living structure within the protoplasm is the spherical or ovoid **nucleus** (plural, **nuclei**). Most organisms have one nucleus per cell, but some of the algae and fungi have cells with two to several nuclei. Well organized and delimited nuclei are probably lacking in certain simple organisms, such as the blue-green algae and the bacteria, but nuclear material is distributed through the protoplasm.

The nucleus is bounded by the **nuclear membrane,** and within this structure may be seen one or more spherical **nucleoli** (singular, **nucleolus**) and irregular strands of **chromatin.** The nucleoli appear to be active centers of protein and ribose nucleic acid synthesis. This latter material, usually abbreviated as RNA, presumably acts as templates that determine the sequence in which amino acids are linked together in protein chains. This will be discussed more thoroughly in Section 17.4. The nuclear membrane has been shown, by electron microscopy, to be double and to contain exceedingly tiny pores. This membrane bulges out into the cytoplasm and forms the extremely convoluted **endoplasmic reticulum,**[1] which is continuous with invaginations from the outer cellular membranes. The remaining part of the nucleus is a clear liquid, the **karyolymph.**

In order to see the various structures more clearly, the cells are placed in certain dyes. The chromatin material stains very deeply and is seen to be in the form of long, coiled, thread-like structures, the **chromonemata** (singular, **chromonema**). These threads are difficult to trace as individuals except when the cell is dividing. When this occurs, the chromonemata become more tightly coiled and shorten, and a matrix forms around each. The condensed matrix stains very deeply and usually obscures the chromonema which it surrounds. This more distinct, rod-shaped structure is the **chromosome;** every type of organism has a characteristic constant number of such chromosomes in each cell. The chromonemata contain distinct submicroscopic particles, the **genes,** which control the characteristic growth and chemical processes of the organism. These genes are basically nucleo-proteins, composed of proteins and the complex nucleic acid. Chemically, then, the nucleus contains a relatively large amount of nucleo-proteins, of which phosphorus is an important constituent.

The nucleus functions as the controlling center for the physiological activities of the cell and also governs the transmission of hereditary characteristics. If the nucleus is removed from the cell, physiological abnormalities occur and death results. The red blood cells of man (erythrocytes) do not contain nuclei when they are mature, but such cells function for only a few days, being replaced by newly-formed erythrocytes. The sieve tube elements (one of the conducting cells in vascular plants) also lack nuclei at maturity. This is the only normal exception in plants. All other cells contain at least one nucleus.

---

[1] Because this structure cannot be seen with the ordinary light microscope, but only with the use of an electron microscope at exceedingly high magnifications, it is not indicated in Figure 2-1. For the same reason, the ribosomes (to be discussed later) have not been shown in this figure.

15 ट~

Cytoplasm. The more fluid portion of the protoplasm, which surrounds the nucleus and in which other formed bodies are contained, is the **cytoplasm.** Recent investigations have emphasized the importance of a submicroscopic structure, and the arrangement of molecules which compose the cytoplasm greatly influences the activities of the cell. Many cellular enzymes [2] are located in the cytoplasm and are important in respiration and various syntheses. In young cells the cytoplasm occupies most of the volume of the cell, but in mature cells the cytoplasm usually occurs as a thin layer lining the walls and with thin strands penetrating throughout the cell.

The cytoplasm frequently can be seen streaming about in the cell. Though there is no movement from one cell to another, many of the distinct bodies found in the cytoplasm are carried about much like wood in a stream. As shown in Figure 2-4, the movement of one cytoplasmic strand may be opposite to that of another; lower layers of the same strand may flow in one direction while the upper layers flow in the opposite direction. Such movement indicates great activity and may be important in the transport of food and other materials.

The surface layers of the cytoplasm are quite distinct from the inner regions and have properties unlike the main mass. Such surfaces are

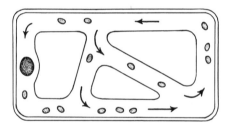

Figure 2-4. Diagram to indicate cytoplasmic streaming. The plastids are swept along by this movement but the nucleus is not.

termed **membranes,** and they are **differentially permeable.** That is, when the membrane is alive, some materials penetrate the membrane quite readily, others penetrate more slowly, and still others do not penetrate at all. This property of membranes is variable, and under some conditions they are more permeable than under others. Upon dying, membranes become freely permeable. This characteristic holds true for all living membranes.

Mitochondria. Small rods or granules, called mitochondria (singular, **mitochondrion**), are abundant in the cytoplasm but are visible only when the cells are stained with certain dyes. Respiratory enzymes

[2] Enzymes are catalysts produced by living cells. A catalyst greatly speeds the rate of a chemical reaction without being used up in that reaction. Without enzymes the activities of living cells would cease.

are oriented in a specific manner in each mitochondrion and function efficiently as a group. Also, plastids probably arise from these small rods. As determined by a study of electron micrographs, the structure of a mitochondrion is basically that of a fluid-filled vessel with a double membrane as the outer boundary. The inner membrane of this double layer has many involutions or infoldings (Figure 2-5). The specific orientation of enzymes quite likely occurs in these membranes.

Figure 2-5. Mitochondrion; the inner layer of the double membrane is very convoluted. (From A. L. Lehninger, *Scientific American*, September 1961.)

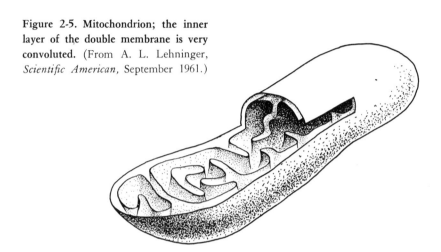

Ribosomes. Within the cytoplasm, located on the endoplasmic reticulum, are exceedingly small granules that are visible only with the use of the electron microscope. These ribosomes are exceedingly rich in ribose nucleic acid (RNA) and are the main site for the synthesis of proteins, especially enzymes. This function will be discussed in more retail in Section 17.4.

Plastids. Also present in the cytoplasm are one to many spherical, ovoid, or lens-shaped bodies which are clearly visible without staining. These **plastids** are sometimes collar-shaped, ribbon-like, or even very irregular in shape, but this is usually true only in some simple plant types. There are three kinds of plastids, all bounded by membranes, and a cell may contain more than one kind: **chloroplast** (green), **chromoplast** (red, orange, or yellow), and **leucoplast** (colorless). The green color of plants, as in leaves, is due to the presence of the green pigments, **chlorophyll a** and **chlorophyll b,** contained in chloroplasts. The yellow carotenoid pigments, **carotene** and **xanthophyll,** are also present in these plastids, but their color is masked by the chlorophylls. The chlorophyll enables the green plant to manufacture food when exposed to light. With the aid of the electron microscope, a chloroplast

17 ϝ⸾

has been shown to have a colorless **stroma** in which small plate-like bodies, called **grana,** are embedded. Each **granum** contains layers of proteins and fatty materials in which the various pigments are located. This detailed structure is, of course, not visible with an ordinary microscope. Very little is known about the structure of other plastids.

The color of a chromoplast depends primarily upon the presence of carotene and xanthophyll. Such plastids are found in fruits, flower

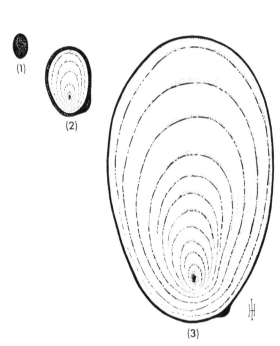

Figure 2-6. Starch grain forming within a leucoplast. The outermost margin represents the membrane of the plastid.

petals, and some other plant parts (e.g., carrot root). These pigments may participate in food manufacture when located in chloroplasts by absorbing light energy and transmitting this excitation to chlorophyll, but their significance in chromoplasts is not clear. Carotene is converted in animals to the essential vitamin A, but this vitamin is not necessary for normal functioning in plants. Leucoplasts contain no pigments and are located most commonly in storage cells where they act as centers for starch formation (a food storage product). The cells of a potato tuber are gorged with starch grains which, on careful observation, can be seen to be enclosed by the leucoplast membrane (Figure 2-6).

In some cells one type of plastid may be converted to another. For example, a developing tomato fruit contains leucoplasts which develop into chloroplasts and eventually into chromoplasts. Chloroplasts multiply by division, in which the plastid constricts in the middle and separates into two parts which then enlarge; this is probably true of all plastids.

INCLUSIONS

Present within living cells are various non-living structures, generally termed inclusions.

Vacuoles. In a mature cell the cytoplasm, nucleus, and plastids are frequently located adjacent to the cell walls, while the greater portion of the cell is occupied by one or more large cavities called **vacuoles.** Within the vacuoles is a fluid, the **cell sap,** composed of water and a great variety of dissolved materials (i.e., sugars, inorganic salts, organic acids and their salts, pigments, alkaloids, and various other water-soluble materials). The pigment found most frequently is **anthocyanin,** which is responsible for many of the red, purple, and blue colors in flower petals, leaves, and even roots (e.g., beet); the color varies with the acid condition of the cell.

Vacuoles are storage areas for food materials and depots for waste materials. In addition to this, they are important in the maintenance of cell turgidity, due to the presence of the differentially permeable **vacuolar membrane,** which is really the inner boundary of the cytoplasm. The outer boundary of the cytoplasm, adjacent to the cell wall, is a similar membrane called the **cytoplasmic membrane.** The movement of materials through cell membranes will be discussed later (see Chapter 4).

 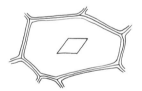 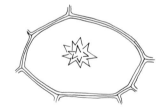

Figure 2-7. Types of crystals frequently found in cells.

Crystals. In the cells of various parts of the plant may be found **crystals,** differing considerably in size and shape (see Figure 2-7), which appear to be waste products, or excretory products, of the protoplasm. They are located primarily in the vacuoles and usually are calcium oxalate crystals, though others are sometimes found.

Stored foods. Visible in many cells are **starch grains** (as in the cells

19 ⟨∾

of potato tubers and many green leaves), **oil globules** (as in the cells of avocado fruits), and **aleurone grains** (stored protein found in the cells of many seeds: for example, wheat). These materials are formed when excess foods are produced by the plant, and may be broken down and utilized by the plant during those periods when food is not being produced in sufficient quantities (or when the seed germinates or the tuber sprouts to form a new plant).

Less frequently found in cells are tannins, gums, resins, and mucilages. These are probably all waste products resulting from the physiological activities of plant cells. Some of these materials are important in water retention (see Section 14.5).

Figure 2-8. Schematic diagram of cell structure based upon studies using the electron microscope. (From J. D. Robertson, *Scientific American,* April 1962.)

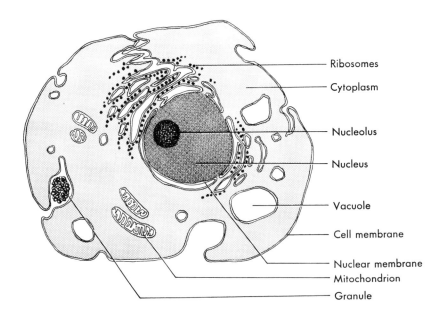

Figure 2-8 is a schematic diagram of cell structure, based upon studies using the electron microscope. The electron micrographs, obtained during these investigations, indicate that the structure of the cell is exceedingly complex. The membranes, for example, are double layers which extend throughout the cytoplasm as a fine network (the endoplasmic reticulum) from the outer cell membrane to the nuclear membrane. All of the basic components of the cell are, therefore, linked together by this framework. Although the cytoplasm appears to be a fluid mass when viewed with a light microscope, the greatly higher magnifications possible with an electron microscope reveal the orderly and integrated structural arrangements that are actually present. The sequential reactions that are known to occur in cells are more readily understandable in the light of this knowledge of structural organization.

2.3 Cell division

All plants are composed of cells, and at least in the multicellular organisms, the number of cells increases greatly as the plant grows. Since new cells develop from pre-existing ones, some means must exist for an individual cell to form more cells. This process is cell division. Cell division includes two distinct processes: **mitosis,** or nuclear division, and **cytokinesis,** which involves the division of the remainder of the cell and the formation of a new wall. Time-lapse photography [3] has enabled the biologist to speed up the apparent rate of cell division so that the tremendous activity can be observed more readily. It is fascinating to watch—much more so than one can possibly put in words on a printed page.

MITOSIS

The division of a nucleus is a continuous process, and no pauses delimit the various phases which will be discussed. However, for ease of discussion, biologists subdivide mitosis, more or less arbitrarily, into several phases. This is similar to discussing the phases of the moon; one phase actually blends into the next. The entire process of mitosis may take from 30 minutes to 22 hours or more and is usually more rapid at higher temperatures.

Metabolic phase, or **interphase.** This phase refers to the condition of a nucleus when it is not dividing. Such a nucleus has at times been referred to as a "resting nucleus," but this term is not acceptable since

---

[3] In time-lapse photography motion picture film is exposed one frame at a time with a lapse of one or more minutes between exposures. When the film is projected at normal speed, all activity is shown much more rapidly than it actually occurs. Such photography can greatly condense movements which take 30 to 60 minutes or even longer. The opening of buds is frequently photographed in this fashion to emphasize the fantastic movements undergone by unfolding leaves and petals.

living activities do not stop merely because a cell is not dividing. In fact, it is during the metabolic phase that new nuclear material is being synthesized. The appearance of the nucleus was indicated earlier in this chapter and is shown in Figure 2-9 and in more diagrammatic form in Figure 2-10A.

Prophase (Figure 2-9 and Figure 2-10B, C). The first indication that a nucleus is about to divide is the shortening and thickening of the chromosomes as the chromonemata become more tightly coiled

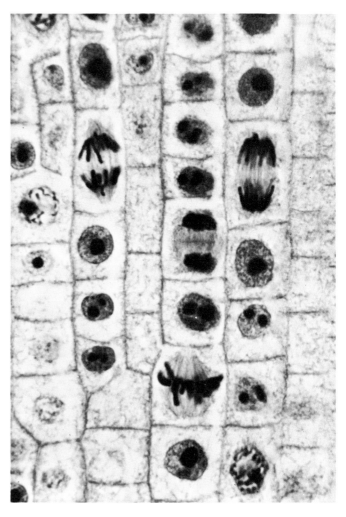

Figure 2-9. Photomicrograph of root tip cells in the process of mitosis. In the row at the left, just above the center, is a cell in prophase. In the next row, slightly higher, is a cell in early anaphase. A telophase with the new cell wall forming and a metaphase are visible in the central row of cells. (Courtesy of General Biological Supply House, Chicago.)

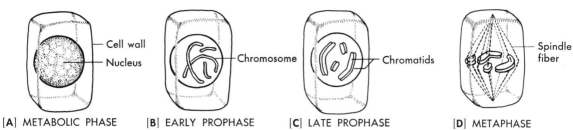

[A] METABOLIC PHASE   [B] EARLY PROPHASE   [C] LATE PROPHASE   [D] METAPHASE

Figure 2-10. Cell division. In **A** and **H** the chromosomes are in the greatly expanded and indistinct condition typical of nuclei which are not dividing. In the other diagrams the chromosomes and chromatids are shown as distinct entities. The formation of the new cell wall is shown in **F, G,** and **H.**

and a matrix forms about each. The nuclear membrane and the nucleolus disappear, and **spindle fibers** become visible. These fibers, some of which are attached to the chromosomes, extend from one end, or **pole,** of the cell to the other in the shape of a spindle. The **kinetochore** (or **centromere**) is the region of the chromosome where a spindle fiber is attached. The chromosomes now move toward the central, or equatorial, region of the cell, and it is apparent that each chromosome has doubled (reproduced itself). This doubling has actually taken place during the previous metabolic phase. Each longitudinal half of a doubled chromosome is termed a **chromatid,** and each chromatid is an exact duplicate of the original chromosome. This duplication possibly is brought about by the original chromosome functioning as a mold or pattern, to which "building blocks" are added from the variety of molecules abounding in the cytoplasm.

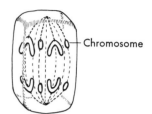

[E] ANAPHASE

Metaphase (Figure 2-9 and Figure 2-10D). When the doubled chromosomes reach the equatorial region, prophase is considered to be over, and nuclear division has reached the metaphase stage. The chromosomes vary considerably in length, and frequently, though the kinetochores are gathered in the central region, the "arms" of the chromatids may dangle in various directions.

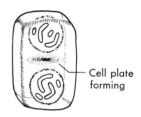

[F] EARLY TELOPHASE

Anaphase (Figure 2-9 and Figure 2-10E). The two parts of the doubled chromosomes separate, forming two identical groups, each going toward a different pole of the cell. Once the chromatids separate, each is considered to be a distinct chromosome. Contraction of the fibers, which are probably strands of colloidal protein material, may aid in this movement of the chromosomal groups. At the termination of anaphase, one group of chromosomes is located at each pole of the spindle.

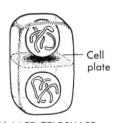

|G| LATE TELOPHASE

Telophase (Figure 2-9 and Figure 2-10F, G). As the spindle fibers disappear, the chromosomal groups at each pole of the cell become reorganized into new nuclei by the development of nuclear membranes

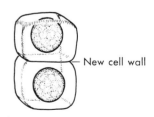

|H| NEW CELLS—METABOLIC PHASE

surrounding each group and by the reappearance of the nucleoli. It should be emphasized that, since the original chromosomes doubled, each of these two groups has the same number and same kind of chromosomes as were present in the cell when mitosis began.

CYTOKINESIS

As mitosis nears completion, granular material appears across the equatorial region. These particles become larger, more dense, and eventually coalesce to form a **cell plate** which extends across the cell from wall to wall. The cytoplasm is thus divided into two portions, each containing one of the new nuclei, and the cell plate becomes the middle lamella of the new cell wall. The two protoplasts of the resultant daughter cells deposit additional cell wall layers on the middle lamella, and cytokinesis is completed (see Figures 2-9 and 2-10F, G, H). In animal cells and in some plant cells, cytokinesis is accomplished by a pinching in of the parent cell until two new cells are formed. Multinucleate cells result if cytokinesis does not follow mitosis, a condition found in various simple plants.

SIGNIFICANCE OF MITOSIS

As a result of the doubling of chromosomes and the subsequent separation of chromatids, each daughter cell contains the same **number** and the same **kind** of chromosomes as did the original (parent) cell. Since genes, which determine hereditary characteristics, are located within the chromosomes, each daughter cell has the same potentialities as the parent cell. The daughter cells enlarge to a mature size, at which time they also may undergo cell division.

Summary

1. Organisms are composed of functional units called cells, which may be variously modified, and all cells come from pre-existing cells.

2. The generalized plant cell consists of a non-living wall enclosing the protoplasm. The cellulose wall is either two or three layers thick and contains certain thin areas, or pits. The more fluid portion of the protoplasm is the cytoplasm, within which various formed bodies are located. These latter are the nucleus, mitochondria, ribosomes, and plastids. Various non-living inclusions may also be present in the cytoplasm (e.g., vacuoles, stored foods, and waste products).

3. Nuclear division is termed mitosis and consists of several intergrading phases: prophase, metaphase, anaphase, and telophase. Cytokinesis refers to the division of the remainder of the cell and the formation of a new cell wall.

1. Diagram a generalized plant cell and label fully.
2. Discuss the functions of the various parts of a generalized plant cell.
3. Describe the changes that take place within a cell during prophase of mitosis, during anaphase, during telophase.
4. Compile three lists, indicating which structures of a green plant cell are visible (a) with an ordinary light microscope, (b) with an ordinary light microscope plus staining the cell, and (c) with an electron microscope.
5. A thin section is made through a plant tissue. When this is examined microscopically, some of the cells are observed to be without nuclei. Suggest two possible explanations.
6. What are plasmodesmata and what is their importance?
7. Cytoplasm is frequently seen to be in motion. What is the possible significance of this movement?
8. How can cells grow if the cell walls are rigid? Is there any practical advantage to the plant of having rigid cell walls?
9. Explain why the term "metabolic nucleus" is more appropriate than "resting nucleus" in describing the nucleus of a cell during interphase.
10. Discuss the reasons for considering a multicellular plant as an organic whole rather than as a community of isolated cells.

SUGGESTED READINGS

Brachet, J. "The Living Cell," *Scientific American,* 205 (September 1961), 50–61.

DeRobertis, E. D. P., et al. *General Cytology.* Philadelphia: W. B. Saunders, 1960.

Mazia, D. "How Cells Divide," *Scientific American,* 205 (September 1961), 100–123.

Seifriz, W. *Protoplasm.* New York: McGraw-Hill, 1936.

Sharp, L. W. *An Introduction to Cytology.* New York: McGraw-Hill, 1934.

Swanson, C. P. *The Cell.* Englewood Cliffs, N. J.: Prentice-Hall, 1960.

Solomon, A. K. "Pores in the Cell Membrane," *Scientific American,* 203 (December 1960), 145–156.

Wilson, G. B., and J. H. Morrison. *Cytology.* New York: Reinhold, 1961.

CHAPTER 3

A Few Basic Physical and Chemical Principles

Explanations of the activities of living organisms have been found by the application of various concepts common to the fields of physics and chemistry. Obviously, a knowledge of these concepts is essential to an understanding of such explanations.

3.1 Molecular structure

All matter (that which has mass and occupies space) is composed of submicroscopic particles, called **molecules,** which are in continuous motion. Such molecules are the smallest subdivision of a substance [1] which still possesses all of the specific properties or characteristics of that substance. Since these particles are not visible, their motility has been determined by various indirect methods. However, a visible indication that water molecules are moving can be obtained by observing what has been termed **Brownian movement.** If small but visible particles (such as India ink) are suspended in a drop of water and observed through a microscope, these particles will be seen to "jiggle" about. Their non-directional trembling movement is not a result of their own molecular composition but of the motion of water molecules striking first from one direction and then from another. The

[1] Substance: a material all samples of which have the same set of properties; it consists of but one kind of molecule.

unequal collisions push the ink particles first to one side and then to another.

The molecules of any material are attracted to each other in varying degrees, and this greatly influences the amount of motility of individual molecules. In solids molecules are strongly attracted, resulting in little movement. In liquids the attraction is less, molecular motion is greater, and the material is fluid. The molecules of a gas have very little attraction for each other, the individual molecules have great motility, and these molecules will move farther and farther apart until the gas completely fills the space available to it. This movement of molecules from one area to another is termed **diffusion** and is a result of the inherent continuous movement of all molecules.

Molecules in turn are composed of **atoms,** the building blocks, which are the smallest particles that will enter into a chemical reaction. Recent evidence indicates that atomic structure is more complicated than had been suspected, but for our purpose we may consider an atom to be made up of a sphere or swarm of **electrons** (negatively charged particles) surrounding a positively charged core.[2] The positive charge is due to **protons** (discrete units of positive charge), but the core also contains particles having no charge at all, the **neutrons.** This central portion contains practically the entire mass of the atom but occupies an extremely tiny portion of the volume; practically all the volume is occupied by electrons. In a neutral atom, the negative charge of the electrons is exactly balanced by the positive charge of the core; the number of electrons is equal to the number of protons. When an electron is removed from a neutral atom, the particle which remains behind is positively charged, or a **positive ion:**

$$Na \rightarrow Na^+ + e^-$$

The electron is shown as e^-. When a neutral atom picks up an electron, it forms a **negative ion:**

$$Cl + e^- \rightarrow Cl^-$$

The symbols Na and Cl refer to sodium and chlorine respectively. Such symbols are the chemists' method of abbreviating the name of an **element,** a substance which cannot be decomposed into simpler substances by ordinary action. Table 3-1 indicates some of the elements which are important in cellular structure and function.

[2] The term "nucleus" (rather than "core") is used by physicists and chemists, but this might lead to confusion in the mind of a beginning biology student, who is more familiar with a cellular nucleus than with an atomic nucleus.

Table 3-1.   Elements Important to Cell Structure and Function

Element	Symbol		Element	Symbol
Boron	B		Magnesium	Mg
Calcium	Ca		Manganese	Mn
Carbon	C		Molybdenum	Mo
Chlorine *	Cl		Nitrogen	N
Cobalt *	Co		Oxygen	O
Copper	Cu		Phosphorus	P
Fluorine *	F		Potassium	K
Hydrogen	H		Sodium *	Na
Iodine *	I		Sulfur	S
Iron	Fe		Zinc	Zn

* These elements are essential for animals, but they have not been proved to be essential for plants. Quite possibly more elements will be added to this list as investigations produce further data (see Section 15.1).

3.2   Compounds and formulae

Some substances are **compounds:** they are capable of being decomposed into simpler substances. Water can be broken down into its constituents, hydrogen and oxygen, but the latter two materials are elements, which cannot be decomposed further. In order to indicate the composition of a compound, a **formula** is written (e.g., H_2O). The formula, utilizing symbols and subscripts, provides the following information: (1) the elements in the compound; (2) the relative number of each atom (subscripts indicate the number of atoms, the number 1 being omitted); (3) the combining weights of the elements, since the symbol refers to an atom and the atomic weights are known; and (4) the molecular weight of the compound, if it is known.

Many compounds are found within plants, but only three of these will be mentioned now. **Carbohydrates** (e.g., sugars, starch, cellulose) are composed of carbon (C), hydrogen (H), and oxygen (O), with the last two occurring in a two-to-one ratio as in water (H_2O). Molecules of the simple sugar glucose ($C_6H_{12}O_6$) are frequently combined by the cell to form more complex carbohydrates, such as starch, which are then stored in the cell. Later these complex molecules may be broken down to simple sugars and utilized. **Fats** and **oils** are also composed only of carbon, hydrogen, and oxygen, but relatively little oxygen is found in proportion to the other two atoms—as, for example, in stearin $C_{57}H_{120}O_6$. At ordinary room temperature, oils are liquids while fats are solids, but there is no general chemical distinction between them. The breakdown of fats and oils results in the production of fatty acids and glycerol (see Section 11.4). **Proteins** contain carbon, hydrogen, oxygen, nitrogen (N), frequently sulfur (S), and sometimes phosphorus (P), as in milk casein $C_{708}H_{1130}N_{180}O_{224}S_4P_4$. These are the most complex molecules found in living cells and can be broken down to simpler substances known as amino acids. Just as complex compounds can be broken down to simpler ones, they can also be synthesized from the simple compounds by living cells. Such complex compounds are usually important constituents of the protoplasm, or they may be storage products.

3.3 Ionization

When dissolved in water, the molecules of many materials will separate into two electrically charged particles, called **ions.** Common table salt is composed of sodium (Na) and chlorine (Cl) and **ionizes,** or **dissociates,** as follows:

$$NaCl \rightarrow Na^+ + Cl^-$$

The plus and minus charges balance. The charged particles are atoms, as above, or groups of atoms, as in the carbonate ion ($CO_3^=$) below:

$$Na_2CO_3 \text{ (sodium carbonate)} \rightarrow 2Na^+ + CO_3^=$$

Such ions are separately mobile and are highly reactive. All acids ionize to form hydrogen ions (H^+):

$$HCl \text{ (hydrochloric acid)} \rightarrow H^+ + Cl^-$$
$$H_2SO_4 \text{ (sulfuric acid)} \rightarrow 2H^+ + SO_4^=$$

All bases dissociate to form hydroxyl ions (OH^-):

$$NaOH \text{ (sodium hydroxide)} \rightarrow Na^+ + OH^-$$
$$Ba(OH)_2 \text{ (barium hydroxide)} \rightarrow Ba^{++} + 2OH^-$$

When acids and bases are mixed, they are **neutralized,** in that the H^+ ions and the OH^- ions combine to form water (H_2O), which is only very slightly dissociated. During neutralization, **salts** are formed:

$$HCl + NaOH \rightarrow H_2O + NaCl \text{ (a salt)}$$

Salts do not form either H^+ or OH^- ions when they ionize.

3.4 Oxidation and reduction

When coal is burned, oxygen combines with the carbon, carbon dioxide (CO_2) is formed, and the chemically bound energy [3] in the coal

[3] Energy is anything that can be converted into work (e.g., heat, electricity, or the potential energy of a coiled spring) or the ability to do work.

is liberated as heat and light. The combination of oxygen with other elements and the consequent release of energy was the original meaning of the term oxidation. However, many oxidations occur, especially in living cells, where free oxygen is not involved—sometimes there is a loss of hydrogens, sometimes a loss of electrons. The basic characteristic of an **oxidation** is that there is a loss of electrons. As far as the living cell is concerned, the important result of oxidation is that bound energy (as in a food molecule) is liberated or made available.

Whenever one material is oxidized, another is reduced. **Reduction** refers to the gain of electrons (sometimes in the form of the addition of hydrogen). In other words, the electrons which are lost when a substance is oxidized are accepted by the substance which is reduced.

3.5 Hydrolysis and condensation

The breakdown and the production of complex compounds that occur so frequently in living cells are actually examples of hydrolyses and condensations. The **digestion** of a complex starch molecule to sugar molecules actually utilizes water and thus is a type of **hydrolysis**—one molecule of water is added for every molecule of sugar that is produced:

$$\text{Starch} + n\,H_2O \rightarrow n\,\text{Sugar}$$

The symbol "n" is used because the size of the starch molecule is unknown, and so the number of water molecules used and the number of sugar molecules produced are unknown. The reverse process, whereby a large number of sugar molecules combine to form starch, with the attendant elimination of water molecules, is termed **condensation** or **synthesis**. Fats, oils, and proteins undergo similar syntheses and hydrolyses.

3.6 Adsorption, capillarity, and imbibition

The molecules of many substances are **polar,** that is, the atoms which make up the molecules join in an angular fashion so that, though the over-all negative and positive charges balance, certain portions of the molecule are more negative and other portions are more positive. This is true of water molecules (H_2O), which should be represented as

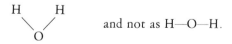

Many materials have charged areas, and molecules or ions are fre-

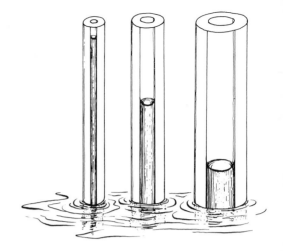

Figure 3-1. Capillarity, diagrammatic. The rise of water into tubes of small diameter depends upon the cohesion of water molecules and their adhesion to the walls of the tubes. The height to which water rises in such tubes depends upon the diameter of the tube, for one thing, as shown in the diagram.

quently concentrated, or held, on various surfaces, a phenomenon termed **adsorption.** For example, the clay particles of soil are negatively charged and hence attract and hold water and positively charged ions. This characteristic of soil particles is of tremendous importance to the growth of plants and will be emphasized in Section 16.4

If the tip of a tube of small diameter is immersed in water, as in Figure 3-1, the level of water in the tube will rise higher than the surface into which the tube was placed. Such a rise of water in tubes, termed **capillary action** or **capillarity,** depends upon the cohesion of water molecules to each other and the adhesion of water molecules to the tube walls.[4] The smaller the diameter of the tube, the higher will be the capillary rise.

The swelling of dry wood when it is placed in water results from the diffusion of water into the wood, the capillary action of water entering tiny cracks, crevices, and tubes of the wood, and the entrance of water between the particles of wood and its adhesion to these particles. **Imbibition** is this entrance of water into solids and the resultant swelling. The wood particles are forced farther and farther apart as the water enters, and the swelling forces may be considerable. The granite blocks used to build ancient pyramids were probably quarried by drilling holes in the stone, pounding dry wood tightly into these holes, and then pouring water on the wood. The resultant imbibitional forces split the granite. Leaky rowboats may become watertight when placed in water, due to the swelling of the dry wood. In a similar manner a

---

[4] Cohesion refers to the attraction of similar molecules to each other (e.g., water molecule to water molecule). Adhesion refers to the attraction between dissimilar molecules (e.g., water molecule to molecule of tube wall).

door may stick as atmospheric humidity rises and the wooden door, or even the door jamb, swells. When a seed germinates, the imbibitional forces resulting from water absorption are sufficient to rupture the tough seed coat, allowing the enclosed embryo to grow. Proteins swell much more than starch which swells more than cellulose. Therefore, the storage tissues of seeds (which contain much protein and starch) swell more than the seed coats.

3.7 Surface-to-volume ratio

Adsorption and absorption are both dependent to a great extent upon exposed surfaces. In the former phenomenon, materials are held to surfaces, whereas in absorption materials pass through a surface. Therefore, the greater the amount of surface, the more adsorption and absorption will take place, other factors being equal. For example, a convoluted soil particle will adsorb more water molecules than a spherical soil particle of similar composition and volume because of the greater surface area in the former.

In general, the smaller or the more convoluted a structure, the greater is the surface-to-volume ratio. A simple way of visualizing this is to think of your textbook, which has a certain volume and six surfaces when closed. When the book is opened to expose each of the pages individually, the volume is unchanged, but the exposed surface area has increased tremendously, just as with any convoluted structure. If the pages are torn out, the total volume does not change, but each page now has surfaces exposed. In effect, the extremely small soil particles, which have developed by disintegration of large particles, are similar to the torn book.

The importance of this principle of surface-to-volume (S/V) ratio will be emphasized several times throughout the text.

Summary

1. All matter is composed of molecules, which are in continuous motion. Spheres of electrons surrounding a central core constitute the atoms of which molecules are composed.

2. Molecules may separate into electrically charged ions.

3. Oxidations provide the energy which is required for normal functioning of the cell.

4. Hydrolysis is the splitting of complex molecules to simpler ones with the utilization of water. Digestions are hydrolyses. Condensations, or syntheses, are the reverse of hydrolyses.

5. Adsorption is the concentration of molecules or ions on surfaces due to the forces of attraction between them. Imbibition refers to the entrance of water into solids and the resultant swelling.

6. The surface-to-volume ratio of structures is important in the processes of adsorption and absorption.

REVIEW TOPICS AND QUESTIONS

1. How could you determine whether the movement of particles in a drop of water was Brownian motion or not?
2. Describe a procedure that you could use to demonstrate diffusion.
3. The starch content of a cell increases while the amount of starch in a neighboring cell decreases. Since there is no other source of carbohydrate, the first cell presumably is obtaining materials from the second cell. Starch is not soluble and cannot penetrate membranes or plasmodesmata. Explain how the observed phenomena are possible if the assumption is correct.
4. List six elements and explain how each is important to living cells.
5. Discuss the advantages of utilizing symbols and formulae, as the chemist does when discussing reactions that occur within a cell.
6. A cube with dimensions of one centimeter is divided into smaller cubes with one millimeter dimensions. What was the original volume? The final volume? What was the original surface area? The final surface area?

SUGGESTED READINGS

Orear, J. *Fundamental Physics*. New York: Wiley, 1961.
Selwood, P. W. *General Chemistry*. New York: Holt-Dryden, 1959.

CHAPTER 4

Diffusion and the
Entrance of Materials into Cells

$\mathbf{M}$ANY materials pass into and out of the various cells of a plant when it is situated in a suitable environment. Water and mineral salts enter the roots from the soil, while carbon dioxide and oxygen gases enter the leaves from the atmosphere. The plant also loses various materials: water vapor and, at times, oxygen and carbon dioxide to the atmosphere. Many such movements result from the diffusion of molecules or ions from one area to another. Gases move through the intercellular spaces, and water and dissolved materials move within the cells. Some of these movements within the plant are accomplished by more complicated mechanisms than diffusion, but these will be discussed in Chapter 7. For the present, we shall be concerned with diffusion, since few, if any, of the physiological processes occurring in plants do not involve diffusion at least in part.

4.1 Diffusion pressure

In order to understand more clearly what is happening when a gas diffuses from one area to another, imagine a large auditorium which contains a great number of small rubber balls bounding about in all directions. A ball's direction of movement will change only upon a collision with a wall or another ball. The result is a zigzag fluctuating movement, and the room becomes filled with flying rubber balls. Similarly, any chamber becomes filled with gas molecules (= rubber balls) because of their inherent motion. The average speed of the entire group will remain constant as long as the temperature does not change. An increase in temperature would result in an increased **kinetic energy** (or motion energy).

Now if the wall between this auditorium and an adjacent one were removed, some of the balls would pass into the empty room because their motion would no longer be impeded by the wall which has been removed. The random movement finally results in an equal number of balls in each room. At this time, the number moving from the first room to the second will be equal to the number moving in the opposite direction, a condition termed **dynamic equilibrium.** Two things should be emphasized: (1) movement is still taking place from one area (room) to the other, and (2) the concentrations in the two areas are equal. The term **diffusion** is best used for the movement of molecules or ions from one location to another, while **net diffusion** is used for the direction of movement of the greatest number of molecules. In other words, net diffusion of the rubber balls was from the first room into the second, and net diffusion ceased (or is zero) at equilibrium, while diffusion continues even at equilibrium.

That such diffusion of gases occurs throughout a room can be demonstrated quite readily by opening a bottle of perfume (or ether) at one end of a room. Persons at that end of the room will detect the odor before individuals at the other end, but eventually the entire room will be permeated with the odor. Diffusion is exhibited by molecules of liquids and solutes (materials dissolved in liquids) also. An example of the diffusion of a solute can be obtained by dropping a cube of sugar in a cup of coffee. Careful sipping at the lip of the cup without tipping (to prevent stirring of the liquid) allows one to taste the increasing sweetness as sugar molecules diffuse, after the sugar dissolves, from the bottom of the coffee to the top layers. In all cases, the rates of diffusion are relatively slow because of the many collisions that occur and because of the vast spaces, in comparison to molecular dimensions, which humans use in measuring distances.

The direction of diffusion of one material is independent of the direction in which a second material is diffusing. The rate may slow down a bit because of collisions between the two different molecules, but the direction depends upon factors concerning each type of molecule separately. Quite possibly, and in fact usually, as certain molecules diffuse into a cell, others are diffusing out.

Diffusion and mass movements should be clearly distinguished from one another. If, in our example of solute diffusion, the coffee had been stirred with a spoon, sugar molecules would have been carried about by the mass movement of the coffee, much as twigs are carried by streams of water. Air currents would have the same effect on gas molecules.

Gases may exert considerable pressures upon the walls of containers. For example, if a rubber balloon is placed in a closed bottle of carbon dioxide gas, the balloon becomes distended because rubber is readily permeable to carbon dioxide molecules. If the temperature remains constant, the pressure exerted by any gas is directly proportional to the number of molecules per unit volume, in other words, its concentration. The net diffusion of gases results from a difference in gas pressures in the two areas under discussion. When the pressures are equal, the condition is that of a dynamic equilibrium. Such pressures, in discussing diffusion, are termed **diffusion pressures**. Liquids and solutes can also be thought of as possessing a diffusion pressure. For reasons that will be clarified in a moment, to state that the net diffusion of a substance is from a region of its greater diffusion pressure to one of lesser diffusion pressure is more correct than to interpret this movement on the basis of concentration differences.

4.2 Factors influencing diffusion

TEMPERATURE

An increase in temperature results in an increase in the speed of diffusion. This is because of the increased activity of molecules as the temperature is raised; the average speed with which a molecule moves is greater at high temperatures than at low temperatures. Another way of putting it is that the diffusion pressure increases directly with temperature.

CONCENTRATION GRADIENTS

As was indicated previously, diffusion pressure increases with an increase in concentration of the molecules. The greater the difference in diffusion pressures between two regions, the more rapid will be the net diffusion of molecules. However, this rate is also influenced by the distance between the two regions, so that the rate decreases as the distance increases. The term concentration gradient implies the application of concentration differences over a specific distance. To visu-

[A]

[B]

[C]

[D]

Figure 4-1. Representations of concentration gradients. The top of the hill represents the higher concentration, the bottom of the hill represents the lower concentration, and the stone represents the material which is moving from one area to the other. **A** and **B**: The concentrations are the same but the distance is greater in **B**. Therefore, the material moves more rapidly in **A**. **C** and **D**: The distances are the same but the concentration is greater in **C**. Therefore, the material moves more rapidly in **C**.

Figure 4-2. The effect of an external force on the diffusion pressure of water. The greater force in B causes more water to penetrate the membrane than in A.

[A]

alize what is happening, imagine a stone poised on top of a hill and then rolling to the bottom. The top of the hill represents the higher concentration, and the bottom of the hill represents the lower concentration of an adjacent area. In Figure 4-1A the stone rolls down a much steeper hill and reaches the bottom faster than the stone in Figure 4-1B, even though both started at the same altitude (= concentration). In Figures 4-1C and 4-1D, the horizontal distance is the same, but the stone in "C" moves faster because it started at a higher elevation (= concentration). The steepness of the gradient, thus, may be changed by a variation in either the concentrations or the distance.

[B]

EXTERNAL FORCES

This concept is particularly important in an understanding of water movements through plant cells. If pressure or force is imposed upon water, as by a piston in a closed system, the diffusion pressure of the water in that system is increased by the amount of force applied. As shown in Figure 4-2, the amount of water passing through the membrane increases as the weight on the piston is increased. The production of such forces in plant cells will be discussed in the next section.

SIZE OF MOLECULES

In general, the larger the molecule, the slower is the rate of diffusion.[1]

PRESENCE OF OTHER MOLECULES

An increase in the number of "foreign" molecules causes the rate of diffusion to decrease because of the additional collisions that occur. In other words, a gas diffuses more rapidly through a vacuum than through air. However, the *direction* of net diffusion is not influenced by the presence of other types of molecules.

4.3 Differentially permeable membranes and diffusion

In describing a generalized cell (see Section 2.2), mention was made of various membranes, surface layers which have properties quite distinct from the specialized bits of protoplasm which they enclose. Also stated was the fact that all such living membranes, and also some

[1] Graham's Law of Diffusion: the rates of diffusion of gases are inversely proportional to the square roots of their densities.

non-living ones (e.g., cellophane, parchment, dialysis tubing), are characteristically **differentially permeable,** i.e., to reiterate, for any given membrane, some molecules and ions penetrate quite readily, others more slowly, and some not at all. There are gradations in penetration rates.

The reasons for differential permeability are not fully known at the present time, but it is undoubtedly related to: the structure of the membrane, especially its fat and oil (lipoid) content; the size of the diffusing molecule; and the relative solubility of the diffusing substance in fatty materials and water. Certainly true is the fact that only dissolved materials will penetrate membranes. Even gases first dissolve in the water which impregnates cell walls before penetrating the cell membranes. In the case of non-living membranes such as cellulose, the size of the diffusing particle is the important factor, since such membranes are differentially permeable because the size of the pores (holes) is large enough for small molecules, such as water, but too small for large molecules, such as cane sugar (sucrose) or proteins, to pass through.

Cell membranes regulate the entrance or exit of materials. However, since these are living membranes, various external and internal factors bring about significant changes which influence the penetration of molecules from one moment to another. The general order of penetration remains fairly constant, but individual rates may fluctuate. In other words, "A" may penetrate more rapidly than "B," but under certain conditions both may diffuse through more rapidly, "A" still faster than "B."

OSMOSIS

One of the most important materials which enters cells is water. The term **osmosis** [2] refers to the movement (diffusion) of water through a differentially permeable membrane from a region of high diffusion pressure to a region of low diffusion pressure of water. In plants this movement of water may be from the environment into the cell, as from the soil into a root cell, or from one cell to another.

Osmosis in non-living systems can be demonstrated quite readily. Figure 4-3A indicates a capillary glass tube [3] with an enlarged base

[2] In a strict sense, osmosis refers to the movement of a **solvent** through such a membrane. However, the only solvent involved in living cells is water, so the more restrictive definition will be used.

[3] A glass tube having a very small inner diameter. A small change in volume of the enclosed solution will be readily observed as a fluctuation of the level in the small tube.

submerged in a beaker of distilled (pure) water. The enlarged portion of the tube is filled with a 50 per cent sucrose solution, separated from the distilled water by a differentially permeable membrane (cellophane or dialysis tubing) which allows water to penetrate but not sugar. For ease of observation the sugar solution may be colored with a dye, such as Congo Red, which will not penetrate through the membrane, or a brown syrup. The concentration of water is greater in the beaker than in the **osmometer,** which means that the diffusion pressure of water is higher in the beaker than in the glass tube. Water molecules diffuse more rapidly into the osmometer than they diffuse out, the volume of liquid in the tube increases, and the level of liquid in the capillary rises as shown in Figure 4-3B.

Note that the water molecules diffuse in both directions but that more of them diffuse inwardly. Net diffusion is then from the beaker into the osmometer. If one could greatly enlarge a portion of the membrane so that molecules were visible, the appearance would be approximately as in Figure 4-3C. The water molecules penetrate quite readily, as indicated by the small arrows, but the sugar molecules are restricted by the nature of the membrane. These large sugar molecules occupy space at the surface of the membrane, and thus the number of water molecules on the solution side of the membrane is less than that on the water side. Clearly then, more water molecules are in a position to penetrate into the osmometer than are in a position to diffuse outwardly. The rise of the solution level does not continue indefinitely

Figure 4-3. An osmometer. The sugar solution within the osmometer is separated from distilled water by a membrane that is permeable only to the water. **A:** The original condition. **B:** The condition after equilibrium has been reached. **C:** Representation of the surface of the membrane. The circles are water molecules; the black squares are sugar molecules. **D:** The condition which would result if a piston with weights were placed in the osmometer tube. For additional discussion see the text.

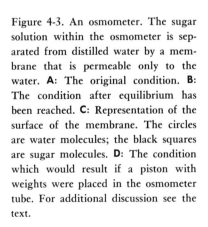

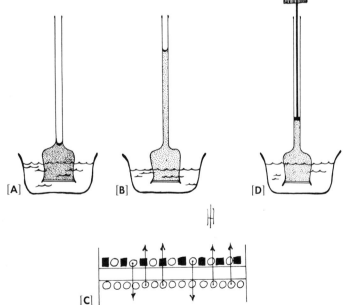

but eventually reaches a definite height.[4] When the level remains constant, the system is at equilibrium. Diffusion is still going on, but now the same number of water molecules is moving out of the osmometer as is moving in from the beaker. At equilibrium, the diffusion pressures of water on both sides of the membrane must be equal. If this were not true, there would be a net diffusion one way or the other, and an equilibrium would not exist. The question then arises as to how the diffusion pressures can be equal even though the concentrations are not equal. Remember that the sugar molecules cannot penetrate the membrane, and thus the water in the osmometer is always less than 100 per cent (which is the concentration of water in the beaker). The explanation arises from an understanding of the influence of external forces on the diffusion pressure of water (review Section 4.2) and the development of hydrostatic pressure in the osmometer.

Water has weight. As the solution rises in the capillary tube, more and more weight presses down on the water within the enlarged portion of the osmometer. The weight of this column of water exerts a force **(hydrostatic pressure)**, which increases the diffusion pressure of water within the osmometer by an amount equal to the external force. With an increase in diffusion pressure, more molecules of water move outwardly. Eventually the increased diffusion pressure, due to a build-up of hydrostatic pressure (an external force), reaches the point where it is equal to the diffusion pressure of water in the beaker and the number of molecules moving in the two directions are equal. The level in the capillary could be maintained at a lower height if a piston and weights were placed in the tube and were pressing down on the solution (as in Figure 4-3D). This is also an external force.

If no capillary tube were on the osmometer, but just the enlarged portion, the hydrostatic pressure would still develop, but it would not be visible as a column of liquid. This is basically the situation found in plant cells. In a mature cell the cytoplasm consists of thin layers adjacent to the cell wall and surrounding the vacuoles. Most of the water entering plant cells passes through the cytoplasm and into the vacuole. Though really two differentially permeable membranes are involved, the entire layer of cytoplasm can be thought of as functioning like a single membrane. As the water concentration increases within the vacuole, the developing hydrostatic pressure forces the cytoplasm out

---

[4] The approximate height can be calculated and depends mainly upon the concentration of sugar solution used. For those students familiar with chemical principles, the concentration must be in terms of molality. In multiplying the molality (50 per cent sucrose equals about 1.5 molal sucrose) by 22.4 by 33, one arrives at approximately 1,100 feet as the height of liquid in the capillary tube. The figures 22.4 and 33 are constants familiar to all chemists; the variable factor is the concentration of sugar which is used.

against the cell walls. Since such walls are rather rigid, their expandability is limited, and pressure develops within the cell. It is this **wall pressure** which increases the outward diffusion of water molecules, until equilibrium is reached and net diffusion is zero.

OSMOTIC PRESSURE AND TURGOR PRESSURE

Hydrostatic pressure against cell walls results in the **turgid** (firm) condition of plant cells and even of an entire structure, such as leaves and non-woody stems. The maximum amount of pressure which can be developed in a solution separated from pure water by a rigid membrane permeable only to water is termed the **osmotic pressure.** Living cells are not immersed in distilled water, except under laboratory conditions, and the theoretical maximum pressure never develops. The actual pressure exerted by the protoplast against the cell wall is the **turgor pressure,** which is always less than the osmotic pressure unless the cell is in distilled water. The difference between these two pressures is similar to that of a car having a maximum speed of 100 miles per hour and actually being driven at 50 miles per hour. Turgor pressure and wall pressure are equal but are exerted in opposite directions. Just as the protoplasm is pressing against the wall with a certain force, so must the wall be exerting a similar force against the protoplast. The crispness of lettuce leaves in a salad depends upon the turgidity of their cells. The longer the exposure to evaporation, the more water is lost, and turgor pressure decreases until the lettuce becomes limp and unappetizing.

4.4 Entrance of materials into cells

Many materials, besides water, enter plant cells: mineral salts from the soil solution; carbon dioxide and oxygen from the air through tiny pores in the leaves or into root cells from the soil atmosphere. These substances are essential to the normal growth and development of a plant.

Perhaps a hypothetical example of movements of materials into and out of a cell would help to clarify the principles involved. Figure 4-4A represents a cell immersed in a bathing solution; the arrows indicate the movement of mineral ions and water when the cell is first placed in the solution. Since the cell membranes are permeable to minerals and water but not to sugar, the sugar molecules diffuse about within the cell but do not diffuse to the exterior in spite of a concentration gradient in that direction. Nitrate salts diffuse out of the cell, sulfates and chlorides move into the cell, phosphates move equally in both directions (no net diffusion), and water enters into the cell. All such

41

movements result from concentration differences and thus from diffusion pressure differences. The direction of *net* diffusion depends upon these differences, and one material readily moves out of the cell as another moves into the cell.

Figure 4-4B indicates the situation when equilibrium has been reached; the arrows indicate an equal diffusion of materials in both directions and thus no net diffusion. Note that the salt concentrations are equal on both sides of the membrane at the equilibrium point but that the water concentrations are *not* equal. The presence of sugar results in the concentration of water always being less within the cell

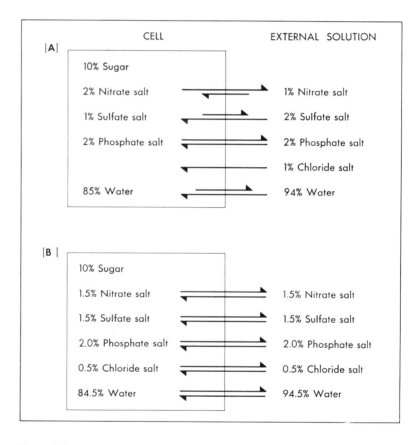

Figure 4-4. A representation of movements of material into and out of a cell. The length of the arrows represent the relative amount of material diffusing in that direction. If the arrows are of equal length, there is no net diffusion; this is the equilibrium point. The cell membrane is permeable to salts and water but not to sugar. Cell **B** is an idealized concept; actual concentrations would depend upon the relative sizes of the cell and the bathing solution.

than outside of the cell.[5] And yet no further net movement of water occurs—the number of molecules diffusing into the cell is equal to the number of molecules diffusing out of the cell. As water begins moving into the cell originally, hydrostatic (wall) pressure builds up. The increasing external force (wall pressure) increases the diffusion pressure of water within the cell. Therefore, the difference in diffusion pressures gradually decreases to zero because the diffusion pressure of water in the cell is raised sufficiently by wall pressure to counteract the higher concentration of water outside the cell.

PASSIVE ABSORPTION

The movement into or out of a cell is in many instances due simply to differences in diffusion pressures. As the cell uses a certain substance, the concentration of that material within the cell decreases, and more of it diffuses in from the environment if the external concentration is now higher than the internal. In the case of solutes (mainly mineral salts), the difference in concentrations is really the only factor which influences diffusion pressures, whereas the movement of water is somewhat complicated by the development of wall pressure. The term **passive absorption** is used to refer to the movement of material into cells as a result of diffusion.

ACTIVE ABSORPTION

In recent years more and more evidence has indicated that the molecules and ions of many substances continue to diffuse into plant cells even when their concentrations, and thus their diffusion pressures, are greater within the cell than they are outside of the cell. In other words the movement is in a direction opposite to that which would be expected on the basis of diffusion phenomena. This accumulation against a concentration gradient is termed **active absorption.** It occurs commonly in root cells of higher plants, but an outstanding example is the accumulation of iodine from sea water by kelp.[6] This iodine, at least 100 times as concentrated as that in the sea, can be extracted for commercial use.

The accumulation of ions and molecules in the vacuoles of cells is attributed to the energy of respiration being used to hold these materials against a gradient. Oxygen and sugars must be available to the cell, and respiratory inhibitors have been shown to prevent this process. Most mineral absorption quite likely is of this type. (See also Sections 8.3 and 15.3.)

[5] Of course, many materials besides sugars and salts are dissolved in cells.

[6] Kelp is a general term referring to the giant brown seaweeds (Division Phaeophyta) found growing in the oceans, as along the Pacific Coast of the United States.

PLASMOLYSIS

As has been mentioned, when water enters, a cell becomes turgid. If a cell is placed in a highly concentrated sugar or salt solution, water diffuses out of the cell (why?) and the protoplast shrinks away from (or collapses away from) the cell wall as turgor pressure is lost. This condition is termed **plasmolysis** (Figure 4-5), and the cell will die if left in that solution. However, if the cell is placed in distilled water or a dilute solution soon enough, recovery will take place, since a higher diffusion pressure of water now exists outside of the cell and movement will be inward. The "burning" of plants after spraying with insecticides or fungicides is actually a result of plasmolysis of leaf cells due to the high concentration of the spray residues. The brown discoloration is an indication of dead cells. Sometimes the excessive addition of chemical fertilizers to the soil may lead to the death of root cells and even the entire plant.

The effect of plasmolysis on living cells is utilized in the salting of meat and fish. The excess salt prevents the growth of decay organisms by plasmolyzing the cells of such molds and bacteria. In a similar manner, jams and jellies are preserved because of the high sugar concentrations which prevent the growth of molds. Undesirable plants can be eliminated by applying salt to the soil at the base of the plant. Though this method may be expensive, it is suitable when one does not wish to dig up the unwanted plant, as with grass growing up through paved driveways. The recent development of arsenical plant-killing solutions has replaced the plasmolytic killing of plants in most instances.

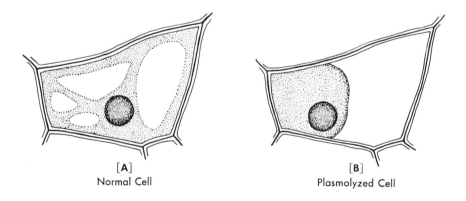

[A]
Normal Cell

[B]
Plasmolyzed Cell

Figure 4-5. **A:** Normal cell. **B:** The same cell in a plasmolyzed condition after it has been placed in a concentrated sugar or salt solution.

Summary

1. Net movement of a substance is always from a region of its greater diffusion pressure to one of lesser diffusion pressure. Diffusion of materials into and out of living cells is primarily influenced by the concentration gradient, by external forces, and by the size of the molecules which are diffusing.

2. All of the membranes of a living cell are differentially permeable. Some materials penetrate such membranes much more rapidly than do others, and some molecules cannot penetrate the membrane at all.

3. Osmosis is the movement of water through a differentially permeable membrane. As water penetrates, a pressure builds up within the cell. This turgor pressure is important in the growth of cells and in the general support of a plant.

4. Materials enter cells passively as a result of diffusion, or they may be absorbed actively as a result of the expenditure of energy by the cell.

5. If a cell is surrounded by a solution which is more concentrated than that within the cell, a net movement of water out of the cell results, and the cell plasmolyzes.

REVIEW TOPICS AND QUESTIONS

1. Explain in detail how you could determine whether the cytoplasmic membranes or the cell walls act as differentially permeable structures.
2. A row of three living cells is immersed in a two per cent salt solution. Cell *A*, which is in contact with cell *B*, contains two per cent sugar and one per cent salt; cell *B*, which is in contact with cell *C*, contains three per cent sugar and three per cent salt; cell *C* contains one per cent sugar and two per cent salt. The differentially permeable membranes of these cells are freely permeable to water and salt but are impermeable to sugar.
    - (a) Explain the direction of initial net movement of all of the materials among the cells and between the cells and the external solution.
    - (b) Explain why such net movement finally ceases, in other words, explain what brings about the equilibrium condition.
3. A living plant cell contains five per cent sugar and the following salts: one per cent nitrates, two per cent sulfates, and one per cent bicarbonates. This cell is immersed in a solution containing the following salts: two per cent nitrates, two per cent sulfates, two per cent phosphates, and one per cent chlorides. The cell membranes are freely permeable to all salts and water but are impermeable to sugar.
    - (a) Explain in detail the reasons for the net movement, or lack of it, of all materials when the cell is first placed in the solution.
    - (b) Explain why such movement eventually ceases.
4. Explain why molds and bacteria usually do not grow upon jams, jellies, and salted meats.

45

5. Human red blood cells do not have walls. Explain what happens to such cells if a drop of blood is placed in distilled water.
6. Living cells are stripped from an onion bulb and placed in a drop of distilled water. They are examined with the aid of a microscope.
    (a) Describe the general appearance of one of these cells as to its turgidity and the location of the protoplasm with respect to the cell wall.
    (b) Describe the appearance of the same cell five minutes after the distilled water is replaced with a ten per cent salt (NaCl) solution, and explain any difference in appearance from that in (a) above.
    (c) Describe the appearance of the same cell after five hours in the ten per cent salt solution, and explain any difference in appearance from (a) or (b) above. (Assume no toxicity.)
7. Frequently after heavy applications of insecticides, yellowish areas appear on the leaves of plants that have been sprayed. Microscopic examination reveals that cells in the yellow areas have died. Since the insect spray is not poisonous to plants, explain the death of the leaf cells.
8. Explain the relation among turgor pressure, wall pressure, and osmotic pressure.
9. Consider an isolated healthy cell bathed in a nutrient solution. Describe and explain the effect each of the following changes will have upon the net ability of the cell to absorb water from the surrounding solution:
    (a) an increase in the turgor pressure of the cell;
    (b) an increase in the concentration of solutes in the external solution;
    (c) an increase in the concentration of solutes in the cell sap.
10. A home-owner decided to triple the amount of fertilizer above that indicated on the label. After adding the dry fertilizer, he sprinkled one half of his lawn for 30 to 40 minutes and then moved the sprinkler to the other half. He went to a movie later, forgetting that the water was still turned on. As a result, the second half of the lawn was thoroughly soaked for over six hours. Several days later, the home-owner noticed that the grass which had received a light soaking was dying, while the rest of the lawn was lush.
    Explain these results.
11. If a crystal (or small piece) of potassium permanganate (violet or purple in color) is placed on a layer of clear agar (or gelatin), the agar gradually becomes violet in color, the color being more intense closer to the crystal.
    (a) Explain in detail this observation.
    (b) Discuss how this general process is important to living cells.
12. A five per cent sugar solution is enclosed within an inelastic unbreakable membrane which is permeable to water but impermeable to sugar. Explain in detail what will happen if this enclosed sugar solution is placed in distilled water.

SUGGESTED READINGS

Curtis, O. F., and D. G. Clark. *An Introduction to Plant Physiology.* New York: McGraw-Hill, 1950.

Ferry, J. F., and H. S. Ward. *Fundamentals of Plant Physiology.* New York: Macmillan, 1959.

Holter, H. "How Things Get into Cells," *Scientific American,* 205 (September 1961), 167–183.

Meyer, B. S., D. B. Anderson, and R. H. Bohning. *Introduction to Plant Physiology.* Princeton: Van Nostrand, 1960.

Miller, E. V. *Within the Living Plant.* New York: Blakiston, 1953.

Solomon, A. K. "Pores in the Cell Membrane," *Scientific American,* 204 (December 1960), 145–156.

CHAPTER 5

The Plant

BEFORE the various types of plants are considered in any detail, the flowering plant will be the example for a discussion of the basic structure and function of plants. Most processes, especially those occurring on the cellular level, are basically alike, whether they take place in a flowering plant or in a one-celled alga. Diffusion and photosynthesis, for example, may be studied in a variety of plants with equal ease and similar results. Differences arise, for the most part, in examining the over-all metabolism of plants which exist in greatly differing environments; land plants have the problems of water loss and conduction of materials, which are trifling or not existent in aquatic plants. Also, the energy-yielding processes of plant cells proceed along one pathway if oxygen is present (respiration) and along a different pathway if oxygen is absent (fermentation). The similarities in structure and function are more numerous and will be discussed first in a general manner. The differences will be emphasized during the discussion of individual groups of plants as they fit into specific niches of the plant kingdom examined from an evolutionary point of view.

Even though no structures or functions of an entire plant are isolated from all others, to separate individual portions or processes for the purpose of logical discussion and understanding is frequently helpful. After individual parts are clear, they can be placed in juxtaposition as one fits pieces of a jigsaw puzzle together to form a finished picture. One of the difficult problems faced during biological investigations is whether or not the one variable factor is influencing a process directly or indirectly by its influence on other processes. The inter-relationships of processes and of structure and function must be kept in mind at all times. Many separations for discussive purposes are purely a matter of convenience and may not appear too logical when viewed on the basis of an entire plant. However, this type of approach, coupled with a final pulling together of the isolated parts, appears to be the best way of treating something as complicated as plant life.

5.1 Vegetative structures

In general, one may lump together as **vegetative structures** those structures of the plant which are concerned with growth and development, i.e., root, stem, and leaf. These parts of the plant are not directly concerned with sexual reproduction. Figure 5-1 represents the various parts of a flowering plant in diagrammatic form and should be referred to for an understanding of the placement and relationships of the portions under discussion.

ROOT

That part of the plant axis which is typically non-green and found beneath the surface of the soil is termed the **root.** This greatly-branched structure's primary function is the absorption of water and minerals

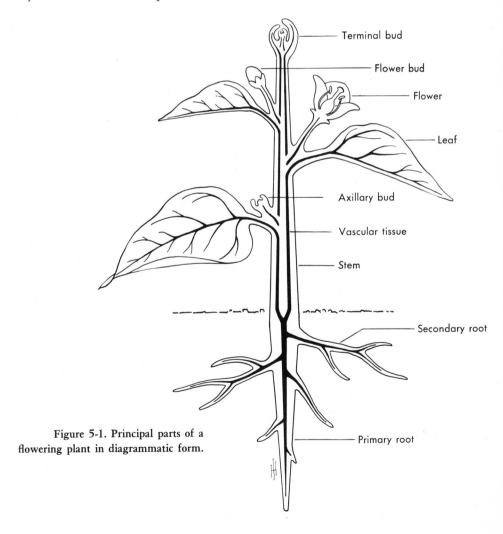

Figure 5-1. Principal parts of a flowering plant in diagrammatic form.

Terminal bud

Flower bud

Flower

Leaf

Axillary bud

Vascular tissue

Stem

Secondary root

Primary root

from the soil. The root, however, has secondary functions. Since those materials which are absorbed are used by all cells of the plant, conduction obviously must take place through the root before such utilization can occur. In addition to conduction, many roots contain much stored food materials, and thus storage must be indicated as another function of this part of the plant. The branching of roots and their penetration within the soil serve to anchor the plant as well as the soil, a significant factor in any area subjected to wind storms and heavy rainstorms. A more detailed discussion of roots will appear later (see Chapter 8).

STEM

The **stem** is the continuation of the plant's axis typically found above the soil surface. No sharp line of demarcation, but a gradual merging of one into the other, exists between root and stem. The stem branches in a variety of ways, resulting in the more-or-less characteristic form associated with different plants (Figure 5-2), and may be woody or

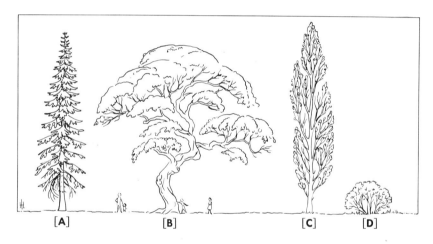

Figure 5-2. Characteristic growth formation of various woody plants. **A**: Pine (*Pinus*). **B**: Oak (*Quercus*). **C**: Lombardy poplar (*Populus nigra* var. *italica*). **D**: Typical bush or shrub.

non-woody. Irrespective of appearances, the stem functions mainly in conducting water and minerals from the root to other parts of the plant and in conducting food materials from the leaves to the rest of the plant. Vascular, or conducting, tissues are well-developed. Stems are involved in the production and support of leaves. Many stems also store food materials and may even manufacture foods if they are green (chlorophyllous). The structural arrangement of tissues and their functions will be discussed in Chapters 6 and 7.

A **leaf,** an outgrowth of the stem, is flat and thin, needle-like, or scale-like. It is green or, if some other color (such as red), the chlorophyll is merely masked by an abundance of accessory pigments. The function of a leaf is closely correlated with the universal presence of chlorophyll. This is the material which enables leaf cells to utilize light energy for the production of food from simple inorganic materials, a process termed **photosynthesis.** Since food for all living organisms is dependent upon this process, considerable discussion will be devoted to it later (see Chapter 10).

5.2 Reproductive structures

Those parts of the plant which are concerned with sexual reproduction and the production of seeds are termed the **reproductive structures.** These are **flowers** or **cones,** which are basically continuations of the stem with specialized structures comparable to modified leaves and branch systems. The seeds which are produced germinate and grow into new individuals similar in type to the parents. The differences between flowers and cones, the manner in which seeds are produced, and the development of fruits will be discussed in subsequent chapters (see Chapters 25 and 26).

5.3 Life span

Once a seed has germinated, the growth and development of the plant are influenced by both the environment and the inherited characteristics of that particular type of plant. Factors of the environment would include such items as: (1) water supply, (2) temperature, (3) supply of minerals in the soil, (4) light, (5) oxygen and carbon dioxide supply, and (6) parasites or herbivores. However, even if all of these factors are conducive to growth, not all plants will grow indefinitely. The length of the life span will depend upon the type of plant: (1) **annuals** grow for one season only, producing their seeds and then dying (e.g., beans, some grasses); (2) **biennials** grow vegetatively during the first season and do not produce seeds until the second year, after which they die (e.g., lettuce, carrot, cabbage); and (3) **perennials** grow for several to very many years, producing a new crop of seeds each year after the first few years (e.g., trees, shrubs). These last include plants which may be hundreds or thousands of years old; the *Sequoiadendron giganteum* in California has been estimated to be probably 3,000 years old. It was already a giant at the birth of Christ, and unless it is attacked by parasites, destroyed by fire, or blown down, there is no reason why some hundreds of years cannot be added to its age. As mentioned previously (Section 1.3), one of the characteristics of plants is their continued growth throughout their life span. Each year this tree, as do others, is increasing in size as well as in age. Who can say when all this will cease?

5.4 Tissues

The complexity of a multicellular organism makes cooperation and correlation amongst its cells essential for any growth and development despite the adversities that are met on every side. For example, the water that is absorbed by the roots is subject to evaporation from the above-ground portions of the plant which are exposed to light and an unsaturated atmosphere. To prevent desiccation, the plant must transport water from roots to leaves much more rapidly than it could by diffusion, or osmosis, from one cell to another. It was fortunate indeed that in some plants there developed conducting tissues which enabled such rapid movement of water. Generally, then, **tissues** are groups of cells which perform essentially the same function and which are commonly of similar structure. They are subdivided into meristematic and permanent types.

MERISTEMATIC TISSUE

The continued growth of plants throughout their lives depends upon the activity of **meristematic tissues.** In such tissues the cells are actively dividing, and new cells are continually being produced. These immature cells, cubical or box-shaped,[1] have thin walls and dense protoplasm, and vacuoles are non-existent or very small. There is no differentiation of cells, one cell being much the same as any other cell of the tissue. **Apical meristems** consist of cubical cells and are located at the tips of both roots and stems. A sample of this tissue (usually a root tip) is used for observing mitosis in the laboratory. The **vascular cambium** consists of elongated (box-shaped) cells, slightly tapered at the ends, and is located as a thin cylindrical sheath between the bark and the wood.[2] It is somewhat difficult to examine because of the tissues bordering on each side, but it is readily detected in cross sections of stems and roots. If a plant is damaged in any way, a **cork cambium** usually de-

---

[1] Technically, a parallelepiped having all right angles.

[2] Bark and wood are general non-technical terms which have been used for convenience. In mature woody stems, the cambium is located between phloem and xylem. The inner part of the "bark" consists of phloem; the "wood" consists of xylem. **See** Chapter 6.

velops. Cells of the injured area become meristematic and produce additional cells which protect the wounded region. The cells which are produced by the activity of these various meristematic tissues eventually differentiate and become the cells of the permanent tissues.

PERMANENT TISSUE

In these tissues the cells are stable and no longer dividing. Although derived from meristematic regions, these cells have considerable structural and physiological modifications. Each type of permanent tissue is composed of specifically differentiated mature cells that make possible an efficient division of labor. For example, the cells of conducting tissues are usually quite elongated, whereas storage cells are short and bulky. Only through the development of a variety of tissues having various specific functions are large organisms capable of existing, especially on land.

The permanent tissues are divided into simple and complex types. The **simple permanent tissues** are composed of cells which are structurally and functionally alike, while the **complex permanent tissues** are composed of several kinds of cells which differ in structure. In this latter type of tissue, the cells are involved in a group of inter-related activities in which one function is usually dominant.

1. Simple permanent tissue. Figure 5-3 consists of diagrams of the kinds of cells that are involved in the formation of simple permanent tissues.

EPIDERMIS (Figure 5-3A). This tissue is one cell in thickness and forms the surface layers of leaves, flowers, and young stems and roots. The outer walls of epidermal cells, at least of the above-ground portions, are covered with **cutin,** a waxy material secreted by the protoplast. The continuous layer of cutin, which is termed the **cuticle,** is quite impervious to water and greatly retards the loss of water from a plant. The conservation of moisture and the protection derived from the fairly thick walls of the epidermal cells are important functions of the epidermis.

In many regions of the epidermis, especially on leaves and green stems, are found tiny pores, or **stomata.** Each **stoma** is really the space between two adjacent, kidney-shaped **guard cells.** The number of stomata per unit area of epidermis varies with the location as well as with the kind of plant. They are usually most numerous on leaf surfaces, and frequently more are found on the lower surface than on the upper surface of a leaf. Such openings provide easy access for the diffusion of gases into or out of the leaf, a situation which is essential for food manufacture. Further discussion of the importance of stomata and the

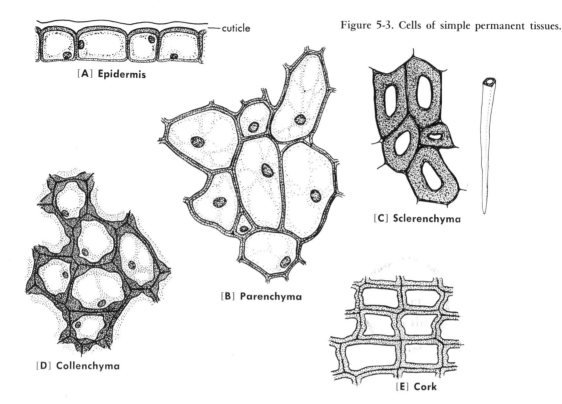

[A] Epidermis

cuticle

Figure 5-3. Cells of simple permanent tissues.

[C] Sclerenchyma

[B] Parenchyma

[D] Collenchyma

[E] Cork

functioning of guard cells will be reserved for Chapters 9, 10, and 14.

PARENCHYMA (Figure 5-3B). The cells of the **parenchyma** are usually more or less spherical, although the shape may be distorted by the pressure of surrounding cells and may appear rather angular or box-shaped. The walls are thin, and the vacuoles are quite large. Various materials are stored in the parenchyma tissues, which are found throughout the plant. If chloroplasts are present, these cells are capable of carrying on photosynthesis under suitable conditions. Cells of this type are capable of becoming meristematic under certain conditions, such as wounding or injury. This is extremely important for recovery from adverse conditions.

SCLERENCHYMA (Figure 5-3C). The cells of this tissue characteristically have extremely thick walls and are dead at maturity. Obviously they are alive as they develop, but the thick walls become impregnated with such materials as lignins, and the protoplast subsequently dies. The gritty texture of many pears is due to the presence of **stone cells,** which are sclerenchyma-type cells. Elongated sclerenchymatous cells are termed **fibers.** Strength, mechanical support, and protection are the main functions of sclerenchyma tissue.

COLLENCHYMA (Figure 5-3D). The cells of this tissue are somewhat elongated, and the walls are irregularly thickened, usually at the corners where the cells meet. This strengthening and supporting tissue is frequently found in young stems near the epidermis.

CORK (Figure 5-3E). This tissue is composed of cells that have thick walls which are impregnated with **suberin,** a waxy material. The cells are dead at maturity and form a rather water-proof layer of tissue. Cork is found as the outer layers of stems and roots of woody plants and also as the protective layers which form when a plant is damaged. Water conservation and protection, then, are the functions of cork. In the case of the cork oak (*Quercus Suber*), such a profuse formation of cork occurs that this tissue is removed and used commercially (e.g., cork stoppers, life preservers, insulation). The cork cambium produces new cork which may again be stripped from the tree in another three or four years.

2. Complex permanent tissue. The **xylem** and **phloem,** which form the vascular or conducting tissues, are complex permanent tissues. The specific kinds of cells which comprise these two tissues will be discussed in the chapter on stems (Chapter 6) so that the location of cells and tissues can be clarified. Since these tissues are somewhat complicated, they can be studied more readily—this is especially true of microscopic examination—in conjunction with their location, and then the individual cells can be examined in detail.

Summary

1. The root, stem, and leaf are vegetative structures and not directly concerned with reproduction. The root is that part of the plant axis which is below ground, while the stem is the part typically found above the soil. The former absorbs water and minerals; the latter conducts material throughout the plant. The leaf is an outgrowth of the stem and carries on photosynthesis.

2. The reproductive structures are flowers and cones.

3. Annual plants grow for one season only, biennials produce seeds during the second year and then die, and perennials grow for many years.

4. A tissue is a group of cells which perform essentially the same function and commonly are of similar structure. In meristematic tissues the cells are actively dividing, as in the apical meristem, vascular cambium, and cork cambium. Permanent tissues are those in which the cells are no longer dividing.

5. Simple permanent tissues are composed of cells which are structurally and functionally alike: epidermis, parenchyma, sclerenchyma,

collenchyma, and cork. The xylem and phloem are complex permanent tissues.

REVIEW TOPICS AND QUESTIONS

1. You are given a slide which contains thin sections, transverse and longitudinal, of a tissue. Discuss in detail the characteristics that you would have to look for in order to determine what kind of simple permanent tissue had been used in preparing this slide for observation through a microscope.
2. You are given a slide which contains thin sections, transverse and longitudinal, of a tissue. Discuss in detail the characteristics that you would have to look for in order to determine whether this was a meristematic tissue.
3. Discuss in detail the changes that occur when a cell differentiates into a fiber. What are the functions of fibers?
4. Describe the difference between annual, biennial, and perennial plants.
5. Discuss the advantages that obtain to a multicellular organism as compared with unicellular or colonial organisms.
6. What is the importance of structure to the function of a cell?

SUGGESTED READINGS

Esau, K. *Anatomy of Seed Plants*. New York: Wiley, 1960.
Foster, A. *Practical Plant Anatomy*. Princeton: Van Nostrand, 1949.
Fuller, H. J., and O. Tippo. *College Botany*. New York: Holt, 1954.
Hill, J. B., et al. *Botany: A Textbook for Colleges*. New York: McGraw-Hill, 1960.

Stem Structure

T HE stem is the pathway whereby foods, which are produced in leaves, and minerals and water, which are absorbed by roots, are transported throughout the plant. Some of these materials nourish the cells of the stem, some are stored there, and the rest merely pass through on their way to other cells and tissues, where they are utilized or stored. In addition to the **translocation** of materials, many stems are also involved in food manufacture, vegetative reproduction, and support. Each of these functions will be discussed in some detail after a discussion of stem structure.

6.1 External structure

An examination of the various kinds of plants that can be found on any campus will indicate that some plant stems are quite woody, while others are not. One can separate plants into two general groups on this basis: those that have herbaceous stems and those that have woody stems. In both types leaves and buds are present at specific locations along the stem, each point of attachment being termed a **node** and the distance between nodes being called an **internode.** The length of an individual stem depends upon the growth of the internode and varies with the type of plant as well as with various environmental conditions (e.g., temperature, light, soil fertility).

HERBACEOUS STEMS

The stems of this group are generally soft and green and have very little, or no, tough woody tissue. There is little growth in diameter, and the plants are usually short-lived. The outer surface consists of a thin epidermis in which stomata are present. The green color, of course, is due to the presence of chlorophyll and indicates the food manufacturing ability of such stems. The support of the leaves depends upon collenchyma, sclerenchyma, and the turgid condition of individual cells.

Figure 6-1. Dormant twig of California buckeye (*Aesculus californica*).

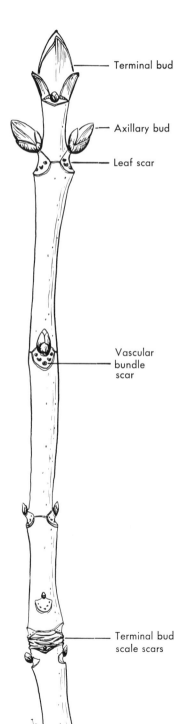

Terminal bud

Axillary bud

Leaf scar

Vascular bundle scar

Terminal bud scale scars

Examples of plants with herbaceous stems are the common garden peas and beans, grasses, clover, alfalfa, wheat (*Triticum* sp.), and corn (*Zea mays*).

WOODY STEMS

In contrast, **woody stems** are hard, thick, and long-lived. The outer surface of the older stems is rough and covered with cork, the common bark of trees and shrubs. In this rough surface are raised areas, or **lenticels,** which are really openings beneath which the cells are loosely arranged with many intercellular spaces. Gaseous exchange can take place through these openings. The bulk of the stem consists of tough woody tissue. A young woody stem may contain chlorophyll and carry on photosynthesis for a short period, but as the diameter increases and cork forms, this ability is lost. Lumber is obtained by cutting the woody tissue of trees into usable sizes and shapes. The difference between a tree and a shrub is merely one of growth-form rather than any intrinsic difference in the internal structure. In a **tree** the stem (or trunk) rises some distance above the ground before branching occurs, while in a **shrub,** several stems of rather equal size arise at, or close to, ground level (see Figure 5-2).

BUDS

New stems and their leaves develop from **buds.** Figure 6-1 indicates a typical arrangement, with a **terminal bud** at the tip of the twig and **axillary** (or **lateral**) **buds** occurring at regular intervals along the stem. The latter type is always located in the angle made by the stem and the leaf stalk. Since the drawing is that of a buckeye (*Aesculus*) twig in its winter condition, after the leaves have fallen, the location of leaves can be determined by the presence of **leaf scars** just below each axillary bud. Since the conducting tissue of the stem is continuous with that of the leaf, this tissue also ruptures when the leaf falls, and **vascular bundle scars** are visible in each leaf scar. In woody plants the more delicate inner structures are protected by the tough hard **bud scales,** which drop off as the new stem develops. (The terminal bud scale scars of previous years are visible on the diagram.) These scales basically are modified leaves, in which the food manufacturing ability has been superseded by a protective function. In herbaceous plants no bud scales are present. Since these plants are generally short-lived, the survival value of protective bud scales is not the significant factor that it is for long-lived woody plants, especially those faced with the problem of severe winter conditions. In this case, those plants in which bud scales evolved (or developed after many generations) would tend to survive much more readily than plants without such protection.

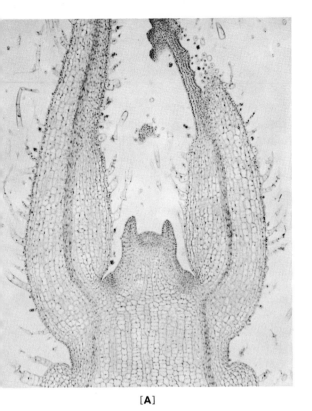

[A]

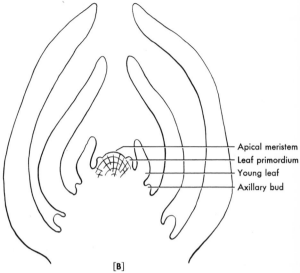

— Apical meristem
— Leaf primordium
— Young leaf
— Axillary bud

[B]

Figure 6-2. **A**: Photomicrograph of a *Coleus* stem tip. Two leaf primordia are present, one at each side of the apical meristem. **B**: Diagram of a terminal bud. (Photo courtesy of General Biological Supply House, Chicago.)

As a bud unfolds, stems, or flowers, or both, may develop. If a bud is sectioned longitudinally while dormant, the similarity in the three types is seen. All buds possess immature leaves, immature buds in the axils of these leaves, meristematic tissue, nodes, and internodes (Figure 6-2). Careful examination will usually make it possible to identify developing vascular tissue. A bud, then, may be regarded as a very much compressed, compact, undeveloped section of a stem. The term **leaf primordia** refers to small projections which will develop as leaves when the bud unfolds but which do not have the characteristic leaf shape as yet. The growth of structures from a bud results from the division of cells of the apical meristem and the subsequent enlargement and differentiation of these cells. As this occurs, the internodes elongate greatly. The growth of axillary buds results in the characteristic branching systems of plants.

The arrangement of buds and leaves is termed **opposite** if two are at a node, **alternate** if only one is present, and **whorled** if three or more are at a node. The growth of axillary buds results in a different type of growth-form for each of the three arrangements.

59 ॐ

6.2 Internal structure of a woody stem

A **transverse** (cross) **section** of the woody stem exposes to view a variety of tissues, which are considered to be **primary tissues** if they develop from an apical meristem and **secondary tissues** if they arise from a cambium. The cells at the tips of stems are young, immature, and undifferentiated, so the section to be examined must be cut at a distance from the end of any stem in order for the plane of section to pass through mature tissues (see Figure 6-3). Low magnification allows the identification of tissues, whereas higher magnification exposes individual cells to observation.

Transverse sections through the apical meristem expose to view parenchyma-type cells in which there is no differentiation, each cell looking much like every other cell (Figure 6-3A). As these cells become older, they will develop into the cells of one of the primary permanent tissues, their growth resulting in the outward extension of the stem tip. Rather than waiting for such cells to mature, we examine tissue which is older already and farther down the stem. In other words, Figure 6-3C represents a transverse section through cells which were once a part of the apical meristem but now have begun to differentiate into definite tissues. Cells in certain areas become vertically elongated and form strands which can be recognized as the beginning of vascular tissue. Between these vascular bundles are parenchyma cells which form a continuous pathway from the central core of parenchyma cells to similar cells located externally to the developing vascular tissue. As more and more vascular tissue is produced, the strands increase in size and eventually fuse, so that the mature stem has a solid cylinder of vascular tissue. The surface cells at this time are also somewhat different from the others and eventually will become even more distinct as the epidermis.

PRIMARY TISSUES

The young woody stem consists of primary tissues alone, and secondary tissues are not produced until near the end of the first year's growth or until subsequent years. All of the cells which comprise primary tissues were produced by cell division in the apical meristem, after which cell enlargement and differentiation resulted in such cells becoming part of one of the mature (permanent) tissues. The tissues and regions will be discussed in order from the outermost to the central area of the stem (see Figure 6-3).

1. Epidermis. As was mentioned previously (see Section 5.4 and Figure 5-3A), the epidermis forms the surface protective layer. It is one cell in thickness, the cell walls are frequently rather thick, and the

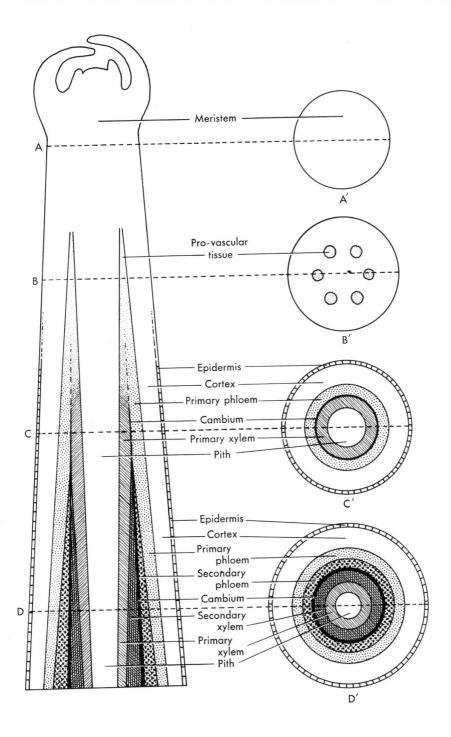

Figure 6-3. Diagram of longitudinal section of a stem tip and diagrams of cross sections at different levels as indicated. Individual cells are not shown; regions and tissues are indicated. The older tissues are the ones farther from the apex.

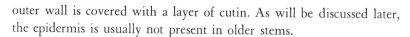

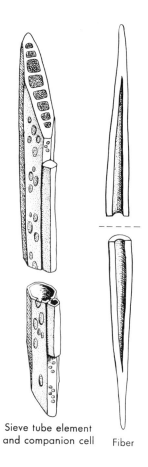

Sieve tube element
and companion cell   Fiber

Parenchyma cell

outer wall is covered with a layer of cutin. As will be discussed later, the epidermis is usually not present in older stems.

2. Cortex. Just under the epidermis is a region containing primarily parenchyma-type cells, the **cortex.** As was indicated previously (see Section 5.4 and Figure 5-3B), the cells are basically spherical, with thin walls and large vacuoles. The amount of this storage tissue varies with the kind of plant, but it is usually many cells in thickness. One may find collenchyma and sclerenchyma cells in the cortex, in which case an additional strengthening and supporting factor is present. Water, minerals, and foods pass through by diffusion from cell to cell. This tissue frequently is also not present in older stems.

3. Primary phloem (Figure 6-4). This is one of the complex permanent tissues which were mentioned in the previous chapter. Several kinds of cells are present in the phloem, which enables the efficient conduction of organic (food) materials from place to place. In addition there are secondary functions of the phloem as a result of the presence of certain supporting and storage cells. The principal conducting cells are the **sieve tube elements,** vertically elongated cylindrical cells, the end walls of which contain numerous thin areas (the **sieve plate**). The cytoplasm of one cell is continuous with the one above and the one below through the **sieve pores.** This contiguity undoubtedly facilitates movement of materials through the **sieve tubes,** which are composed of numbers of sieve tube elements arranged end to end and frequently overlapping. The exact mechanism of phloem transport cannot yet be explained, but the rates of movement are much more rapid than the rate of diffusion alone. When mature, the cytoplasm in the sieve tube element is not as distinct from the large vacuole as in other living cells, and the nucleus has disappeared. Abutting each of these conducting cells is a somewhat shorter, narrower, vertically elongated **companion cell.** The nucleus of the latter cell is present throughout its life. The exact function of the companion cell is not known, but it may have something to do with both conduction and storage (there are pits in the walls between the sieve tube element and the companion cell). The **phloem parenchyma cells,** scattered through the tissue, are similar to such cells discussed previously and are mainly storage cells. In some plants **phloem fibers,** strengthening and supporting cells, are present. These cells are narrow, vertically elongated cells with very thick walls and a small **lumen** (the cell cavity). They are dead at maturity, con-

Ray cell

Figure 6-4. Cells of the phloem. The sieve tube element and fiber are rather elongated cells; the central portion has been omitted in part.

Figure 6-5. Cell (C) of the vascular cambium dividing with the resulting cells differentiating into secondary xylem cells (X^1, X^2, X^3) or secondary phloem cells (P^1, P^2). Note that one of the cells of the two which are formed at each division remains meristematic as part of the vascular cambium. The central region of the stem is to the right while the exterior is to the left. The vascular cambium and other regions external to the xylem are pushed outwardly by the production of secondary xylem. The entire development results in an increase in the diameter of the stem.

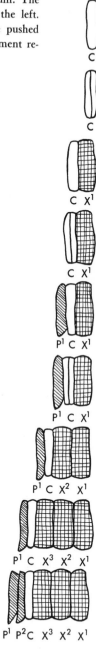

taining no protoplasm. The phloem fibers of the flax and hemp plants are made into linen and rope, respectively. The manner in which such fibers are separated from other cells will be discussed in Section 20.6.

4. Vascular cambium. Meristematic cells form a narrow (one or two cells in thickness) cylindrical sheath of tissue, the **vascular cambium,** immediately internal to the phloem. As these thin-walled cells divide, those cells which mature toward the outer part of the stem develop into various cells of the secondary phloem, while those which mature toward the inner part of the stem develop into cells which form the secondary xylem (Figure 6-5). Usually, more xylem than phloem is produced, and as a stem continues growth, a greater and greater proportion is xylem, or **wood.** The tissues external to the cambium constitute the **bark,** though this term is usually used only after secondary tissues and cork have formed.

5. Primary xylem (Figure 6-6). This is the second of the complex permanent tissues which were mentioned in the previous chapter. Here again one finds several kinds of cells and primary and secondary functions. The conduction of water and minerals occurs mainly through tracheids and vessel elements of the xylem. The **tracheids** are thick-walled, elongated, and tapering cells which are dead at maturity. Pits are located in the walls, and usually spiral or ring thickenings add to the strength of the cell. The hollow cavity (lumen) of each cell, the pits which are present, and the overlapping ends of tracheids in stems and roots enable water and minerals to be transported very rapidly in a vertical direction. **Vessel elements** function as do tracheids but are more efficient in that they are much larger in diameter, many pits are present, and the end walls as well as the protoplasm have disappeared when the cells are mature (see Figure 6-7). In addition to this, vessel elements are arranged end to end, like barrels on top of each other, forming long, vertical tubes, the **vessels,** which may be several feet in length. These are the main conducting structures in the xylem of flowering plants (angiosperms) but are not found in certain plants, such as gymnosperms (e.g., pine, spruce). The tracheids, on

63 ⅋

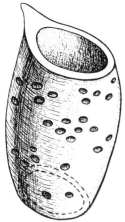

Vessel element

Parenchyma cell

Ray cell

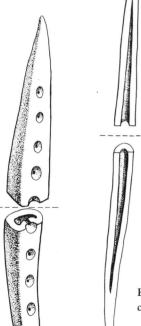

the other hand, are present in all xylem tissue. **Xylem parenchyma cells** and **xylem fibers** are similar to the parenchyma cells and fibers found in the phloem, although fibers may be more numerous in the xylem. In gymnosperms (e.g., *Pinus*) typical fibers are rare. In these plants the xylem is quite homogeneous, consisting mainly of tracheids.

6. Pith. The central portion, or core, of the stem consists of parenchyma-type storage cells.

SECONDARY TISSUES

The presence of the cambium in woody stems is responsible for the tremendous growth in diameter of which they are capable (observe any old tree). The tissues which develop from the cambium constitute the **secondary tissues** which reinforce or replace certain primary tissues. The cells of the cambium divide in two planes (radially and tangentially), thus producing an increase in circumference as well as in diameter. No epidermis, cortex, or pith is formed by the cambium.

1. Secondary phloem. With one difference, the cells which comprise the secondary phloem are very similar to those of the primary phloem as far as structure and function are concerned. The difference lies mainly in their mode of origin. All of the cells of the phloem which have been mentioned are vertically elongated or spherical. Two of the difficulties encountered by land plants are conduction along a considerable length of stem and the support of this stem and the leaves, flowers, and fruits which are attached to it. Vertically elongated cells are well-suited to these functions. However, as the stem increases in diameter, more horizontal conduction is necessary to supply tissues located internally and externally with regard to the vascular tissue as well as the cells of the vascular tissue itself. The **phloem ray cells,** not found in primary vascular tissue, are parenchyma-type cells which are elongated horizontally (radially) and function quite readily in transporting materials across the stem (see Figure 6-4). The relatively large simple pits in the walls of these cells facilitate such conduction from cell to cell. These cells are oriented end to end, forming the **phloem ray,** which is usually several cells deep. Various materials are quite likely also stored in these ray cells.

2. Secondary xylem. As is true of the secondary phloem, the cells of the secondary xylem differ from those of the primary xylem mainly with respect to the tissue from which they develop. Here also, the exception is the **xylem ray cell** (Figure 6-6), which is similar to cells found in the phloem. A **xylem ray** to the cambium plus the continua-

Figure 6-6. Cells of the xylem. The tracheid and fiber are rather elongated cells; the central portion has been omitted in part.

Fiber

Tracheid

tion as a phloem ray into the secondary phloem is termed a **vascular ray.**

Concentric rings that form in the secondary xylem can be seen quite readily whenever a tree is cut down. One ring usually develops each year, and so the term **annual ring** has come to be used, although **growth ring** is more appropriate. The appearance of alternate light and dark bands is due to differences in the tracheids (and vessels) produced during periods of rapid growth and those produced during periods of slow growth. When growth is rapid, usually during the spring, the cells are larger in diameter and have thinner walls than when growth is slow, as in summer. The sequence of events, then, is rapid growth, slow growth, and no growth, followed by a repetition of this differential process. These events result in large, relatively thin-

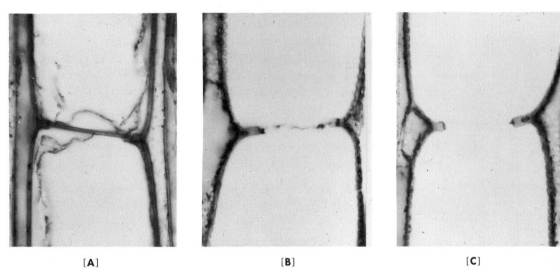

[A]   [B]   [C]

Figure 6-7. Photomicrographs of longitudinal sections showing stages in the development of a vessel in *Zea mays*. **A:** End wall between vessel elements intact. This wall is primary in nature but the secondary thickenings of the longitudinal walls are visible on the sides. The protoplast is present. **B:** End wall broken down; remnants still visible. Note pits in side walls. Protoplast gone. **C:** End wall gone although the rim persists. No protoplast. (Courtesy of Katherine Esau.)

walled cells gradually merging into smaller, thick-walled cells—this is one ring; no distinct line of demarcation appears between the two types of cells. However, since a period of no growth (or very little growth) is followed by the period of rapid growth, a very sharp line can be seen between the thick-walled cells of one year and the relatively[1] thin-walled cells of the subsequent year. Viewed without the

[1] The term "relative" must be emphasized. Remember, these are tracheids. Compared with parenchyma cells, even the relatively "thin-walled" tracheids would be considered to have thick walls.

aid of a microscope, the area of thick-walled cells appears dark (much wall, little lumen), whereas the area of thin-walled cells appears lighter (less wall, more lúmen). Since the formation of rings in the secondary xylem depends upon growth differences, lack of water, damage, or other environmental factors might result in the production of fewer than one ring each year; more than one ring may form if recovery from some hazard occurs during the same year. For this reason the term "growth ring" is preferable.

Figure 6-8 represents a stem cut to show three views of the woody tissues. In the transverse section the growth rings can be seen quite clearly, and the slender xylem rays radiate outwardly much like the spokes on a wheel. The longitudinal cuts have been made in two planes so that the rings and rays can be seen in surface view and in face view. In a radial section the rays (in surface view) have the appearance of a brick wall, while the growth rings are seen as vertical lines. In a tangential section, however, the rays are seen "head on," appearing somewhat elliptical in shape. The beautiful grains that are present in boards used for cabinet work result from the slanted cuts that are made through the secondary xylem; the growth rings generally appear as vertical or curved lines. The vascular rings of branches from the main trunk add to the intriguing patterns found in wood, and some of the most beautiful cabinet work utilizes wood with large rays in radial sections.

3. Cork cambium and cork. The cambium which produces xylem and phloem is frequently termed the **vascular cambium** to differentiate it more vividly from the **cork cambium.** As was mentioned previously (Section 5.4), parenchyma cells are capable of becoming meristematic under certain conditions, even though such cells are considered to be portions of permanent tissues. Damage to a tissue results in such meristematic activity and the formation of a cork cambium. As the cells of the cork cambium (or **phellogen**) divide, the outer ones develop into **cork cells,** and the inner ones may develop into a tissue known as the **phelloderm,** in which the cells are of the parenchyma type. Cork (or **phellem**) consists of box-shaped cells, similar to the cork cambium from which they are derived but whose walls are impregnated with suberin. The presence of this waxy material in the cell walls and the lack of intercellular spaces result in cork being relatively impermeable to water and gases. Cork, then, is a protective tissue. The protoplasts of cork cells die after suberin is deposited in the walls.

Though cork forms as a result of damage to tissues, this is not an unusual occurrence. In fact, all woody stems have cork as the surface layers by the second year's growth; often cork begins forming before

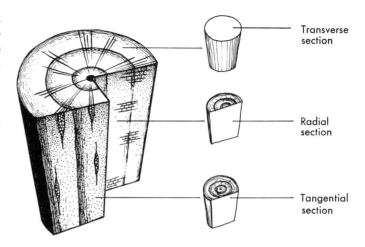

Figure 6-8. Woody tissues of stem shown in three views. In the transverse (cross) section the growth rings are visible as concentric rings; xylem rays radiate like spokes on a wheel. In the radial section rays are seen in surface view, appearing like a brick wall; growth rings are visible as vertical lines. In the tangential section the rays are seen "head on"; again, the growth rings are visible as vertical lines.

Transverse section

Radial section

Tangential section

the end of growth during the first year. The reason is quite simple. The production of secondary vascular tissue results in an increase in the diameter of a stem. The epidermis and cortex are permanent tissues and thus can no longer increase in size. These outer tissues rip and tear as more and more vascular tissue develops internally. Cork forms as a result of this damage and frequently before the damage is apparent. Since cork is impervious to most materials, any cells external to this tissue die and are sloughed off. In older plants all of the epidermis, cortex, primary phloem, and even parts of the secondary phloem may be lost in this fashion, cork cambium eventually forming from parenchyma cells of the secondary phloem. The so-called "bark" then consists of secondary phloem, cork cambium, and cork.

6.3   Stem types

At the beginning of this chapter, herbaceous and woody stems were mentioned. An examination of their tissues indicates that we should actually subdivide herbaceous stems into two groups: **monocotyledonous** and **dicotyledonous.** These two terms will be discussed more fully in Section 26.10, but suffice it to say now that all flowering plants can be termed either monocotyledonous or dicotyledonous. Plants in the former group have one **cotyledon,** or seed leaf, in the seeds, the leaves are parallel-veined, and the flower parts are in threes; common examples are grasses, lilies, and corn. The dicotyledons have two cotyledons in each seed, net-veined leaves, and flower parts in fours or fives; common examples are oaks, tomatoes, beans, and pears. Except for the palms, almost all of the monocotyledons have herbaceous stems, whereas the dicotyledons may have herbaceous (e.g., tomato, bean) or

67 ᢓᢀ

woody (e.g., oak, pear) stems. Basic internal differences for each group will be considered.

HERBACEOUS MONOCOTYLEDONOUS STEM

The vascular tissue exists as scattered bundles of xylem and phloem (Figure 6-9A). Except for the palms and certain other large monocots which have an anomalous cambium, no cambium, and thus no secondary tissue, is present; the little growth in diameter is dependent upon enlargement of the cells of primary tissues. Even though no definite arrangement of vascular bundles exists—the xylem and phloem never form continuous cylinders of tissues—the xylem is always located on the inner side of a bundle and the phloem to the outer side. The greater part of the stem consists of parenchyma tissue. Usually, however, directly adjacent to the epidermis and frequently surrounding the vascular bundles are sclerenchyma and collenchyma cells which strengthen and support the stem.

HERBACEOUS DICOTYLEDONOUS STEM

In these stems (Figure 6-9B) the vascular tissue is also arranged in discrete bundles, but the bundles themselves are arranged in a very orderly ring and not scattered. The cambium, which is visible between the xylem and phloem, may be restricted to the individual bundles or may be continuous from bundle to bundle. Whatever the arrangement, secondary tissues are poorly developed, and the stem remains nonwoody. Frequently the cortex may contain many collenchyma cells and the vascular tissue may contain fibers, both of which aid in the support of these stems. The parenchyma cells, between vascular bundles, are continuous with those of the pith and cortex.

WOODY DICOTYLEDONOUS STEM

This is the type of stem (Figure 6-9C) that was utilized for the discussion of primary and secondary tissues in earlier sections of this chap-

Figure 6-9. Stem types in transverse section. **A:** Herbaceous monocotyledonous stem with scattered vascular bundles. Vascular bundles are more numerous toward the periphery of the stem. In each bundle the xylem is toward the center of the stem and the phloem forms the outer portion of the bundle. **B:** Herbaceous dicotyledonous stem; the vascular bundles are arranged in an orderly ring-fashion. **C:** Woody dicotyledonous stem; the vascular tissue is arranged in concentric cylinders which appear as circles in a transverse section. (In this diagram growth rings are not shown; neither is any distinction made between primary and secondary tissues.)

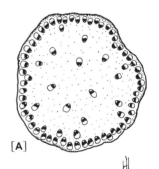

[A]

ter. Though the very young stem has vascular bundles, the conducting tissues of mature woody stems are in the form of concentric cylinders, in which the great development of secondary xylem results in the characteristic woody condition. These stems usually have much less pith than the herbaceous dicotyledonous stems.

Summary

1. Herbaceous stems are generally soft and green, have little tough woody tissue, and are short-lived. Woody stems are hard and long-lived. In both types leaves and buds are located at nodes, and the interval between them is the internode.

2. New stems and their leaves develop from terminal or axillary buds. Bud scales are present in woody plants.

3. Primary tissues develop from apical meristems, and secondary tissues arise from a cambium. A transverse section through a mature woody stem would expose the following tissues and regions: epidermis, cortex, primary phloem, secondary phloem, vascular cambium, secondary xylem, primary xylem, and pith. As additional secondary tissues develop, the outer regions of the stem split and tear, which results in the formation of cork from a cork cambium.

4. The cells which may be found in the phloem are: sieve tube elements, companion cells, phloem parenchyma cells, and phloem fibers. In the xylem may be found: vessel elements, tracheids, xylem parenchyma cells, and xylem fibers.

5. The rings which are visible in the trunk, or stem, of a cut tree are formed in woody stems as a result of the differential growth of the secondary xylem.

6. Herbaceous monocotyledonous stems contain vascular tissue that is present as scattered bundles of xylem and phloem. Herbaceous dicotyledonous stems contain similar vascular bundles, but these are arranged in an orderly ring. In the woody dicotyledonous stem, the vascular tissues are in the form of concentric cylinders.

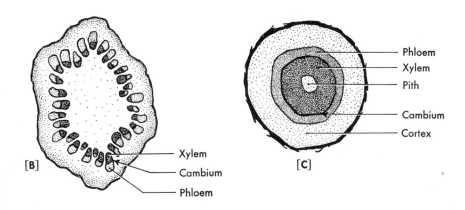

[B]
— Xylem
— Cambium
— Phloem

[C]
— Phloem
— Xylem
— Pith
— Cambium
— Cortex

REVIEW TOPICS AND QUESTIONS

1. Diagram in cross-section a woody stem with a vascular cambium but no secondary tissues. Label all regions or tissues, but do not show individual cells.

2. Diagram the stem of the previous problem after a year's cambial activity. Label all regions or tissues, but do not show individual cells.

3. Diagram in longitudinal (radial) section the stem of the previous problems after six years of growth. Label all regions or tissues, but do not show individual cells.

4. Describe each of the cells which are (or may be) common to both xylem and phloem, and list the main function of each.

5. Describe each of those cells which are located in the xylem or phloem but not in both, indicate in which tissue each is found, and list the main function of each cell.

6. For each of the following, name a plant cell which has that function, describe the structure of the cell, and discuss how such structure is an adaptation for that function: (a) support, (b) conduction of water, (c) food storage, and (d) conduction of food.

7. In terms of internal anatomy, compare a mature herbaceous dicotyledonous stem with a mature herbaceous monocotyledonous stem.

8. A branch was cut from a willow tree which was over three years old. If you were given the branch, explain how you could prove: (a) its age at the time of cutting, and (b) the time of year at which it was cut.

9. Explain why tissues outside the cambium of a stem are frequently cracked, torn, and sloughed off.

10. In what ways is a vessel better modified than a series of tracheids for the conduction of water?

SUGGESTED READINGS

Esau, K. *Anatomy of Seed Plants.* New York: Wiley, 1960.

Foster, A. *Practical Plant Anatomy.* Princeton: Van Nostrand, 1949.

Fuller, H. J., and O. Tippo. *College Botany.* New York: Holt, 1954.

Schulman, E. "Tree Rings and History in the Western United States," *Economic Botany,* 8 (1954), 234–250.

Williams, S. "Wood Structure," *Scientific American,* 188 (January 1953), 64–68.

CHAPTER 7

Stem Function

THE preceding chapter was devoted primarily to a discussion of the external and internal structure of the stem. As each structure was described, a specific function correlated with that particular structure was indicated. The correlation between structure and function in storage, supporting, and strengthening tissues or cells is rather straightforward and simple. Storage cells are thin-walled, which enables materials to penetrate readily, and have cytoplasm and large vacuoles in which such materials are stored. The metabolic activity of these cells enables them to accumulate storage products against a concentration gradient or to store products in a non-soluble form (e.g., starch). Strengthening and supporting cells are vertically elongated and have thick walls and small lumen; sometimes additional ring or spiral wall thickenings are present. However, difficulties arise in finding a similar correlation between structure and the conduction of various materials through a stem.

7.1 Movement of organic materials

Experiments have demonstrated quite conclusively that organic materials, such as foods, are transported by the phloem. In these experiments all tissues external to the cambium are removed in a band around the stem. Though this removes the phloem, the xylem is not disturbed, and water quite readily passes the **ringed** (or **girdled**) area. Any such interruption of the phloem prevents the transport of organic compounds, usually sugars, from one side of the ring to the other; both upward and downward movement ceases. In control plants—those in the normal condition with intact phloem—movement of sugar occurs quite naturally. Some investigators have even removed sections

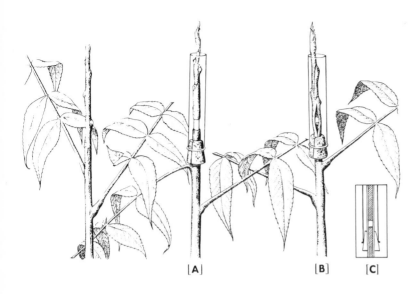

[A]   [B]   [C]

Figure 7-1. Diagrams to indicate one technique of investigating the movement of materials in stems. **A**: The phloem has been removed by excising the tissues external to the cambium (ringing). **B**: The xylem has been removed. **C**: Sectional view of **B**. The cut area of the stem is enclosed in a water jacket to keep the exposed tissues from drying in each instance. (Redrawn from O. F. Curtis, *The Translocation of Solutes in Plants.* New York: McGraw-Hill. Copyright 1935 by the publishers and used by permission.)

of the xylem without destroying the phloem (see Figure 7-1) and have found sugar movements to be normal, provided care is taken that the phloem does not dry out. Botanists accept the statement that organic materials move upwardly (to growing stem tips, for example) and downwardly (to storage areas in the root, as an example) in the phloem. This is not meant to exclude diffusionary movements from cell to cell. The great amount of rapid movement, however, occurs in the phloem.

The difficulties that arise in discussing **translocation** (or transport) in the phloem relate to the mechanisms involved, not the tissue. Many measurements have been made of the rate of movement through the phloem, and all data indicate a rate which is at least a thousand times the rate that could be accounted for by diffusion alone. If translocation is faster than diffusion, what is the mechanism? Several suggestions have been made. Some plant physiologists are more or less convinced that a **mass flow** of materials through the sieve tubes occurs as a result of higher turgor pressure on the supplying end of such tubes. Others consider **protoplasmic streaming** to be important. The flowing movement of cytoplasm can be observed in many cells, but not in all, while mass flow would be rather difficult through sieve plates or through cells containing cytoplasm. Another suggestion is that of **activated diffusion,** in which the metabolic activity of living cells speeds up diffusion. Actually, all of these suggestions have their proponents and opponents, and no hypothesis has yet knitted the data together in a suitable explanation. The simple fact is that the mechanism whereby organic compounds move through the phloem is yet unknown. This is another one of those problems of living organisms which cause us to look with great anticipation to the future.

7.2 Movement of minerals

Ringing experiments and other types of investigations, even with the use of radioactive materials, have not been as conclusive with regard to mineral transport as they have been with regard to sugar movements. The majority of evidence, however, indicates that minerals are, for the most part, transported in the xylem. One of the difficulties in these investigations is that certain minerals are very rapidly utilized in the formation of organic compounds which then move in the phloem. This is quite likely true of nitrogen and phosphorus. Another difficulty is that salts transfer radially to the phloem and other tissues and may accumulate in living cells. Most probably, however, minerals diffuse into the xylem and are then carried upward in the streams of water that fill the tracheids and vessels.

7.3 Movement of water

That most of the water absorbed is transported throughout the plants by means of the tracheids and vessels in the xylem has been conclusively shown. The difficulty again is in explaining the mechanism involved. Capillary movement of water through the xylem cells could account for a rise of water of only a few feet, even if the smallest diameter of a tracheid is used as a basis for calculation. As was indicated previously, the most efficient conducting cells are the large-diametered vessel elements, in which water would rise much less by capillarity than it would in a tracheid. Imbibitional movements within the submicroscopic channels of the cell walls must be ruled out, because water moves in the lumen; plugging the lumen prevents water conduction. For a time, some plant physiologists thought that root pressure forced water upwardly. Such pressures have been demonstrated in many plants and depend upon the activity of living root cells. However, other plants do not develop root pressure, root pressures are not great enough to force water to the top of tall trees, and water movement through stems continues even though roots have been removed.

(Note almost any cut flowers in the home.) Another suggestion was that the loss or utilization of water at the tops of the plant produced a vacuum and that atmospheric pressure pushed water up the hollow tubes of the xylem. Unfortunately, atmospheric pressure could account for only a rise of approximately 33 feet, and many trees are taller than that.

Strange as the idea may appear at first reading, botanists are now convinced that water is *pulled* up the stem of a plant. Chemists and physicists have demonstrated that water molecules are very strongly attracted to one another; water molecules in thin columns are difficult to separate, and considerable tension (pull) is necessary to accomplish separation. This fact was made use of by plant physiologists in explaining water movements. As water is lost or utilized [1] in the cells at the top of a plant, more moves into these cells by osmosis from neighboring cells. (Why?) One or more of these cells is next to a tracheid or vessel element from which water is removed.[2] At this point, the **cohesive** strength between water molecules enters our explanation. Since the molecules cling together, as some are removed at the top of the xylem, the rest are pulled upwards—just as pulling on the end link of a chain will cause the entire chain to move along. These water columns are under tension, a phenomenon which demonstrates itself by a decrease in the diameter of a tree trunk during times of great water loss and movement. Just as an external force increases the diffusion pressure of water, a tension decreases the diffusion pressure. (Review Sections 4.2 and 4.3 if necessary.) The result is that the diffusion pressure of water in the tracheids and vessels is lower than that of the living root cells, and water diffuses from the latter to the former. This lowers the diffusion pressure of water in the cells adjacent to the xylem cells, and an osmotic movement of water takes place through living root cells from the soil solution. Note that water movement is osmotic through living cells and cohesive through the non-living cells (tracheids and vessels). Cohesion is not the basis for all water movement but is really limited to those areas where non-living cells are involved.

In this discussion of translocation, various mechanisms other than diffusion were emphasized. This should not be interpreted to imply a relatively unimportant role for the process of diffusion. Movements from one parenchyma type cell to another are by diffusion, termed "osmosis" in the case of water. However, the known rates of diffusion

---

[1] Lost by evaporation (transpiration); utilized in various life processes (photosynthesis, digestion).

[2] Imbibition likely is involved in water movements through the walls of the tracheid and the adjacent cell.

are much slower than the known rates of translocation through the xylem and the phloem. Obviously, then, rapid vertical movements are brought about by other, or additional, mechanisms and not by diffusion alone. Radial (horizontal) movements, as through vascular rays (xylem rays plus phloem rays), is a slow process dependent upon diffusion.

7.4 Specialized stems

In a number of plants, the stems are greatly modified as to structure and function. Many such modifications are concerned with **vegetative** or **asexual reproduction**—reproduction not involving fusion of **gametes** (sex cells) or the production of seeds. Other structural modifications result in a variety of protective and supporting devices. However, even though the stems may be very different from the "typical," they can be recognized if one looks for nodes (and their attendant buds and leaves) and for the development of branches from the surface. Secondary, or branch, roots originate from internal tissues, and roots do not have nodes.

RUNNERS

The strawberry plant (*Fragaria*) has a long, slender stem that grows horizontally along the surface of the ground. New leaves and roots develop where a node touches the ground, and these are new plants as soon as the **runner** (or **stolon**) dies (Figure 7-2). In many areas the strawberry is used as a ground cover because of its rapid reproduction and spreading characteristics.

Figure 7-2. Strawberry plant (*Fragaria*). **The oldest plant is second from the left. Other plants have developed at intervals along horizontal stems.**

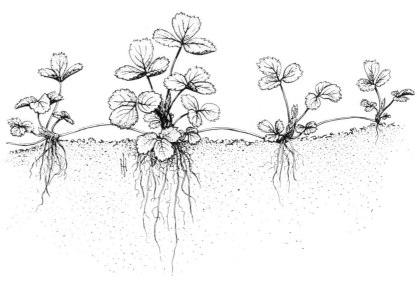

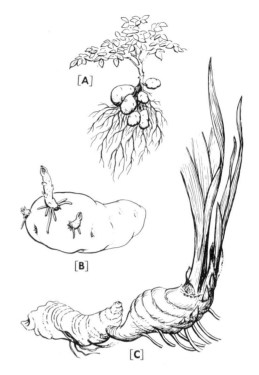

Figure 7-3. Some specialized stems. **A**: Irish potato plant (*Solanum tuberosum*) with tubers. **B**: Potato tuber sprouting. **C**: Iris rhizome sprouted.

RHIZOMES

As exemplified by iris and fern plants, a **rhizome** (Figure 7-3C) is an underground, horizontal stem which may be bulky and contain much stored food. Most rhizomes live through the winter, even though the shoots may die, and new shoots develop the next spring from the buds which are located at nodes. Breaking of the rhizome will not destroy the plant but merely separates the new shoots which are produced. As long as a node with its bud is present, each piece of rhizome is capable of producing a new plant, provided it has sufficient stored food.

TUBERS

The **tuber** (Figure 7-3A, B) of an Irish potato (*Solanum tuberosum*) is a bulky, short terminal portion of an underground stem. The "eyes" are actually buds at nodes, and the bulky appearance results from the compressed, unexpanded internodes. As long as the piece of tuber contains at least one "eye" when it is planted, shoots and roots will develop, and a new plant results. The food value of potato tubers for humans results from the enormous numbers of starch grains that are stored in the cortical and pith cells. However, the sweet potato (*Ipomoea batatas*) and yam (*Dioscorea alata*) are storage roots.

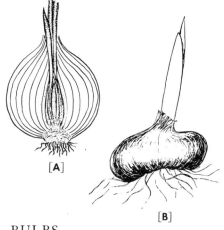

[A]

[B]

Figure 7-4. Some specialized stems. **A:** Onion (*Allium cepa*) bulb. **B:** Gladiolus corm.

BULBS

Actually, a **bulb** (Figure 7-4A), as in the onion (*Allium cepa*), consists of a very small piece of stem tissue bearing numerous fleshy leaves. Terminal and lateral buds are present, and both may develop into shoots. Frequently, in slicing an onion which has been stored for some length of time, one will notice that the buds have already begun to grow. In this structure the fleshy leaves are the storage organs and contain large amounts of sugar but no starch. The odor and tear-producing characteristics of onions are due to aromatic oils.

CORMS

A **corm** (Figure 7-4B), as in gladiolus, consists of a bulky, short, vertical stem which contains stored foods.

SPINES AND THORNS

The protective thorns (Figure 7-5A) of rose bushes (*Rosa* spp.) and spines (Figure 7-5B) of cacti (*Opuntia* spp.) are examples of stem outgrowths or modified stems. These sturdy, sharp-pointed structures are probably of survival value in decreasing the amount of browsing damage to these plants by herbivores (and probably decrease damage caused by humans also). The spines of some plants are modified leaves.

Figure 7-5. **A:** Thorns of a rose (*Rosa*). **B:** Spines of a cactus (*Opuntia*).

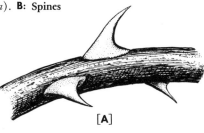

[A]

[B]

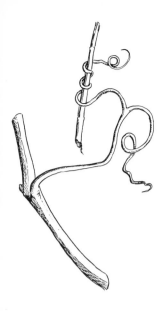

Figure 7-6. Tendril of a grape
(*Vitis*) coiled about a twig.

TENDRILS

In some plants, such as the grape (*Vitis* spp.), certain of the stems develop as long, thin, coiling structures which attach the plant to a support (Figure 7-6). Due to unequal rates of growth, the tips of tendrils move slowly back and forth as they elongate. As soon as a tendril comes in contact with a solid object, rapid growth responses result in the tendril coiling about the object. The tendrils of Boston ivy (*Parthenocissus tricuspidata*) end in flattened disks which adhere to surfaces and enable the plant to "climb" vertical walls. Tendrils may also be modified leaves, but in any case such structures support the photosynthetic areas where they will be exposed to light, a function performed by mechanical tissues (composed of fibers and tracheids mainly) in many plants.

7.5 Grafting and rooting

Stems are frequently used in the vegetative propagation of desirable varieties of plants. In some instances the cultivated variety, although producing large yields of good quality,[3] is more susceptible to root diseases than is the naturally-occurring variety. Buds or branches of the susceptible variety may be grafted to the stem of the resistant variety. In **grafting,** the freshly-cut surfaces of two stems are bound together firmly, so that, as new cells are formed, the tissues fuse and form a union. Generally [4] the cambial layers must be in contact. Grafting wax or a similar compound is used to cover the wound surfaces to prevent tissues from drying out and to prevent fungi from entering.

The **scion** is the stem cutting which is grafted to a rooted portion, the **stock.** Neither the scion nor the stock influence each other's growth habits, except for nutritional materials which may be transported through the graft union. Therefore, to graft several varieties of apples on the same root stock is possible; each cutting then bears a different type of apple. Although plants of two different genera within a family can sometimes be grafted, most successful grafts are between members of the same species. The general growth and tissue differentiation must be quite similar for graft unions to be substantial enough to resist rupture. Figure 7-7 represents several common methods of grafting.

[3] Such cultivated varieties are usually a result of plant breeding programs.
[4] A few monocotyledonous plants have been grafted successfully.

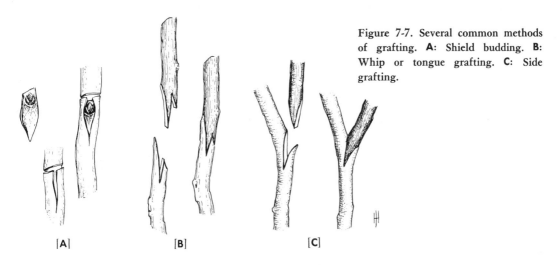

Figure 7-7. Several common methods of grafting. **A**: Shield budding. **B**: Whip or tongue grafting. **C**: Side grafting.

[A]   [B]   [C]

Many citrus (orange, lemon) trees consist of a resistant root stock variety to which other varieties have been grafted. The navel orange is probably the best example of the usefulness of grafting. Because these oranges are seedless, they can be propagated only by grafting. In fact, the entire navel orange industry is dependent upon trees which are all asexual descendants of a single tree found in South America almost 100 years ago. To perpetuate such a desirable variety, it has been necessary to propagate it vegetatively by grafting.

Another method of vegetative propagation which can be used with some kinds of plants is to make stem cuttings and then place the cut ends in moist sand or peat moss. Plants, such as *Coleus,* willow, rose, geranium, and grape, develop adventitious roots (see Section 8.1) at the cut end when handled in this manner. Increased formation of such roots can frequently be obtained by treating the basal portions of cuttings with plant growth regulators (see Section 28.8). Figure 7-8 represents the rooting of cuttings, some of which were treated with naphthalene acetic acid. Some cuttings will not root unless treated in this fashion. The cuttings are usually kept in a shaded area with a humid atmosphere to reduce water loss and thus water requirements. Until roots form, these cuttings are very susceptible to wilting because of poor water absorption.

[A]

These two methods of vegetative propagation are frequently useful in maintaining varieties without the changes that so frequently occur as a result of sexual reproduction. The plants that result from grafting and from rooting of cuttings have the same characteristics as the plants from which the stems were taken. Plants which develop from seeds

Figure 7-8. Rooting of cuttings. **A**: Untreated controls. **B**: Treated with naphthalene acetic acid (a growth regulator).

[B]

are frequently different from the plant which produced those seeds, as will be explained in Chapter 17.[5]

7.6 Economic aspects of stems

In addition to lumber, wood pulp for paper, and fibers for linen and rope, man has utilized plant stem tissues and their products in many ways. The bark of the cork oak (*Quercus Suber*) is useful for stoppers, insulation, life preservers, and padding. Quinine, an alkaloid used in the treatment of malaria, is extracted from *Cinchona* bark. During World War II, when *Cinchona* bark could not be obtained, a synthetic drug, atabrine, replaced quinine to a great extent. For similar reasons, synthetic rubber was used in place of natural rubber from *Hevea brasiliensis* (a tropical tree). The potato tuber has already been mentioned as a food source, but just as important are sugar and molasses from sugar cane (*Saccharum officinalis*). To flavor food, one can use spices from *Cinnamomum zelylanicum* (cinnamon from the bark). Tars, resins, turpentine, and wood alcohol are distilled from hardwood trees. In recent years many materials have been developed which utilize cellulose as a base: celluloid, cellophane, rayon, and lacquers (ethyl cellulose). The cellulose is obtained from wood (plant cell walls).

The foregoing is only a very brief indication of the economic uses of stems, usually in the form of tree trunks and branches. Any economic botany text can be consulted for a more detailed discussion of these and other uses of plants and their products.

Summary

1. Organic materials are transported in the phloem, while water and minerals are transported primarily in the xylem. Due to the cohesive strength between water molecules, the columns of water in the xylem are under tension as they are pulled to the tops of the plant.

2. In some plants stems are variously modified as: runners, rhizomes, tubers, bulbs, corms, spines, and tendrils.

3. In grafting, the cut surface of the scion is tightly bound to that of the stock so that the new cells which form will tend to fuse and form a union.

4. Many stem cuttings will root if the cut portion is placed in moist sand or peat moss. The application of certain plant growth regulators to the basal portion of such cuttings frequently stimulates root initiation.

[5] Seeds from an apple tree will always produce apple trees, of course, but the size, shape, quality, or yield of apples may vary from tree to tree. This is not the case with vegetative reproduction.

5. Man has found many uses for plant stems: lumber, wood pulp for paper, wood fibers for cloth and rope, cork, quinine, rubber, food, resins, alcohol, and plastics.

REVIEW TOPICS AND QUESTIONS

1. A water molecule, originally in the conducting tissue of a stem, eventually is utilized in the growth of a cell of the apical meristem. Discuss the movement of this water molecule, including the cells concerned and the forces which bring about such movements.
2. Explain why most trees will die if all tissues external to the xylem are removed in a ring around the stem.
3. Describe in detail an experiment that would demonstrate whether or not organic materials are transported in the phloem.
4. Describe in detail an experiment that would demonstrate whether or not root pressure is involved in supplying water to the top of a plant.
5. Describe five types of modified (or specialized) stems, and indicate the importance of each to the plant involved.
6. Discuss the importance of grafting to humans.
7. List ten items, commonly used by humans, which are made from plant stems or from parts of plant stems.
8. List five products which humans extract from plant stems.
9. The trunk of a tree is split. In order to save the tree, the owner decides either to place a metal bolt through the trunk or a metal band around the trunk, and asks you for advice. Explain which method he should use.
10. During their honeymoon at a mountain cabin, a couple fastened a wooden bench firmly between two trees. They returned on their fiftieth anniversary. Would they be able to use the bench? Explain, assuming the trees are still living and had grown at the rate of one foot per year.

SUGGESTED READINGS

Biddulph, S., and O. Biddulph. "The Circulatory System of Plants," *Scientific American,* 200 (February 1959), 44–49.

Crafts, A. S. *Translocation in Plants.* New York: Holt, Rinehart and Winston, 1961.

Curtis, O. F., and D. G. Clark. *An Introduction to Plant Physiology.* New York: McGraw-Hill, 1950.

Ferry, J. F., and H. S. Ward. *Fundamentals of Plant Physiology.* New York: Macmillan, 1959.

Gourley, J. H., and F. S. Howlett. *Modern Fruit Production.* New York: Macmillan, 1946, Chapter 15.

Greulach, V. A. "The Rise of Water in Plants," *Scientific American,* 187 (October 1952), 78–82.

Hill, A. F. *Economic Botany.* New York: McGraw-Hill, 1937.

Meyer, B. S., et al. *Introduction to Plant Physiology.* Princeton: Van Nostrand, 1960.

Zimmerman, M. H. "Movement of Organic Substances in Trees," *Science,* 133 (1961), 73–79.

CHAPTER 8

Roots

THE roots of a plant are the below-ground structures through which materials move from the soil to the various parts of the plant. Water and minerals are the primary essential nutrients which the plant obtains from the soil, and these nutrients are either utilized in the roots themselves or are transported to other parts. Note that the root cells are closest to the supply of water and minerals, and the amount of transport out of the roots is influenced by requirements of root tissues themselves. In addition to absorption and conduction, roots serve to anchor the plant, are frequently storage areas, may serve in supporting the plant, and are extremely important in holding soil particles in place.

8.1 Gross structure of roots

The roots are a continuation of the main axis of the plant, and no sharp line of demarcation exists between what is root and what is stem. When a seed germinates, the root grows down into the soil as the stem grows up and eventually out of the soil. As additional roots are produced, the root system develops as one of two general types: (1) a **diffuse,** or **fibrous,** root system, or (2) a **tap** root system. In the former, as exemplified by grasses (Figure 8-1A), are numerous slender main roots which are nearly equal in size. Such a root system has a high surface-to-volume (S/V) [1] ratio and is a rather efficient organ of absorption. In some plants, such as the sweet potato (*Ipomoea batatas*), certain of the larger roots may develop as enlarged storage areas. Because of their root systems, grasses are utilized in preventing **erosion** (the wearing away of soil by wind and water). The small, abundantly-branched roots are intertwined throughout the soil particles and tend to anchor both plant and soil in place.

[1] Refer to Section 3.7 for a discussion of the importance of S/V ratios.

In a tap-root system, such as found in beets, dandelions, and carrots, the primary root grows most rapidly, enlarges considerably, and remains the dominant part of the underground structure. This main, or tap, root contains much stored food materials when the plant is mature, but most of the absorption of materials is accomplished by the secondary and tertiary (branch) roots. As indicated in Figure 8-1B, if a carrot is carefully removed from the soil, the small branching roots are readily seen. Whereas the outer layers of the mature tap root usually consist of cork cells, this is not true of the tiny younger roots through which materials enter the plant.

In many plants **adventitious roots** frequently develop. These are roots which arise from stems and leaves. The prop roots of corn are adventitious. They arise from the lower part of the stem and grow out and down into the soil, serving to brace the plant. The rooting of stem cuttings depends upon the development of adventitious roots, as does the rooting of African violet (*Saintpaulia ionantha*) leaf cuttings. The roots which form from tubers and corms, as when white potatoes and gladiolus are planted, are also adventitious (see Figures 7-3B and 7-4B).

8.2 The root tip

The root tip (Figure 8-2) is more elongated than the stem tip and is not enclosed by developing or protective leaves or scales. Its growth regions, therefore, are somewhat easier to examine closely.

Figure 8-1. A: Diffuse or fibrous root system of a grass. **B:** Tap root system of a carrot (*Daucus carota*).

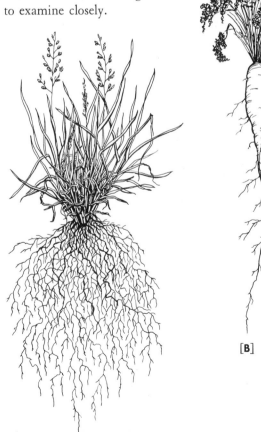

[B]

[A]

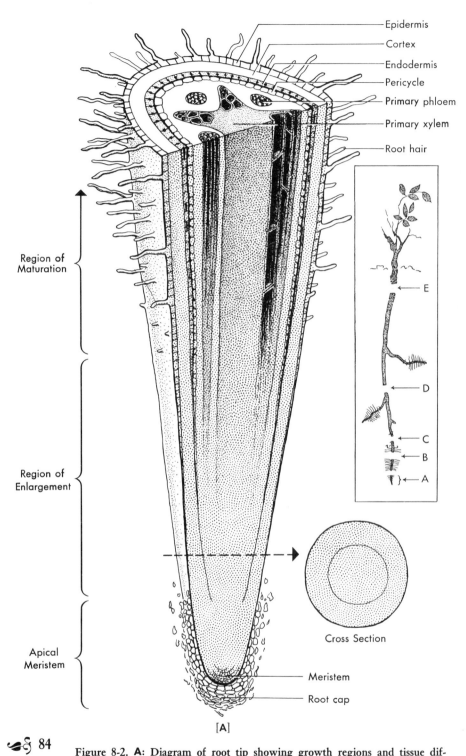

Epidermis

Cortex

Endodermis

Pericycle

Primary phloem

Primary xylem

Root hair

Region of
Maturation

Region of
Enlargement

Apical
Meristem

E

D

C

B

A

Cross Section

Meristem

Root cap

[A]

Figure 8-2. **A**: Diagram of root tip showing growth regions and tissue differentiation. The enclosed figure indicates the regions at which sections were made. In **B** and **C** on the facing page, lateral (or secondary) roots are visible.

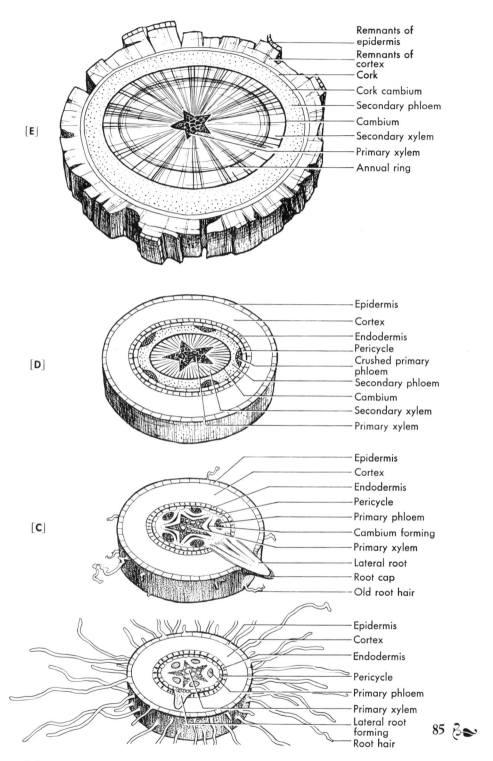

[E]
- Remnants of epidermis
- Remnants of cortex
- Cork
- Cork cambium
- Secondary phloem
- Cambium
- Secondary xylem
- Primary xylem
- Annual ring

[D]
- Epidermis
- Cortex
- Endodermis
- Pericycle
- Crushed primary phloem
- Secondary phloem
- Cambium
- Secondary xylem
- Primary xylem

[C]
- Epidermis
- Cortex
- Endodermis
- Pericycle
- Primary phloem
- Cambium forming
- Primary xylem
- Lateral root
- Root cap
- Old root hair

[B]
- Epidermis
- Cortex
- Endodermis
- Pericycle
- Primary phloem
- Primary xylem
- Lateral root forming
- Root hair

85 ᘓᕷ

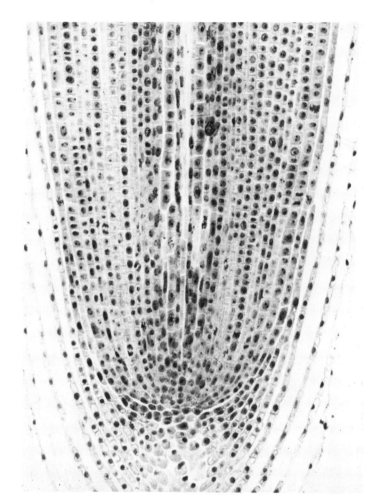

Figure 8-3. The root-cap area consists of the somewhat loosely arranged cells at the bottom of the photomicrograph. The apical meristem is directly behind the root cap (above in the photograph) —the more densely packed cells. (Courtesy of General Biological Supply House, Chicago.)

APICAL MERISTEM AND ROOT CAP

As was mentioned previously (see Section 5.4), at the tips of roots and stems are the apical meristems, regions in which the cells are actively dividing so that new cells are continually being produced. The cells are small, thin-walled, and cubical, and contain dense protoplasm (few or no vacuoles). Protecting this delicate meristematic tissue in the root is a covering which consists of a thimble-shaped mass of cells, the **root cap** (Figure 8-3). As the root grows and the tip advances through the soil, cells of the root cap are sloughed or rubbed off, and new cells are continuously added by divisions of the apical meristem cells directly behind it. The cells of the apical meristem become a part of the root cap, enlarge and mature as permanent root tissues, or continue to divide as a part of the apical meristem. In this way, additional tissue cells are produced, while the meristematic area remains fairly constant in size.

These new cells which are produced at the distal [2] end of the meristematic region become enlarged as they mature, and this region of cell growth is usually termed the **area of cell enlargement.** Again, remember that no sharp distinction exists between the apical meristem and the area of cell enlargement; one blends into the other. The small vacuoles of the cell coalesce and expand, an increase in protoplasmic contents takes place, and the cell wall stretches. New cellulose molecules are added between the old particles, and additional wall layers are secreted. The cells gradually assume separate identities, and indications of tissue development are clearly visible.

AREA OF CELL MATURATION OR DIFFERENTIATION

The enlarged cells eventually develop into the various more-or-less specialized cells of the mature tissues. Those cells which have already differentiated can be seen farther back from the root tip. In the **area of cell maturation,** specific types of tissues are clearly visible, and a division of labor here becomes evident: certain tissues store materials, while others transport materials.

As cells divide, enlarge, and differentiate, the root cap and apical meristem regions are forced farther and farther through the soil. Actually, the sizes of the root cap, apical meristem, and cell enlargement areas remain fairly constant; the area of cell maturation is what increases greatly in size. A cell starts its life as part of the apical meristem. As it ages (if it does not become a root cap cell), the cell next

[2] Distal refers to areas away from the apex or, in this case, to the older areas of the meristematic tissue.

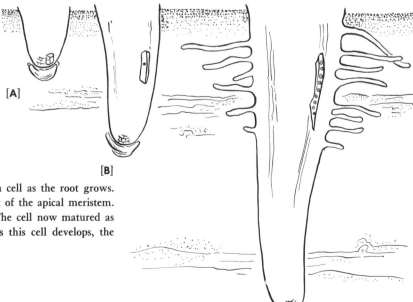

Figure 8-4. Maturation of a cell as the root grows. **A:** The cell is at first a part of the apical meristem. **B:** The cell enlarging. **C:** The cell now matured as a tracheid in the xylem. As this cell develops, the root tip grows downward.

exists as a part of the enlargement region and finally as a cell in what is now the region of maturation. The cell has not changed positions; it has merely changed in structure and function. Figure 8-4 represents this forward, or downward, growth of a root, in which a single cell is shown in its various stages of development. For the sake of simplification, other cells have not been shown, but one must remember that many cells are undergoing a similar maturation.

In a transverse section through the region of mature cells in the root of a woody plant, the various tissues and regions can be diagrammed as in Figure 8-2; outlines of tissues and regions, but not the individual cells, are indicated. Only primary tissues are found at levels *B* and *C*, whereas secondary tissues have developed at level *D*, which represents older tissues.

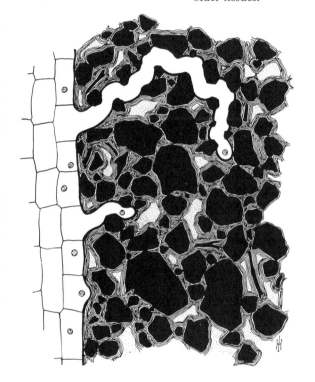

Figure 8-5. Development of root hairs. The soil particles are surrounded by films of water. The stippled areas represent air spaces.

Epidermis (Figure 8-2). This tissue is similar to the epidermis of the stem except for the presence of root hairs in the youngest portion of the region of maturation. A **root hair** (Figures 8-5 and 8-6) is an elongation of an epidermal cell, which becomes intimately associated with soil particles as it develops. Viscous secretions serve to maintain such contact, and root hairs are probably more important in erosion control than are the roots themselves. These hair-like appendages grow very rapidly but have only a transitory existence, dying within a few

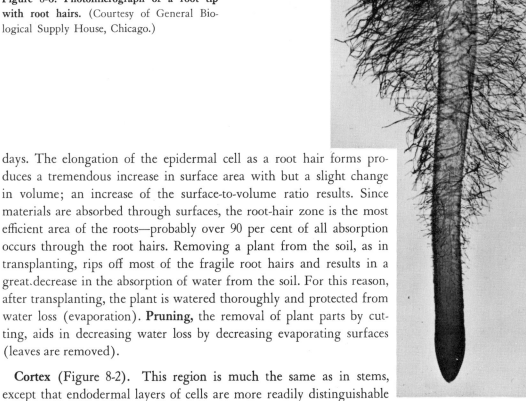

Figure 8-6. Photomicrograph of a root tip with root hairs. (Courtesy of General Biological Supply House, Chicago.)

days. The elongation of the epidermal cell as a root hair forms produces a tremendous increase in surface area with but a slight change in volume; an increase of the surface-to-volume ratio results. Since materials are absorbed through surfaces, the root-hair zone is the most efficient area of the roots—probably over 90 per cent of all absorption occurs through the root hairs. Removing a plant from the soil, as in transplanting, rips off most of the fragile root hairs and results in a great decrease in the absorption of water from the soil. For this reason, after transplanting, the plant is watered thoroughly and protected from water loss (evaporation). **Pruning,** the removal of plant parts by cutting, aids in decreasing water loss by decreasing evaporating surfaces (leaves are removed).

Cortex (Figure 8-2). This region is much the same as in stems, except that endodermal layers of cells are more readily distinguishable in the root. The **endodermis** consists of a sheath-like layer, one cell in thickness, which marks the inner boundary of the cortex. Many of the cells of this layer have thickened walls.

Pericycle (Figure 8-2). The **pericycle** consists of parenchyma-type cells which are located between the endodermis and the vascular tissues. All branch roots arise from the cells of the pericycle, force and digest their way out through the cells external to them, and then penetrate out into the soil. Frequently, the root cap is visible before the branch (or secondary) root has completely reached the exterior (Figure 8-7). Tertiary roots are those which form from the pericycle of secondary roots.

Primary xylem (Figure 8-2). Though the cells which constitute this tissue are similar to those of the stem, the location of the xylem as the central core of the root is quite different from its location in the stem.

89 ठ⁀

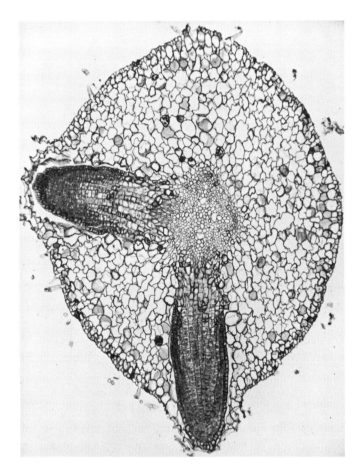

Figure 8-7. Photomicrograph of a transverse section of a willow (*Salix*) root with developing secondary roots. (Courtesy of General Biological Supply House, Chicago.)

The general shape of the xylem, as seen in transverse section, is that of a star.

Primary phloem (Figure 8-2). Located between the projecting arms of the primary xylem are clusters of cells which constitute the primary phloem. Once again, the cells are similar to those found in the primary phloem of the stem; only the location of the tissue is somewhat different.

As the root matures, a **vascular cambium** forms from parenchyma cells between the primary xylem and primary phloem and from some of the cells of the pericycle. As in the stem, secondary xylem and phloem cells develop from the vascular cambium. Figure 8-2E represents a transverse section through a root containing secondary vascular tissues as well as cork, which forms as the increase in diameter tears apart the original outer (primary) tissues. Eventually the production of secondary tissues results in the cylindrical arrangement of vascular tissues. As in the stem, the epidermis and cortex are frequently

sloughed off and are no longer present in older roots. Such roots absorb little, if any, materials because of the cork which now forms the
outer layers.

8.3 Absorption

The absorption of water depends upon osmotic forces, as was indicated previously. The student should review Sections 4.2 and 4.3 for
a discussion of diffusion pressure, wall pressure, and turgor pressure.

Basically, water will be absorbed by the root whenever the diffusion
pressure of water within the root cells (usually root hairs) is less than
the diffusion pressure of water in the soil solution. This is usually the
case, since water is utilized by the various cells of the plant as well as
lost to the atmosphere by evaporation, resulting in water movement
from the root hairs to other cells. The resultant lowering of turgor
pressure, water concentrations, and diffusion pressure within the root
hair brings about further absorption from the soil solution.

The absorption of minerals from the soil is not influenced by the
absorption of water, except for the concentration increase in the soil
mineral content that results when water is removed. The two processes
are independent of each other, just as the absorption of one salt is
independent of the absorption of a second salt. Salts may enter a root
hair because the membranes are permeable and the concentration of
that salt is greater in the soil solution than in the root cell. Utilization
of salts within the plant tends continually to decrease the amount of
salts dissolved in the root cells. Recent evidence, however, indicates
that **active absorption**—when salts are absorbed against a concentration
gradient—is exceedingly important. This is especially prevalent in the
actively metabolizing cells of the root tip. (See Sections 4.4 and 15.3
for additional discussion of this phenomenon.)

Minerals may be absorbed as molecules or as ions. Since these latter
particles are charged, they cannot be absorbed alone without upsetting
the electrostatic equilibrium between positively and negatively charged
particles. When a positively charged ion is absorbed by a cell, either
a positively charged ion is lost from the cell (**ion exchange**) or a negatively charged ion must accompany the one which has a positive
charge. Respiration occurring in a root cell results in the production
of carbon dioxide (CO_2), which forms carbonic acid (H_2CO_3) when
dissolved in water. Since the cells contain considerable quantities of
water, carbonic acid is present and ionizes to form hydrogen ions
(H^+) and bicarbonate ions ($HCO_3{}^-$). These ions may then be exchanged for similarly charged ions of the soil solution (e.g., H^+ exchanged for K^+, potassium; $HCO_3{}^-$ for $NO_3{}^-$, nitrate). It is also

likely that a direct exchange **(contact exchange)** takes place between ions adsorbed to soil particles and the ions of root cells without the ions of the soil actually entering into the soil solution. The extremely close attachment of soil particles to root hairs makes this possible.

8.4 Economic aspects

The roots of many kinds of plants have been utilized for their food value since the beginning of recorded history and probably even earlier. The digging and eating of raw roots of wild plants gradually gave way to the cultivation of plants specifically for roots. The parts are now usually cooked before eating, but many are quite palatable raw. Through plant breeding programs, plants have been produced which develop tap roots of considerable size and of enormous commercial value. The roots most commonly used for food include: beet (*Beta vulgaris*), carrot (*Daucus carota*), radish (*Raphanus sativus*), parsnip (*Pastinaca sativa*), turnip (*Brassica rapa*), sweet potato (*Ipomoea batatas*), and yam (*Dioscorea alata*). The last four are also frequently used as feed for cattle and hogs. The sugar beet is increasing in importance in various countries as a source of sugar, over 5 million tons being produced annually, with the by-products being utilized as cattle fodder, manure, and the molasses for industrial alcohol production. Some plant roots contain drugs which are frequently utilized: ipecac, an emetic and expectorant, from *Cephaelis ipecacuanha;* rhubarb, for indigestion and as a laxative, from *Rheum officinale;* and ginseng, a stimulant, from *Panax ginseng.*

Summary

1. In a fibrous root system are numerous slender main roots which are nearly equal in size, whereas in a tap-root system the primary root remains the dominant part of the underground structure. Adventitious roots are those which arise from stems or leaves.

2. The apical meristem at the end of the root is protected by the root cap. The cells which are formed in the apical meristem eventually enlarge and differentiate into the cells which comprise the various primary tissues of the root.

3. The tissues and regions of a mature root consist of: epidermis, cortex, pericycle (from which branch roots arise), primary phloem, secondary phloem, vascular cambium, secondary xylem, and primary xylem. In a young root the epidermal cells may be greatly elongated as root hairs. In older roots the outer regions are frequently ripped and torn because of the increased diameter that results from the develop-

ment of secondary tissues. In such cases a cork cambium forms from the pericycle, and cork is rapidly produced.

4. Water is absorbed whenever the diffusion pressure of water is lower within the root cells than in the soil solution. Minerals are absorbed as a result of diffusion along a concentration gradient, ion exchange, contact exchange, or against a concentration gradient by actively metabolizing cells.

5. Roots of many kinds of plants are used as food, in alcohol production, and as a source of various drugs.

REVIEW TOPICS AND QUESTIONS

1. Contrast the development of stem branches and root branches.
2. Contrast the roles in plant growth of the apical meristem and the vascular cambium.
3. Diagram a one-year-old woody root in transverse section, and label all structures. It is not necessary to show cells. Secondary tissues should be shown, but no cork has formed.
4. Describe the structural characteristics of roots which increase the efficiency with which they function.
5. You are given an unlabelled microscope slide containing a transverse section of a young woody plant. Explain how you could determine whether the section was made through a root or a stem.
6. As the root tip grows, cells of the root cap are rubbed off by contact with rough soil particles. Explain why a root cap is still present after 20 or 30 years.
7. Since root hair cells do not have a greater ability to absorb water than do other cells of the root, then explain why root hairs are more important in the absorption of water than are other epidermal cells of the root.
8. Would the soil of a cultivated field of beets erode more rapidly or more slowly than the soil of a field of grasses? How would your explanation differ if a field of corn was compared with the field of grasses?
9. Discuss the ways in which minerals may be absorbed by a plant. In what area of the root would most of the active absorption be likely to occur?
10. List ten ways in which plant roots are important to humans.
11. In discussing root tips, one frequently refers to the apical meristem, region of enlargement, and region of differentiation. Explain why these regions cannot be sharply delimited.
12. Compare a root tip with a stem tip, indicating (a) similarities and (b) differences.

SUGGESTED READINGS

Esau, K. *Anatomy of Seed Plants.* New York: Wiley, 1960.
Foster, A. *Practical Plant Anatomy.* Princeton: Van Nostrand, 1949.
Fuller, H. J., and O. Tippo. *College Botany.* New York: Holt, 1954.
Hill, A. F. *Economic Botany.* New York: McGraw-Hill, 1937.

CHAPTER 9 ☙

Leaves

THE food manufacturing process which occurs mainly in the green leaves of plants will be discussed separately in the next chapter, while this chapter will be devoted more to the structural aspects of leaves, since a knowledge of structure is essential to an understanding of function. A clear comprehension of why leaves are the centers of photosynthesis (food manufacture) results only from an investigation of the structural arrangement of the tissues concerned.

9.1   External structure of leaves

Although tremendous variations occur in the size and shape of leaves, certain basic structures are distinguishable (Figure 9-1). The **petiole** (or leaf stalk) is a continuation of the stem and contains vascular tissue which is continuous from that of the stem proper to the rest of the leaf. The **blade** is the flattened, expanded portion of the leaf and is usually green in color, due to the presence of many chloroplast-containing cells. Some leaf blades are needle-like, as in pine (*Pinus*), or scale-like, as in cypress (*Cupressus* spp.). Most of the food manufacture occurs in the blades, and much of this food is then conducted through the petiole to other parts of the plant. Water and minerals move into the blade through the petiole. Small, leaf-like **stipules** are frequently found at the base of the petiole, along with an axillary bud. The development of an axillary bud results in the production of secondary branches, flowers, or both, depending upon the type of bud.

In Figures 9-2 and 9-3, examples of variations from this general type are shown. The gigantic *Victoria* leaf and the tiny leaf of *Lemna* are

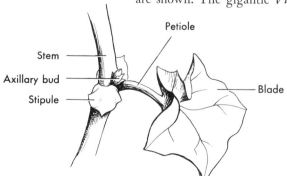

Stem

Axillary bud

Stipule

Petiole

Blade

Figure 9-1. The basic parts of a leaf. The ivy geranium (*Pelargonium peltatum*) was used as the model for this drawing.

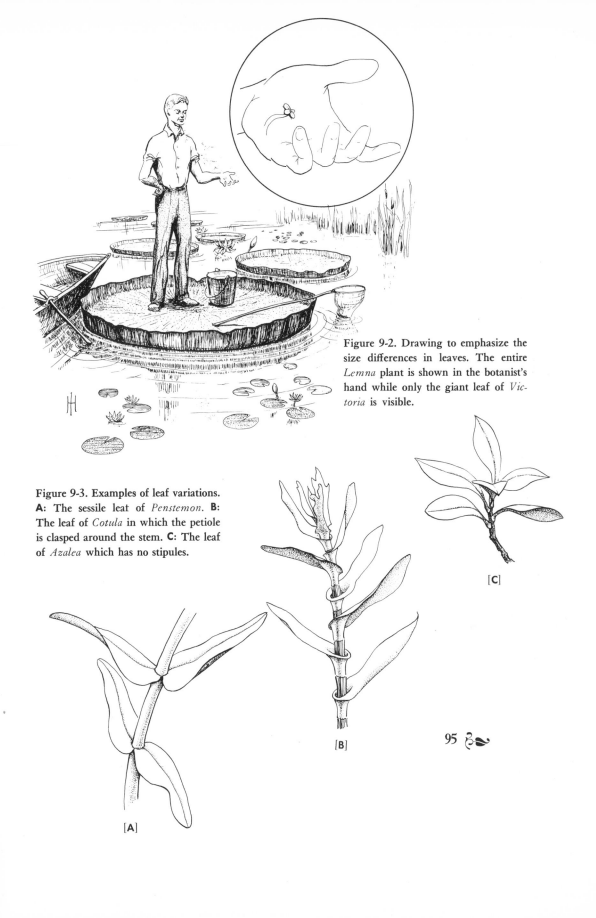

Figure 9-2. Drawing to emphasize the size differences in leaves. The entire *Lemna* plant is shown in the botanist's hand while only the giant leaf of *Victoria* is visible.

Figure 9-3. Examples of leaf variations. **A**: The sessile leat of *Penstemon*. **B**: The leaf of *Cotula* in which the petiole is clasped around the stem. **C**: The leaf of *Azalea* which has no stipules.

[C]

[B]

[A]

95

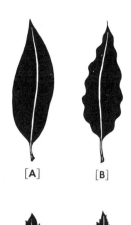

[A]   [B]

Figure 9-4. Examples of variations in leaf margins. **A**: Entire. **B**: Undulate. **C**: Serrate. **D**: Double-serrate. **E**: Lobed. **F**: Parted.

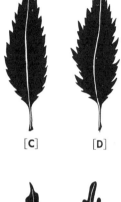

[C]   [D]

[E]   [F]

drawn to indicate extremes in size. Stipules are not present in *Azalea* spp., the leaf of *Penstemon* is **sessile** (no petiole is present), and the petiole of a *Cotula* leaf is clasped about the stem. Leaves also vary in the type of leaf margin or edge, as is indicated in Figure 9-4.

SIMPLE AND COMPOUND LEAVES

The leaf blade may be subdivided into several separate expanded parts, or **leaflets.** Such a leaf is termed **compound,** as distinguished from a **simple** leaf, which has a single expanded portion (Figures 9-5 and 9-6). Each leaflet may consist of an expanded portion and a short stalk, or **rachis,** which is a continuation of the petiole (Figure 9-6A). In order to determine whether the structure is a leaflet or a small leaf, the base of the stalk must be examined: buds occur only in the axils of leaf petioles, and stipules are found only at the bases of petioles. Leaves may be more than once compound (Figure 9-6C).

LEAF VENATION

Vascular tissue extends from the stem through the petiole and into the blade of the leaf, where it forms a network of **veins,** which may be arranged in several ways. **Parallel venation** is a characteristic of mono-cotyledonous plants, such as onion (*Allium cepa*), lily (*Lilium*), corn (*Zea mays*), and grasses. In such plants numerous veins of approximately equal size extend side-by-side from base to tip of the blade and are inter-connected by small and inconspicuous veins (Figure 9-5C). **Net venation** is found in dicotyledonous plants, such as oak (*Quercus*), maple (*Acer*), bean (*Phaseolus*), pea (*Pisum*), and syca-more (*Platanus*). In these plants one or more veins are prominent, and the smaller veins form a conspicuous network. If a leaf has one main vein from which the others branch off, it is termed **pinnately**

Figure 9-5. Examples of simple leaves. **A**: Dwarf ivy (*Hedera helix* var.) leaf, palmately net-veined. **B**: Grape (*Vitis*) leaf, pinnately net-veined. **C**: Bamboo (*Bambusa*) leaf with parallel venation.

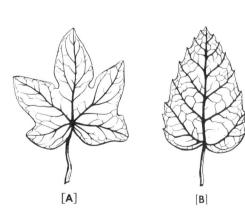

[A]   [B]   [C]

[A]   [B]   [C]

Figure 9-6. Examples of compound leaves. **A:** *Akebia,* palmately compound. **B:** Brazilian pepper (*Schinus terebinthifolius*), pinnately compound. **C:** *Acacia,* double pinnately compound.

net-veined (Figure 9-5B), whereas a **palmately** net-veined leaf has several main veins extending from the base (Figure 9-5A). Leaves may also be **pinnately compound** (Figure 9-6B) or **palmately compound** (Figure 9-6A).

LEAF DEVELOPMENT

As was mentioned in the discussion of buds (see Section 6.1), leaves develop as lateral outgrowths from the terminal meristems of the stems. In most leaves growth is rather generalized—growth regions are not localized—and cell division ceases rather early. Further increase in size is a result of enlargement of cells already present. Leaves, therefore, are determinate (or limited) in growth, as compared to the indeterminate (or unlimited) type of growth found in roots and stems (due to the presence of an apical meristem and sometimes a cambium).

In some monocotyledonous plants, such as the grasses, the basal portion of each leaf remains meristematic, and the leaf continues to grow. Lawn-mowers are necessary for this reason—even though the top part of the grass leaf is cut off, this does not stop the leaf from growing, and subsequent mowing is necessary.

9.2 Leaf modifications

The leaves of certain plants are so modified as to lack the appearance of leaves. Just as some stems are modified as supporting tendrils (see Section 7.4), so also may leaves or leaflets function in a similar manner. The twining tendrils of *Vicia* are modified leaflets (Figure 9-7A). Other leaves may be modified as thorns and spines, as in Ocotillo (*Fouquieria splendens*) (Figure 9-7B) and in some cacti.

Leaves borne on different parts of the same plant may vary considerably in structure. Leaves exposed to the sun tend to have a thick cuticle, a palisade layer (see next Section) several cells in thickness, and relatively small intercellular spaces in the spongy mesophyll, whereas shaded leaves on the same tree are more likely to have thin cuticles, a palisade layer one cell in thickness, and considerable inter-cellular spaces. Probably the most important factors involved in such growth are differential water contents and variations in light intensity and quality (wave lengths or colors). The leaves in the sun lose more water, the cells are less turgid, and cell enlargement would tend to be curtailed—remember that such enlargement depends to a great extent upon turgor pressure. With a curtailment in cellular expansion, addi-tional food supplies might be available, for example, during the develop-ment of a relatively thick cuticle. The higher light intensities imping-ing upon exposed leaves would also result in rather high rates of food manufacture (photosynthesis; see the next Chapter). In addition to these effects, various wave lengths (colors) of light are also known to influence significantly the structural development of plants. However, the precise mechanisms involved in the morphological differentiations that have been observed in leaves exposed to the sun and similar leaves not so exposed have not yet been demonstrated.

Many plants growing in dry areas have very thick, succulent leaves which store large quantities of water. Water-storage cells, really the parenchymatous cells of the mesophyll, contain copious quantities of hygroscopic [1] mucins, which greatly retard water loss. Examples of these plants are found in many rock gardens of the southern United States: *Sedum,* century plant (*Agave*), ice plant (*Mesembryanthe-mum*), and *Crassula.*

In some aquatic plants, such as *Ranunculus aquatilis,* the leaves which develop submerged in water are quite different in appearance from those which develop above the surface. As indicated in Figure 9-7C, the former are subdivided into a many-branched structure, while in the latter the blade is unbranched. The finely divided submerged leaf may be advantageous as far as diffusion of materials into the leaf is concerned (i.e., CO_2 for photosynthesis, O_2 for respiration).

[1] Hygroscopic materials adsorb water.

[A]

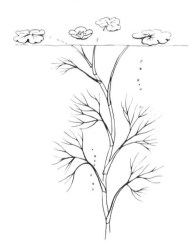

(1)

(2)

[B]   [C]

Figure 9-7. Examples of leaf modifications. A: Twining tendrils of *Vicia.* B: Thorns of Ocotillo or Jacob's Staff (*Fouquieria splen-dens*); (1) an early stage with the blade present, (2) later stage. C: Submerged and exposed leaves of *Ranunculus aquatilis.*

9.3 Insectivorous plants

Much has been written about "carnivorous plants," and these will be discussed in more detail later (Section 13.5), but this phrase is really a misnomer, since these plants do manufacture their own food and only insects have ever been found to be utilized. At least three plants have leaf modifications which enable the plant to partake of insects. Probably the most interesting is the Venus'-Flytrap (*Dionaea muscipula*) (see Figure 13-6), in which the hinged leaf closes about such things as flies and entraps them. The bodies are digested by enzymes[2] secreted by certain cells of the leaf, and the leaf cells undoubtedly absorb such digested materials. In the Sundew (*Drosera* spp.) (see Figure 13-5), certain leaves are basically short stalks with an enlarged end, from which project slender hairs having a sticky knob at the end. Insects stick to these hairs and are digested by enzymes secreted by the hairs. The leaves of the pitcher plant (*Sarracenia* spp.) (see Figure 13-4) are somewhat funnel-shaped, with stiff hairs on the inner surface projecting downward. Insects fall into the leaf and drown in the water which partly fills the leaves, since they cannot crawl out past the hairs.

9.4 Internal structure of leaves

Figure 9-8 is a stereoscopic view of a leaf, showing the location of various cells and tissues. The leaf blade has both an upper and a lower epidermis, which form a relatively waterproof layer because of the waxy cuticle present on the outer surfaces of the cells and the lack of intercellular spaces. Cutin, a waxy material, is secreted by the epidermal cells and forms this impermeable layer. At intervals are specialized, kidney-shaped epidermal cells, the **guard cells,** between which are pores, or **stomata.** These openings, which may be present in both epidermal layers (though usually more frequent or more numerous in the lower epidermis), provide a pathway for gaseous exchange between the intercellular spaces within the leaf and the external atmosphere. In darkness, the guard cells are limp, and the stoma is closed; in the presence of light, the guard cells become turgid by absorbing water, and the stoma is open (Figure 9-9). Guard cells are the only cells of the epidermis that contain chloroplasts, an important factor in bringing about their turgor changes, as will be discussed later (Section 14.4).

Between the epidermal layers is a parenchyma tissue, the **mesophyll,** usually arranged in two layers. The layer beneath the upper epidermis is the **palisade layer,** which consists of cylindrical cells whose long axes **99** &

[2] See Section 11.2 for a discussion of **enzymes.**

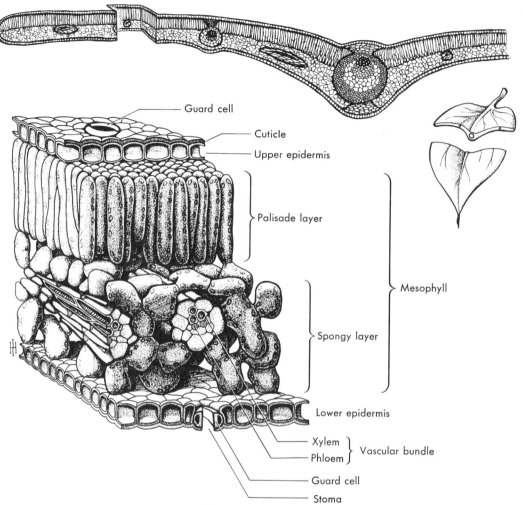

Figure 9-8. Stereoscopic diagram of a leaf showing the location of various cells and tissues.

Figure 9-9. **A**: The two guard cells are relatively limp and the stoma is closed. **B**: The guard cells are turgid and the stoma is open.

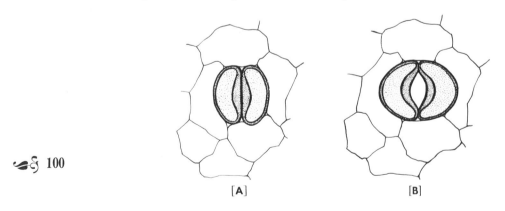

[A]　　　　　　　　　[B]

are at right angles to the epidermis so that they appear to hang down like closely packed stalactites. Though usually only one layer of cells is present, this is influenced by environmental conditions, and many leaves, when exposed to the sun, tend to have a palisade layer several cells in thickness. Between the palisade layer and the lower epidermis is a mass of loosely arranged, irregularly-shaped cells which comprise the **spongy layer.** All cells of the mesophyll contain numerous chloroplasts. The intercellular spaces of the two layers form a continuous pathway through which gas molecules or water vapor molecules may diffuse from atmosphere to cell by way of the stomata, or vice versa.

Extending throughout the mesophyll are strands of vascular tissue, the leaf veins, which ramify and inter-connect forming a network within the leaf. The number of veins and their profuse branching insures that the location of any leaf cell is in the vicinity of some vascular tissue. In fact, probably no leaf cell is more than five cell-diameters away from a vein. Such an extensive vascular network, continuous as it is with the vascular tissue of the stem and thus with the root, enables rapid transport of materials into and out of the leaves.

9.5 General function of leaves

The most important function of leaves is the manufacture of organic material from carbon dioxide and water, a process **(photosynthesis)** which will be discussed in considerable detail in the next chapter. Leaves also may be areas in which food or water is stored. The onion bulb (*Allium cepa*) consists mainly of large fleshy leaves in which copious quantities of food are stored, while the century plant (*Agave americana*) provides us with an example of leaves which store quantities of water when it is available.

9.6 Economic aspects of leaves

The leaves of many plants are utilized as a source of food by humans: cabbage (*Brassica oleracea* var. *capitate*), kale (*Brassica oleracea* var. *acephala*), lettuce (*Lactuca sativa*), spinach (*Spinacia oleracea*), celery (*Apium graveolens*), and rhubarb (*Rheum Rhaponticum*). In the last two, it is mainly the petiole which is usually eaten. The leaves of certain plants are a source of fibers: bowstring hemp (*Sansevieria thyrsiflora*), manila hemp (*Musa textilis*), New Zealand flax (*Phormium tenax*), and sisal (*Agave* spp.). Tea leaves (*Thea sinesis*) are used to make a beverage, while tobacco leaves (*Nicotiana* spp.) are the basis for a billion-dollar industry. A few drugs, condiments, and flavorings are also obtained from leaves: belladonna and atropine from *Atropa bella-*

donna, purgatives from *Aloe* spp., cocaine from the coca shrub (*Erythroxylon coca*), digitalis from *Digitalis purpurea*, and witch hazel from *Hamamelis virginiana*; sage from *Salvia officinalis*, basil from *Ocimum Basilicum*, thyme from *Thymus vulgaris*, bay leaves from *Laurus nobilis*, and marjoram from *Majorana hortensis*; spearmint from *Mentha spicata*, wintergreen from *Gualtheria procumbens*, and peppermint from *Mentha piperita*.

Summary

1. The basic structures of the leaf are the petiole, the blade, and the stipules. However, leaves vary greatly in size, shape, and as to whether or not a petiole or stipules are present.

2. Simple leaves have a single expanded portion, whereas the leaf blade of a compound leaf is subdivided into several parts called leaflets. The vascular tissue in the blade forms a network of veins in which the main veins extend parallel to each other or in which main veins and subsidiary veins form a branching system.

3. The leaves of various plants are modified as tendrils, thorns, or spines; others are enlarged succulent structures which store copious quantities of water. The leaves of some plants are so modified as to trap insects, which are then consumed.

4. Between the epidermal tissues of the leaf is the mesophyll tissue, which is differentiated into an upper palisade layer and a more loosely arranged spongy layer. The cells of the mesophyll contain numerous chloroplasts and are important in food manufacture. The vascular tissue extends throughout the mesophyll. In the epidermal layers are found numerous stomata through which gaseous exchange occurs.

5. The leaves of some plants are exceedingly important economically: food, tobacco, fibers, tea, drugs, condiments, and flavorings.

REVIEW TOPICS AND QUESTIONS

1. Diagram a leaf in cross-section, and label all structures. Individual cells of the vascular tissue need not be shown.
2. Diagram a leaf as it appears when the section is cut parallel to the epidermis and through the palisade mesophyll. This is a paradermal section. Do not show individual cells of the vascular tissue.
3. Diagram a leaf as it appears when the section is cut parallel to the epidermis and through the spongy mesophyll. Do not show individual cells of the vascular tissue.
4. Why is it possible to find vascular tissue in both transverse and longitudinal views when examining the cross-section of a leaf?
5. List seven plants the leaves of which are used as food by animals (including humans).

6. In what ways are leaves used by humans other than as a source of food?   **Leaves**

SUGGESTED READINGS

Ashby, E. "Leaf Shape," *Scientific American,* 180 (April 1949), 22–29.
Gibbs, R. D. *Botany*. Philadelphia: Blakiston, 1950.
Hill, A. F. *Economic Botany*. New York: McGraw-Hill, 1937.
Hill, J. B., et al. *Botany*. New York: McGraw-Hill, 1960.

Photosynthesis

10.1 Nutritional types

In the preceding chapter the structure of the leaf was emphasized, and but a brief mention was made of the functions involved. However, the most important aspect of a study of plants is probably the food manufacturing process (photosynthesis), which occurs primarily in green leaves. This activity of green cells provides the food and the oxygen for all organisms, including animals and non-green plants, as well as the requirements of the plant which itself contains such cells. An organism, such as a green plant, which can manufacture its own foods from simple inorganic substances (usually carbon dioxide and water) is termed an **autotrophe.** Autotrophes are of two types, **photosynthetic** and **chemosynthetic,** which differ in that the former utilize radiant (light) energy and the latter utilize energy derived from chemical reactions (see Chapter 20, especially Section 20.5). Those organisms which cannot manufacture their own food are **heterotrophes. Parasites** are those heterotrophes which obtain their food from the living cells or tissues of another organism, while **saprophytes** obtain their food from non-living organic matter (i.e., dead plants and animals, excretions and secretions from plants and animals). Humans are, of course, heterotrophic, just as are all animals and the non-green plants.

10.2 Photosynthesis

The manufacture of food, mainly sugar, from carbon dioxide and water in the presence of chlorophyll, utilizing light energy and releasing oxygen gas, is termed **photosynthesis.**[1] This process has been under intensive investigation for many years, but the exact mechanisms in-

[1] Some bacteria are photosynthetic but do not utilize water or produce oxygen. The activity of these organisms is insignificantly small in comparison with the green plants.

volved are not yet completely understood. The raw materials and major end products have been known at least since the work of Sachs in the 1860's, but the complexity of the steps between these end points is only now being clarified. Certainly ten or more steps, some of a cyclic nature, are involved.

10.3   Essential factors in photosynthesis

Any factor whose presence is required before a reaction proceeds is termed an **essential factor.** This is not a relative term: if any one such factor is absent, the reaction cannot take place. The raw materials, or substrate, of a reaction are essentials, but so also in many instances are certain environmental factors. In photosynthesis the essential factors are: carbon dioxide, water, energy (light), chloroplasts, and a suitable temperature.

RAW MATERIALS

Because of the concentration gradient that results from its use as a substrate, carbon dioxide diffuses through the stomata from the atmosphere into the intercellular spaces of the leaf. The content of carbon dioxide in the atmosphere is rather constant at about 0.03 per cent (3 parts per 10,000 parts of air), a seemingly small amount but totalling approximately 2,000,000,000,000 (2×10^{12}) tons in the atmosphere surrounding the earth. This gas is continually being added to the air by the respiration (Chapter 12) of plants and animals, by the decay of organic materials, by the combustion of fuels, by the weathering of rock, and by volcanic activity, although, in fact, the respiration of plants, including micro-organisms, supplies more carbon dioxide to the atmosphere than comes from all other sources combined. The oceans of the world contain tremendous amounts of dissolved carbon dioxide, probably more than is found in the atmosphere, and act as a great reservoir of this material. Once in the intercellular spaces, the molecules of carbon dioxide dissolve in the water which saturates the walls of the mesophyll cells and diffuse into the cytoplasm and eventually to the chloroplasts of these cells, where photosynthesis takes place.

Water, the other substrate, is absorbed by the roots of the plant and is transported to the leaves through the various cells and tissues as indicated in previous chapters.

ENERGY

In the synthesis of any material, energy is required in order to convert simple molecules into more complex ones. As the name implies, the energy source in photosynthesis is light energy, with the red and

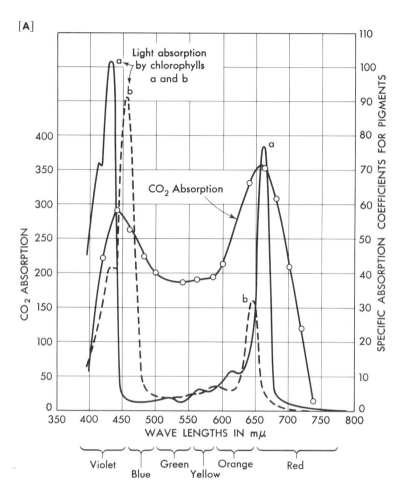

[A]

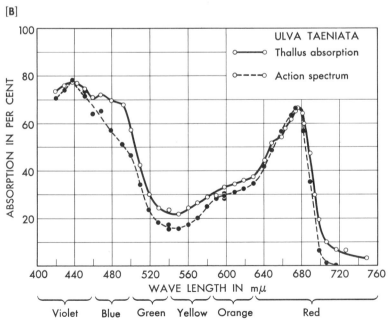

[B]

Figure 10-1. Light absorption curves of chlorophyll superimposed on the curve of photosynthetic rate as a function of wavelength of light. **A: In wheat plants.** (From O. F. Curtis and D. G. Clark, *Introduction to Plant Physiology.* New York: McGraw-Hill. Copyright 1950 by the publisher. Used by permission.) **B: In** *Ulva,* **a green alga.** (From F. T. Haxo and L. R. Blinks, *Jour. Gen. Physiol.,* **33** (1950), 389–422.)

blue wave lengths (colors) being the most effective. The greens and yellows are mainly reflected from and transmitted through the leaf and have much less effect on the process. The sun normally is the source of such radiations, but electric lights can also be used. Only those wave lengths which can be absorbed by chlorophyll are useful in photosynthesis. The process may be considered as one in which radiant energy is converted to chemical energy and stored in the form of the carbohydrate end product—an energy-storing or energy-absorbing process. Even though only about two per cent of the light energy striking a leaf is actually stored in the resultant sugar molecules, the process is more efficient than this would appear to be: most of the light from the sun is reflected, transmitted, or absorbed as heat, but approximately 30 per cent of what is actually absorbed is converted to chemical energy (as sugar).

PIGMENTS

The presence of the green pigment chlorophyll [2] enables green plants to absorb light energy and to use this energy in the production of sugars. The absorption spectrum for chlorophyll indicates that red and blue wave lengths are absorbed much more than green, and this correlates rather closely with the effect of wave lengths on photosynthesis (see Figure 10-1). Chlorophyll transfers this absorbed energy to the compounds involved in the reaction and also acts as a catalyst.

The **carotenoid** pigments, **xanthophylls** (yellow) and **carotenes** (yellow-orange), are always present in chloroplasts along with the chlorophyll. Recent evidence indicates that such associated pigments, in algae at least, may absorb light and pass this excitation (or energy) to chlorophyll. They may supplement chlorophylls as light absorbers, but they are not capable of acting as catalysts in photosynthesis. In higher plants no example of photosynthesis has been found where the cells did not contain chlorophyll. Even those plants that have red leaves are found to contain chlorophyll which is merely masked by the red pigment. Boiling such leaves in water removes the red **anthocyanin,** which is water-soluble and located in the vacuoles of the leaf cells; the green chlorophyll is then visible.

[2] Actually, several chlorophylls (indicated by letters a, b, c, d, e, etc.) have been found, but chlorophyll "a" is the pigment to which the others transfer energy which they have absorbed as light. Green plants contain chlorophylls "a" and "b," whereas the other chlorophylls are present in certain of the algae (see Chapter 19).

The yellowish pigments are usually not noticed, because they are masked by the color of the chlorophylls and come into prominence only during the fall of the year in many plants. The autumn coloration of many trees results as chlorophyll synthesis decreases while chlorophyll destruction continues. Eventually the carotenes and xanthophylls are no longer hidden; the leaf color changes from green to yellowish, as in the tulip tree (*Liriodendron tulipifera*), elm (*Ulmus*), aspen (*Populus tremuloides*), and hickory (*Carya ovata*). In some trees additional red pigments, anthocyanins, develop, especially if large supplies of carbohydrates are available to the leaves. Red maple (*Acer rubrum*), sumac (*Rhus*), and many oaks (*Quercus*) become quite prominent in the landscape as a result of their dominant red color. As the leaves die, the pigments decompose, and only the brown **tannins** remain. The gorgeous hues of northern forests result from these pigment changes that take place near the end of the growing season. Frost does not bring about this coloration. In fact, early frosts tend to decrease the color display, especially with regard to the red pigments, by bringing about the early death of leaves and the rapid appearance of the brown tannins. However, exceptionally brilliant autumn coloration usually occurs if fairly low night temperatures, which retard the removal of food from leaves, are associated with bright sunny days, which favor photosynthesis and sugar production.

TEMPERATURE

Photosynthesis generally takes place over a range of temperature from 5 to 40°C., the rate increasing as the temperature rises, up to approximately 35°C., after which a rapid decline in rate occurs. This decrease in rate is probably due to enzyme inactivation at the higher temperatures. Since the process is influenced by temperature as well as by light, it is apparent that both chemical and photo-chemical reactions are involved because the latter are independent of temperature. This will be discussed more fully later. The enzymes that are involved have not all been identified, but the evidence for their presence is quite conclusive. More refined techniques will undoubtedly clarify this situation in the future.

ADDITIONAL ESSENTIAL FACTORS

Present in chloroplasts, along with the pigments already mentioned, are various carrier molecules whose functions have only recently been elucidated. They are important in transferring hydrogen atoms and in transferring energy. These activities are discussed in more detail in Section 10.6.

10.4 Materials produced as a result of photosynthesis

As investigations continue, photosynthesis is found to be an extremely complicated process in which a variety of substances may be produced, even though the simple sugar, glucose (a carbohydrate), is the principal end product in the majority of plants. The substances produced quite possibly may vary with the kind of plant as well as with the environmental conditions which influence the process. The discovery of all the steps whereby water and carbon dioxide are converted to sugar would be of tremendous importance, especially if correlated with an understanding of how manipulation of the environment might bring about the increased production of one or another of the products that now appear to be formed in relatively small amounts (e.g., organic acids, fatty acids, amino acids, etc.). Further discussion along these lines will be found in Section 29.6. Because most of the food produced is usually in the form of glucose, this compound will be used for discussions in the subsequent sections of this chapter.

The oxygen produced by photosynthesis either is utilized within the cells or diffuses out of the leaves by the same pathway that was available to the carbon dioxide molecules diffusing into the leaves. Fortunately for the heterotrophic organisms, much more oxygen is produced by green plants than is utilized by them. This excess oxygen (excess as far as the green plant is concerned) is used by man, other animals, and the aerobic non-chlorophyllous plants. Anaerobic, or fermentative, fungi do not utilize oxygen, of course, but are nevertheless dependent upon autotrophic organisms for a supply of food, just as are the aerobic heterotrophes. See Chapter 12 for a further discussion of respiration and fermentation.

10.5 The over-all reaction

The equation for photosynthesis is frequently written as:

(1) $$6CO_2 + 6H_2O \xrightarrow[\text{light energy}]{\text{chloroplast}} C_6H_{12}O_6 + 6O_2$$

This equation indicates that six molecules of carbon dioxide and six molecules of water react in the presence of chloroplasts and light to form one molecule of glucose (a six-carbon sugar, or hexose) and six molecules of oxygen. In the early 1940's a series of investigations by Ruben resulted in a revision of this basic equation. Ruben utilized **isotopes**[3] of oxygen to label atoms in the water; until isotopes were

[3] Isotopes are atoms which are identical in chemical properties but which differ in mass. This mass difference is a result of differences in the number of neutrons

used, these oxygen atoms could not be distinguished from those in the carbon dioxide. In a similar manner, radioactive atoms are now used to distinguish, for example, the first carbon atom in glucose from the other five. When the oxygen atoms in the water molecules were labeled, Ruben found that these atoms formed the free oxygen that was produced and were not present in the sugar molecule; the oxygen atoms from the carbon dioxide molecules, on the other hand, were found in the glucose. Just how startling this was to a chemist or physiologist can be seen more clearly if we re-write equation #1 as follows:

$$(2) \qquad CO_2 + H_2O \rightarrow [CH_2O] + O_2$$

(The chemical formula CH_2O is a general one for any carbohydrate; equation #2 is really the same as #1, in that carbon dioxide and water react to form a carbohydrate and oxygen.) Physiologists used to think that carbon dioxide was split during photosynthesis, the carbon adding to water to form the carbohydrate and the oxygen being liberated to form oxygen gas. This could not be the case, however, since Ruben's work showed that the oxygen gas was derived from water. The dilemma was solved by the understanding that new water is actually formed during photosynthesis; water is used and water is produced:

$$(3) \qquad CO_2 + 2H_2O^* \rightarrow [CH_2O] + O_2^* + H_2O$$

The asterisk indicates labeled atoms. The water which is produced is not the same as the water that has been used. Note that the oxygen atoms in the water molecules to the right of the arrow have come from some of the oxygen atoms that were originally present in the carbon dioxide molecules. To represent photosynthesis in a manner similar to equation #1:

$$(4) \qquad 6CO_2 + 12H_2O \xrightarrow[\text{light energy}]{\text{chloroplast}} C_6H_{12}O_6 + 6O_2 + 6H_2O$$

This, then, is a more accurate version of the over-all photosynthetic reaction. It is also an excellent example of the importance of being able to label atoms so that the atoms in one reactant can be differentiated from similar atoms in other reactants.

---

in the core of the atom (Section 3.1). Therefore, we can differentiate between such atoms on the basis of weight. Isotopes may or may not be radioactive; radioactive isotopes can be produced by bombardments with alpha particles, utilizing such devices as the cyclotron. For further information the reader is referred to any good, modern, general chemistry text.

10.6 The mechanism of photosynthesis [4]

The fact has been mentioned previously that two types of reactions are involved in photosynthesis: (1) photochemical and (2) enzymatic, or chemical. Any detailed discussion of the various steps involved in these two types is beyond the scope of this text, but a few comments are in order.

The photochemical reactions utilize light energy to bring about the decomposition (photolysis) of water whereby the hydrogen atoms are made available for the enzymatic reduction of carbon dioxide to carbohydrate. Chlorophyll absorbs light energy and is activated. This energy is utilized in the splitting of water molecules and in the formation of high-energy phosphate bonds. The chlorophyll returns to its original condition, as a result of losing energy, and is ready to absorb more light energy.

(5) $\quad$ Chlorophyll + light energy $\rightarrow$ Activated chlorophyll

(6)
$$4H_2O \quad\diagup\quad \text{Activated chlorophyll}$$
$$4[H] + 4[OH] \diagup\diagdown \text{Chlorophyll}$$

Some of the hydrogens [H] are accepted by (or attached to) an organic compound, triphosphopyridine nucleotide (TPN), while the hydroxyls [OH] form oxygen and new water.

(7) $\qquad$ $TPN + 2[H] \rightarrow TPNH_2$

(8) $\qquad$ $4[OH] \rightarrow O_2 + 2H_2O$

Other hydrogens and hydroxyls recombine with an evolution of energy that results in the formation of high-energy phosphate bonds,[5] as adenosine diphosphate (ADP) is converted to adenosine triphosphate (ATP).

(9)
$$[H] + [OH] \quad\diagup\quad \text{ADP + Inorganic phosphate}$$
$$H_2O \quad\diagup\diagdown \text{ATP}$$

---

[4] The discussion in this section is based upon recent evidence and upon general hypotheses that fit most of the data that have been accumulated. However, as additional information is obtained, one should not be too surprised if a revision of at least parts of this section would be necessary. Similar revisions in various aspects of biology have been made many times in the past as a result of further investigations. Photosynthesis is an exceedingly complex process, and the difficulties inherent to research on the molecular level should be apparent to everyone. Also, this discussion has been greatly simplified in order to remain within the purview of a general botany text.

[5] High-energy phosphate bonds ($\sim$P) are extremely important in transferring energy from place to place and in the various syntheses that occur in living cells. A more intensive discussion of such bonds can be found in Chapter 12, especially Section 12.6.

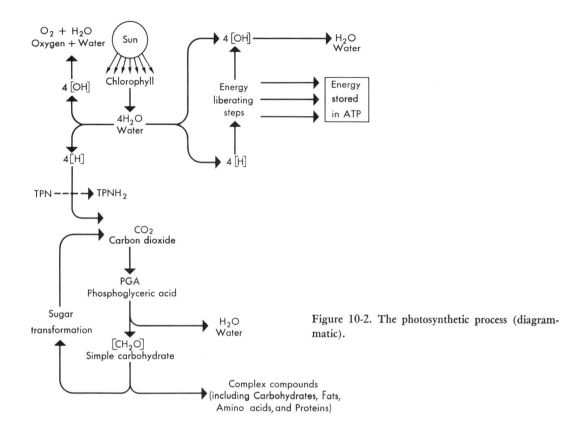

Figure 10-2. The photosynthetic process (diagrammatic).

Activated chlorophyll is also capable of converting ADP to ATP, a process in which energy is transferred to high-energy phosphate bonds.

(10)

$$\text{ADP} + \text{P} \quad \overset{\text{Activated chlorophyll}}{\underset{\text{Chlorophyll}}{\bigtimes}} \quad \text{ATP}$$

After the preceding reactions have occurred in the light, the rest of the reactions of photosynthesis may take place in the dark. These latter reactions are influenced by temperature, whereas the photochemical ones are not. As a first step in the "dark reactions," [6] carbon dioxide is added to a pre-existing five-carbon sugar-phosphate, which immediately splits into two molecules of **phosphoglyceric acid,** the first identifiable product. This acid is a phosphorus-containing organic compound with three carbon atoms. A number of chemical reactions, some of them cyclic, reduce phosphoglyceric acid molecules to a variety of

[6] The term "dark" indicates that these reactions *may* take place in the dark, *not* that they require dark. The "light reactions," on the other hand, do *require* light.

sugars; eventually more of the five-carbon sugar is formed, as well as glucose (a six-carbon sugar), the principal product of photosynthesis. The end result of these various reactions is that carbon dioxide molecules are reduced to a carbohydrate by the addition of hydrogens obtained from $TPNH_2$ and through the utilization of energy residing in ATP.

(11)

$$CO_2 + 2TPNH_2 \qquad\qquad ATP$$
$$[CH_2O] + H_2O + 2TPN \qquad ADP + P$$

In this whole series of reactions, several materials are changed from one form to another and then back to the original—they are not used up. This is true of chlorophyll, TPN, and ADP. Carbon dioxide and water, however, are used up as glucose and oxygen are produced. Thus, even though reactions number (3) and (4) indicate the over-all photosynthetic process, Figure 10-2 represents the process more accurately. The transformation of simple carbohydrates into complex compounds may take place quite rapidly, which would explain the observations (by various investigators) that other materials besides glucose are produced.

10.7   The fate of the sugar molecules

That simple sugars provide the basic building blocks for all of the complex molecules that constitute a living cell, its secretions, and its excretions, cannot be emphasized too strongly. Glucose undergoes many chemical transformations, which result in the formation of starch, cellulose, fats, proteins, vitamins, hormones, and many other compounds. Some of these materials are structural components of the cell (e.g., cellulose, proteins), some are storage products (e.g., starch, proteins, fats), and others are necessary for the normal metabolism of the cell (e.g., vitamins, hormones, enzymes). Glucose frequently is transported from the mesophyll cells of the leaf to other, non-chlorophyllous cells, where such reactions then take place. In addition to glucose being used as a basis for syntheses, many of the sugar molecules are utilized as a source of energy in the respiratory processes of cells. Respiration is that process which occurs in all living cells and which makes energy available for cellular functions. This energy-yielding process will be discussed in more detail in Chapter 12.

The rapid conversion of sugar to starch, a storage product, frequently enables physiologists to utilize the convenient iodine test for starch as an indication of the occurrence of photosynthesis. In many leaves excess sugars (excess in that more sugars are produced during photosynthesis than are used by the leaf) are rapidly converted to starch,

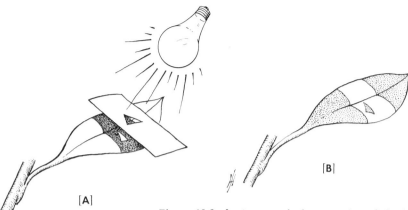

Figure 10-3. **A**: A cover shades a portion of the leaf. Actually the cover is placed directly on the leaf, but in the diagram it has been shown in a raised position to emphasize the shading effect. **B**: The stippled area indicates a positive starch test. Note that the covered area is devoid of starch.

which yields a blue-black color when treated with iodine-potassium iodide solution. If photosynthesis is prevented in half of the leaf by covering this portion with black paper, only the other half of the leaf will yield a positive starch test (Figure 10-3). The chlorophyll is usually first removed by boiling the leaf in alcohol so that the green color does not interfere with the test. In some leaves (e.g., onion, lily) starch is not formed, and this test could not be used. In fact, it must be clearly understood to be an indication of photosynthesis and not really a test for the end product of the reaction, which is glucose. To test for starch is merely more convenient than to test for sugar, and the test is valid as long as its limitations are understood.

10.8 Limiting and retarding factors

Photosynthesis is the first metabolic (chemical) process of the plant which has been mentioned in any detail, and this is an excellent opportunity to utilize a process to point out examples of limiting and retarding factors. Remember, however, that these concepts or principles are valid for all chemical reactions.

A **limiting factor** is any essential whose deficiency slows down the rate of a reaction. As the amount of this material is increased, the rate of the process will increase. For example, during the night, light is limiting the rate of photosynthesis. As the sun rises and the light intensity increases, the rate of the process increases, up to the point where something else becomes limiting or retarding (see below). A similar situation may prevail with any of the essential factors, even though light is most often limiting under natural conditions. It is certainly possible that on a bright summer day at noon carbon dioxide may be a limiting factor, or temperature, during the winter, in evergreens. The influence of two factors is indicated in Figure 10-4. As the concentration of carbon dioxide is increased, photosynthesis increases up to a certain rate; beyond this, the rate remains constant, even though a further increase in the amount of carbon dioxide is available to the green cells (curve ABC). The point at which the

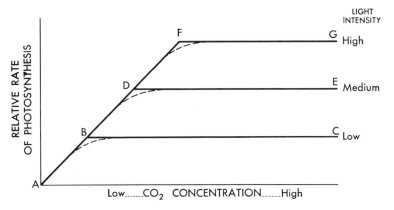

Figure 10-4. A series of curves to indicate the concept of limiting factors. The slope of curve ABDF demonstrates the effect of increasing CO_2 when this factor is limiting. The horizontal portions of the curves demonstrate the lack of effect of CO_2 when light is limiting. (For further discussion see the text.)

curve levels off indicates that carbon dioxide is no longer limiting but that some other factor now is. In this instance it is a low light intensity. If the light intensity is increased to a medium level, the curve assumes the shape ADE; at a high light intensity, the curve is AFG. In each case, the rate increases directly with an increase in carbon dioxide concentration until light becomes limiting: beyond points B, D, and F, respectively, there is sufficient carbon dioxide but not enough light. The solid line curves are theoretical. Under field conditions, no abrupt change in shape as is indicated at B, D, and F takes place, but rather a gradual transition from an increasing rate to a constant rate as indicated by the broken lines. This discrepancy results because no single factor is limiting or retarding the process for the plant as a whole or even in all cells of a single leaf. What usually happens is that the rate of photosynthesis may be limited by a deficiency of carbon dioxide in some cells and by a low light intensity in other cells of the same leaf, especially if any portions of the leaf are shaded.

A **retarding factor** is any factor whose presence in excess slows the rate of a reaction. The accumulation of end products of a reaction will tend to slow the reaction; for example, as sugar accumulates in the afternoon, the rate of photosynthesis decreases. Poisons may also be considered as retarding factors. The rate of photosynthesis increases as temperature rises, up to approximately 35°C., after which a rapid drop in the rate occurs; temperature was first a limiting factor and then a retarding factor.

Throughout a full day under general field conditions, first one and then another limiting and/or retarding factor is the principal agent governing the rate of photosynthesis, and more than one may be operative at any given instant. Usually light is the primary limiting factor in the morning, carbon dioxide around noon, and light again in the evening and certainly at night. The accumulation of sugar (retarding factor) aids in bringing about the decrease in the afternoon, while temperature may be too low in the morning and too high in the afternoon. Obviously, therefore, in discussing the influence of a particular factor on the rate of a process, the assumption must be made that this one factor is either limiting or retarding the process. If this were not so, a variation in that factor would have no influence on the rate of the process. Why?

Water, even though essential to photosynthesis, is never directly a limiting factor. Most cells which carry on the food manufacturing process contain 80 to 98 per cent water. Before water could become so deficient as not to be available for photosynthesis, the normal activities of the cell would have been disrupted. The decreased rate of photosynthesis observed when water becomes deficient in the soil is due to a lack of carbon dioxide (limiting) or an increased concentration of sugar (retarding). When water content is low, the leaves wilt, the stomata close (Sections 9.4, 14.3, and 14.4), and carbon dioxide cannot diffuse into the leaf. The decrease in water content of mesophyll cells (which is what brings about the wilted condition) also results in an increased sugar concentration of those cells, even though the total amount of sugar does not increase.

10.9 Efficiency of leaf structure

In the more complex plants, such as the flowering ones, almost all of the food manufacturing process is restricted to the leaves whose structure is quite conducive to the carrying on of photosynthesis. They are broad, flat, and thin, which insures the exposure of all cells to light, especially since many leaves are oriented with the expanded surface at right angles to the incident rays. Those cells near the lower epidermis receive light which penetrates through the relatively thin tissues above. The large number of stomata and extensive intercellular (air) spaces of the leaf enable carbon dioxide molecules to diffuse from the atmosphere to all photosynthesizing cells. Such cells (the mesophyll tissues) contain abundant chloroplasts with their chlorophyll pigments, which are so necessary to the process. To these characteristics of a leaf must be added the numerous branching veins which carry water and minerals to the mesophyll and sugars away from this tissue.

Summary

1. An autotrophic organism can manufacture its own foods from simple inorganic substances, whereas a heterotrophic organism is dependent upon an external supply of food. Photosynthetic autotrophes utilize light energy, while the chemosynthetic autotrophes obtain energy from chemical reactions. Parasites are those heterotrophes which obtain food from living cells or tissues, while saprophytes utilize non-living organic matter.

2. Photosynthesis is the manufacture of glucose from carbon dioxide and water by chloroplasts utilizing light energy and releasing oxygen gas. The reactions of photosynthesis that require light result in the production of high-energy phosphate bonds and in the splitting of water, which provides hydrogens. The subsequent reactions utilize the hydrogens and high-energy phosphates to reduce carbon dioxide molecules to carbohydrates (assimilation of CO_2).

3. The sugar molecules produced during photosynthesis are utilized in the various syntheses of the plant, are respired, or are stored.

4. A limiting factor is any essential whose deficiency slows down the rate of a reaction. A retarding factor is any factor whose presence in excess slows the rate of a reaction. Under natural conditions, a process within a plant can be influenced by both limiting and retarding factors simultaneously.

5. The structure of the leaf makes it the most efficient part of the plant for photosynthesis.

6. All living things, except for a few groups of bacteria, depend upon photosynthesis for their existence. Besides being the sole source of oxygen, this process is the only significant food-producing mechanism on the earth.

REVIEW TOPICS AND QUESTIONS

117

1. Describe in detail what you would have to do to determine whether or not a red-leaved plant contains chlorophyll and carries on photosynthesis.

2. In discussing the over-all photosynthetic reaction, one usually states that carbon dioxide and water in the presence of light and chloroplasts are converted to carbohydrates, oxygen, and newly constituted water.

(a) Explain why the word "chloroplast" should be used rather than "chlorophyll." Does the use of the former term imply that chlorophyll is not essential to the process?

(b) Explain why one says that water is both used and produced in the process.

(c) Explain how a plant might possibly carry on photosynthesis without oxygen gas being liberated into the atmosphere.

3. A labeled atom of carbon originally is found as part of a carbon dioxide molecule in the atmosphere over a field of potato plants and eventually is found as part of a starch molecule in a potato tuber. Trace in logical sequence the movement of this atom, indicating the tissues through which it moves, the kind of chemical substances in which it occurs, the processes to which it is subjected, and the energy relations of these processes. Your discussion should include those forces which bring about movement and changes.

SUGGESTED READINGS

Arnon, D. I. "The Role of Light in Photosynthesis," *Scientific American,* 203 (November 1960), 104–118.

Conant, J. B. (ed.) *Harvard Case Histories in Experimental Science.* Cambridge, Mass.: Harvard, 1957.

Galston, A. W. *The Life of the Green Plant.* Englewood Cliffs, N. J.: Prentice-Hall, 1961.

Lehninger, A. L. "How Cells Transform Energy," *Scientific American,* 205 (September 1961), 62–73.

Meyer, B. S., et al. *Introduction to Plant Physiology.* Princeton: Van Nostrand, 1960.

Rabinowitch, E. I. "Photosynthesis," *Scientific American,* 179 (August 1948), 24–35.

Rabinowitch, E. I. "Progress in Photosynthesis," *Scientific American,* 189 (November 1953), 80–85.

Enzymes and

Digestion

11.1 Metabolism

The cell, besides being the basic structural unit of living organisms, is a marvelously complex little "factory" in which a great number of chemical reactions are all going on simultaneously. Some materials in the cell are utilized as "fuel" to supply energy, while others are converted to the more complex components of the cell utilizing this energy. Complex molecules are broken down to simpler ones; small molecules are combined to form more complex ones; protoplasmic constituents "wear out" and are replaced; materials move about within the cell; and in some instances various chemical reactions may result in motility or the production of light (bioluminescence of certain micro-organisms). The term **metabolism** refers to all of these various reactions. **Anabolism** includes any metabolic reactions which result in the construction or synthesis of materials, whereas any reactions which involve the breakdown or destruction of substances are termed **catabolism.**

Cells are dynamic, not static. Even when cells are not growing or reproducing (dividing), maintenance is a problem. Just as parts of an engine wear out and are replaced, so also are many parts of the cell replaced. The use of nitrogen isotopes has shown a turn-over of approximately 50 per cent of the protein content of a rat's liver within a week's time. In other words, half of the protein molecules have been replaced by new ones during that week (similar to the replacing of the fuel pump or a spark plug in an automobile). Such replacement, or maintenance, is undoubtedly typical of all cells, although the rate may vary. Probably 90 per cent of the cellular components of an organism are replaced during its lifetime.

11.2 Enzymes

A question which naturally arises when considering the number of reactions occurring within a living cell is whether these reactions occur spontaneously. In many cells sugars are utilized as the building blocks in the synthesis of starch, but sugars dissolved in water and placed in a test tube do not form starch. In many cells the reverse process also may occur, starch being broken down to sugars. This process can be brought about in a test tube, but concentrated acid (usually hydrochloric) and a high temperature are necessary factors which are not present in the cell. In fact, the cell would die if exposed to such concentrated acid or high temperature, Chemical reactions which occur in the laboratory at negligible rates, except possibly at high temperatures, are brought about in living cells because of the presence of molecules called enzymes.

In order to understand the functioning of an enzyme, we should first consider a simple chemical reaction. If hydrogen gas (H_2) and oxygen gas (O_2) are mixed in a chamber, no perceptible reaction occurs. Adding finely ground platinum results in an immediate and vigorous reaction in which water is formed:

$$2H_2 + O_2 \xrightarrow{\text{platinum}} 2H_2O$$

The platinum promotes the reaction without itself being used up; it is a **catalyst.** In the absence of platinum, the hydrogen and oxygen molecules very seldom come into close enough proximity for them to react. When these molecules are adsorbed to the surfaces of the platinum, they are concentrated together in one location, and reactions between molecules occur with great rapidity. Also, stresses and strains probably are established in the adsorbed molecules as a result of the union between the catalyst and these molecules. The molecules, therefore, become more reactive, i.e., are activated. In this condition they undergo changes at a more rapid rate than when present in the free state.

Enzymes are exceedingly large complex organic compounds which are produced by the living cell and which act as catalysts. They are protein molecules, although additional less complex organic molecules, called **coenzymes,** are frequently necessary for the normal catalytic activity. In some enzyme systems, certain metallic ions (e.g., Mn^{++} and Mg^{++}) are essential for normal activity. The colloidal nature of protein molecules results in the very large surface area per unit of volume which is characteristic of enzymes. The protein portion of enzyme systems also provides the specificity which is so typical of enzyme activity. Although many enzymes are specific as to the substrate upon which they act, this specificity resides in many cases in the type of action which is catalyzed rather than the substrate. For example, diphosphopyridine nucleotide (DPN) is the coenzyme for various dehydrogenase enzyme systems. In the presence of a dehydrogenase protein, DPN is capable of removing two hydrogen atoms from the substrate molecule. The specific action involving DPN is the removal of hydrogens; the protein portion [1] of this system determines from which specific substrates the hydrogens will be removed. For example, DPN can remove hydrogens from malate (a 4-carbon compound) if malic dehydrogenase is present, or the hydrogens can be removed from ketoglutarate (a 5-carbon organic compound) if ketoglutaric dehydrogenase is the protein portion of the enzyme system that is present. Neither the DPN nor the dehydrogenase can function alone; both must be present.

Enzymes are quite sensitive to changes in acidity and are most active over a rather narrow range of acidity. Any increase or decrease of acidity beyond the confines of this narrow range results in a decrease of enzyme activity.

Enzymes, as well as proteins in general, are inactivated by moderate heat (60–70°C.) when in the moist condition characteristic of most cells. This is probably a basic explanation of the upper temperature limits of life and also indicates why dry seeds and spores tend to be rather resistant to adverse environmental conditions. In a dried (or dehydrated) condition, enzymes are quite stable. Most of the reactions occurring within a cell proceed at a faster rate with an increase in temperature, up to a maximum beyond which a decrease takes place as enzymes become inactivated.

Enzymes are extremely efficient; minute quantities of them are capable of catalyzing reactions of large numbers of molecules in short periods of time. For example, one molecule of catalase (enzyme) will catalyze the breakdown of approximately 5,000,000 molecules of hydrogen peroxide in one minute. The substrate molecules are adsorbed to the enzyme surface, the reaction takes place, the resultant molecules are released from the surface, and they are replaced by other substrate molecules. The enzyme molecule is used over and over again, since it is not changed by the reactions occurring at its surface. Though the cell contains many different kinds of enzymes, none of them are present in any high concentration. This is in no way detrimental to

---

[1] **Apoenzyme** refers to the protein portion; **coenzyme** refers to the non-protein portion, or **prosthetic group**, of an enzyme system.

the cell, since even low concentrations of enzymes bring about reactions of large numbers of substrate molecules.

11.3 Mechanism of enzyme action

Any conceptual scheme [2] of enzyme function must be consistent with greatly speeded up reactions occurring at surfaces and without any change of that surface. The present viewpoint is that the surface configuration of the protein portion of the enzymes (the apoenzyme) determines which substrate molecules will be adsorbed. If a coenzyme is an integral part of the enzyme system, the protein must have at least two reactive spots or areas where molecules are adsorbed; the substrate becomes adsorbed in one location, the coenzyme in the second reactive

Figure 11-1. An enzyme catalyzed reaction. Only molecules X and Y fit into the surface configuration of the enzyme. The close proximity of these two molecules results in the formation of product Z.

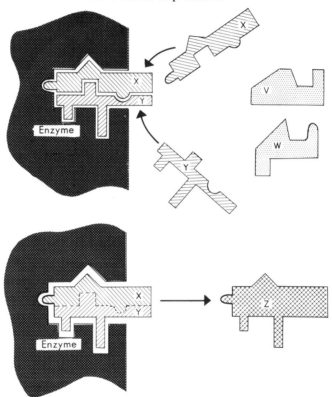

spot, in close proximity to the substrate. Only those molecules which fit the configuration of the enzyme protein will be adsorbed to any great extent. Such fitting of molecules into a surface results in a "selection" of certain molecules from a mixture—the specificity of enzyme action.

[2] A conceptual scheme fits a variety of facts into a relatively simple theory.

Figure 11-1 represents what may happen as an enzyme catalyzes a reaction between molecules **X** and **Y** to form product **Z**. In the mixture only **X** and **Y** fit the enzyme surface and are adsorbed; **V** and **W** are not adsorbed. In the adsorbed condition, **X** and **Y** are oriented in such a way that a rapid reaction takes place between them; the product **Z** is released from the surface, which then is available for the adsorption of more **X** and **Y**. When free in solution, the molecules of **X** and **Y** would very seldom be oriented as they are when attached to the enzyme surface, and non-enzyme-catalyzed reactions would hardly ever occur.

11.4 Digestion (hydrolysis)

Just as complex molecules are continually synthesized from simpler ones in living cells, so are many compounds broken down to simpler ones. **Digestion** is the process whereby complex or non-soluble molecules are converted to simpler molecules or molecules which are water-soluble. Since water is used in this process, it is a type of **hydrolysis.** Some of the more common digestion reactions are indicated below:

(1)   Starch + Water $\xrightarrow[\text{amylase}]{\text{enzyme}}$ Sugar molecules

(2)   Protein + Water $\xrightarrow[\text{proteinase}]{\text{enzyme}}$ Amino Acid molecules

(3)   Fats + 3 Water $\xrightarrow[\text{lipase}]{\text{enzyme}}$ 3 Fatty Acid molecules + Glycerol

In every case, digestion is catalyzed by a specific enzyme which acts upon one substrate but not all. The reactions yield little or no energy and are of no consequence in fulfilling the energy requirements of the cell. The reverse reactions are **syntheses,** which require energy, the energy being made available by respiratory processes of the cell.

Digestions of one sort or another probably occur in all cells, and some digestions occur outside of the cell. In the latter cases, enzymes are secreted by the cells. If yeast plants are placed in a solution of sucrose (a 12-carbon sugar), sucrase (an enzyme) is secreted, and the sucrose is broken down to two 6-carbon sugars, glucose and fructose. The glucose and fructose molecules are then absorbed and utilized. Such extra-cellular digestions occur throughout the alimentary canal (mouth, stomach, and intestines) of humans.

When foods are stored, they are usually in the form of non-soluble materials. Before such foods can be utilized, they must first be converted to a soluble form. For example, when a seed is planted and watered, the first thing that happens (after water is absorbed, swelling the seed) is the digestion of starch, fats, and proteins. The resultant sugars, fatty acids, glycerol, and amino acids are then available and are utilized in the subsequent production of new cells which develop into roots, stems, and leaves. Once the leaves have formed, the plant is no longer dependent upon the foods stored in the seed; photosynthesis can now take place, and foods are produced.

Summary

1. Metabolism refers to all the complex chemical reactions occurring within a cell. Enzymes, produced by the cell, are the catalysts which make possible these various reactions.

2. Enzymes are colloidal proteins which are sensitive to acidity changes and to moderate heat. Substrate molecules are thought to be adsorbed to the enzyme surface, this orientation making reactions possible.

3. The conversion of complex or non-soluble materials into simpler or soluble ones is termed digestion. It is a type of hydrolysis which occurs in all cells.

REVIEW TOPICS AND QUESTIONS

1. Discuss the importance of the fact that enzymes are not used up in the reactions that they catalyze.
2. Enzymes are colloidal proteins. In what way does this characteristic of enzymes influence the activities of living cells? What is the importance of a protein structure to enzyme activity?
3. Discuss the importance of digestion to plants. In what ways do digestions in a flowering plant differ from digestions in a human? In what ways are digestions in these two organisms similar?
4. Explain how you could determine the rate of enzyme activity. Describe an experiment that could be used to test your method.

SUGGESTED READINGS

Doty, P. "Proteins," *Scientific American,* 197 (September 1957), 173–178.

Frieden, E. "The Enzyme-Substrate Complex," *Scientific American,* 201 (August 1959), 119–125.

Fruton, J. S. "Proteins," *Scientific American,* 182 (June 1950), 32–41.

Pfeiffer, J. E. "Enzymes," *Scientific American,* 179 (December 1948), 28–39.

Swanson, O. P. *The Cell.* Englewood Cliffs, N. J.: Prentice-Hall, 1960.

Synthesis, Energy, and Respiration

12.1 Syntheses

Whenever a cell enlarges, or when a cell divides into two which then enlarge, additional protoplasmic materials are produced in addition to larger walls or new walls. The reproduction or doubling of chromosomes is an excellent example of a cell manufacturing new living materials from the various non-living substances found within the cell. The total of all such processes whereby living material is produced constitutes **assimilation,** whereas the production of any type of cellular matter, living or non-living, is generally termed a **synthesis.** Of course, many kinds of syntheses occur during the development of a cell. Various kinds of carbohydrates (including cellulose), fats, and proteins (including enzymes) are produced, as well as vitamins, hormones, aromatic oils, and many, many other substances. In addition to making its own food, the green plant is capable of synthesizing all of its necessary complex organic compounds from this food plus the minerals it absorbs from the soil. Obviously, much work is carried out by individual cells, and much energy is expended. The production of any more complex molecule from simpler ones entails an expenditure of energy, just as a man expends energy in making a fireplace from a pile of bricks and some concrete. Energy and the source of energy, thus, are important factors in an understanding of cellular function.

12.2 Energy

Energy may be thought of as the ability to do work. The work includes syntheses, maintenance, movement, accumulation, luminescence, and possibly other functions, and in every case such energy is obtained from a complex series of chemical reactions occurring within the cell. During such reactions, energy is made available in a step-wise fashion, similar in a way to the slow unwinding of a mainspring which enables the watch mechanism to keep time.

The potential (chemical) energy of a food molecule is converted to available energy, which the cell uses to rearrange the atoms of simple molecules to form the various arrangements characteristic of more complex molecules of the cell. In this way new protoplasm and cell walls are produced. Even cells which are not growing or reproducing still require energy for the ordinary maintenance of normal cell function. Various molecules are unstable and are replaced by new, though similar, molecules. Most component molecules of a cell probably are replaced at one time or another during the lifetime of the organism.

Of the many reactions occurring in a cell, some produce energy and others require it. The energy obtained from the former processes is utilized to run the latter, which otherwise would not occur. Energy has not been created; the cell is merely making use of that energy stored in chemical compounds as a result of the original synthesis of the compounds. All organic materials contain potential energy. This potential energy of organic compounds is a result of the conversion of light energy to "chemical" energy during photosynthesis. Such materials may be burned, producing heat energy, or they may be utilized by living organisms, producing both heat and the energy used to form cellular components or to carry on cell activities. During these conversions of energy, a decrease of useful available energy always occurs, since some useless heat is always produced. This is, of course, not to be considered a loss of energy, because heat itself is a form of energy—energy can be neither created nor destroyed, but it can be, and is, readily transformed from one form to another.

12.3 Respiration

Note that breathing and respiration are not synonymous. **Respiration** refers to the series of complex oxidation-reduction reactions whereby living cells obtain energy through the breakdown of organic material; some of the intermediate (or partial breakdown) materials can be utilized for various syntheses. **Breathing** is merely an exchange of gases which, in the human and in various other animals, takes place in the lungs. All living cells respire, an important feature of this process being the energy that is made available. In breathing, energy is used as muscular movement aids in the exchange of gases.

AEROBIC RESPIRATION

Respiration which proceeds in the presence of abundant gaseous oxygen is termed **aerobic respiration** or, sometimes, merely respiration. The oxygen is reduced (to water), as the substrate, usually glucose, is oxidized. The over-all reaction may be indicated as follows:

$$\text{Glucose} + \text{Oxygen} \xrightarrow{\text{enzymes}} \text{Carbon dioxide} + \text{Water} + \text{Energy}$$

The amount of energy produced from a glucose molecule is the same as the amount stored in that molecule during photosynthesis (see Section 10.5). Unfortunately, some of this energy is in the form of heat, which is wasted as far as the cell is concerned. The water is usually retained within the cell, while the carbon dioxide diffuses out of the cell or is used in photosynthesis. In most organisms this "metabolic water" is of no significance because of the large quantities of water obtained in other ways (i.e., absorption).[1] A broken arrow appears in the over-all equation to emphasize that many steps are involved, the complexity of which will be mentioned later.

[A]

Figure 12-1. Heat production during respiration. **A**: Dead seeds. **B**: Germinating seeds. Note the much higher temperature of **B**.

The amount of heat produced during respiration may be considerable, especially in densely-packed storage tissues. Figure 12-1 indicates the condition which prevails when vacuum jars are tightly packed with seeds, lot "A" consisting of germinated but dead seeds (treated with formaldehyde) and lot "B" consisting of germinating (actively respiring) seeds. The temperature in lot "A" is equal to the room temperature (21°C.), while the temperature of lot "B" is considerably higher (31°C.). Under certain conditions, as in wheat storage bins where the seeds have become moistened or in barns where moist hay has been stored, respiratory heat may result in such high temperatures that the material bursts into flame—**spontaneous combustion**. The presence of bacteria and other micro-organisms undoubtedly adds to the respiratory activity and subsequent heat production.

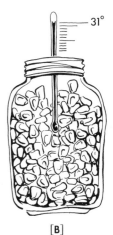

[B]

Though the substance most frequently used as a substrate in respiration is glucose, other materials may be utilized. Fats and proteins may be digested, the products of such reactions then serving as respiratory substrates. This is true in the case of storage organs, such as seeds, and in any cell during extreme starvation.

[1] In the case of the kangaroo rat of the desert, however, this appears to be the only source of water.

127

ANAEROBIC RESPIRATION

Many micro-organisms are capable of carrying on incomplete oxida-tion-reduction reactions in the absence of gaseous oxygen. This is termed **anaerobic respiration,** or **fermentation,** and the energy released from the substrate is a result of molecular rearrangements. The end products are not carbon dioxide and water but various organic com-pounds and sometimes carbon dioxide. As with aerobic respiration, fermentation results in the production of energy, some of which is then available to the cell.

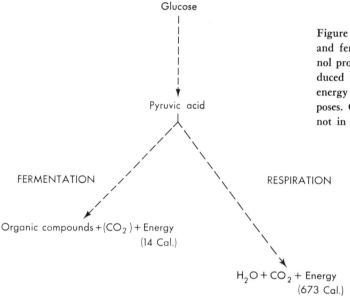

Figure 12-2. A schematic comparison of respiration and fermentation. In alcoholic fermentation (etha-nol production) the caloric value of the energy pro-duced would be as indicated. The two values for energy liberated are presented for comparative pur-poses. CO_2 is produced in many fermentations but not in all.

COMPARISON BETWEEN
AEROBIC AND ANAEROBIC RESPIRATION

In general, the substrate is the same—glucose, a simple 6-carbon sugar. A series of reactions results in the production of a relatively small amount of energy, as a glucose molecule is converted to two molecules of **pyruvic acid,** a 3-carbon compound. These steps in respira-tion, which result in the production of a key intermediate compound (pyruvic acid), are collectively termed **glycolysis.** Oxygen is not utilized in glycolysis, and the pathway of glucose degradation is the same up to this point in both types of respiration. The processes diverge in the reactions that occur after the formation of pyruvic acid, as indicated schematically in Figure 12-2.

Aerobically, the pyruvic acid molecules are further changed by means of a cyclic pathway in which carbon dioxide is given off at intervals and where hydrogens are removed, also at intervals. The loss of hydrogen is a type of oxidation: large amounts of energy are made available, and oxygen is simultaneously reduced to water. As a result, the pyruvic acid molecules are eventually converted to carbon dioxide and water, and the energy of the original glucose molecule is converted to usable energy or heat.

Anaerobically, the pyruvic acid molecules are oxidized (by the removal of hydrogens) to various organic compounds,[2] such as alcohol and organic acids, with or without the production of carbon dioxide. The amount of energy produced is much less than that made available in aerobic respiration: at least 20 to 40 times as much energy is produced aerobically as is produced anaerobically. The difference in available energy results because pyruvic acid is not completely oxidized to carbon dioxide and water in fermentation reactions, and much potential energy still resides in the alcohols, organic acids, and other materials that are produced. Some organisms (bacteria) can respire these materials and thus make use of such residual energy.

12.4 Vitamins

At this time we should indicate the value of vitamins in the activity of cells. **Vitamins** are organic compounds which are essential to organisms but which are not utilized as a source of food or energy. Most of the vitamins in plants participate in enzyme systems. A deficiency of one of the vitamins results in abnormal metabolism and may result in characteristic symptoms. No clear-cut definition of a vitamin exists, because a substance which is considered to be a vitamin for one organism may actually be synthesized by another. For example, thiamine[3] (vitamin B_1) is essential in the respiration of both plant and animal cells. While in man a deficiency of thiamine in the diet results in characteristic symptoms (beri-beri), green plants are capable of synthesizing thiamine if they are provided with carbon dioxide, water,

---

[2] Various alcohols, such as ethanol, isopropanol, butanol, and glycerol; various organic acids, such as formic, acetic, propionic, butyric, lactic, and succinic; and acetone may be produced. The products which result from the fermentation of glucose depend upon the organism involved, and more than one organic compound may result from the activity of a single type of organism.

[3] The nomenclature with regard to vitamins is complicated by the frequent use of letters to designate specific vitamins. Such letters (e.g., vitamin A, vitamin B_2 and B_6, vitamin C, etc.) were used as a convenient method of designating an unknown component of man's diet. As soon as the molecular structure is known with any degree of accuracy, the letter designation should be dropped in favor of a more descriptive term. The situation with regard to "B" vitamins became even more complex when vitamin "B" was discovered to be a *group* of vitamins.

minerals, and light. In the strict sense, then, such a material is not a vitamin for green plants. Non-green plants are usually like animals in their requirements. As one example, the fungus *Phycomyces blakeslee-anus* cannot synthesize thiamine and must have a supply of this vitamin in its food.

Vitamins in general are obtained from the green plants which form the basic food materials for all organisms. Vitamin A and vitamin D (calciferol) are obtained as precursors from plant material, and then the vitamin itself is synthesized by the animal. Table 12-1 indicates

Table 12-1.   Some Important Vitamins

Vitamin	Some Sources	Role in Green Plant	Some Deficiency Symptoms in Man
Converted carotene * = A	Yellow vegetables, eggs, butter, liver oils	Pigment involved in phototropisms; possibly accessory pigment in photosynthesis	Night-blindness
Thiamine = B_1	Yeast, whole grains, meat	Part of enzymes involved in respiration	Beri-beri, a disease of the nerves
Riboflavin = B_2	Same as thiamine	Part of enzymes involved in respiration	Skin ailments
Pyridoxine = B_6	Same as thiamine	Part of enzymes involved in synthesis of amino acids	Not certain
Niacin = nicotinic acid	Same as thiamine	Part of enzymes involved in respiration	Pellagra
Ascorbic acid = C	Fresh fruits (especially citrus) and vegetables	Participates in oxidation-reduction systems	Scurvy
Calciferol = D	Liver oils, eggs, almost all plants	None known	Rickets, defective growth of bones

* Beta-carotene + $2H_2O$ → 2 vitamin A.

some of the important vitamins and their sources. In the case of those vitamins which have a known function in green plants, such as thiamine, riboflavin, and pyridoxine, plants and animals do not differ in their requirements for these vitamins but only in their ability to synthesize the compounds.

Because of the many processes or reactions taking place within a living cell, many compounds different from the ones that were originally present in the cell are produced. Some of these latter compounds are transitory stages, or intermediates, in a long series of steps during which the original material is converted to a final product. Organic compounds undergoing such changes contain varying numbers of carbon, hydrogen, and oxygen atoms, as well as smaller numbers of other atoms. Ordinarily, one carbon atom cannot be distinguished from another, or one hydrogen atom from another. However, as has been mentioned previously (Section 10.5), certain atoms in a molecule can be labeled by using isotopes, which may be radioactive. In this manner a physiologist can frequently determine which of a series of intermediates has been formed first, in other words, which compound has the greatest concentration of isotopic atoms at a particular time. Also possible in many instances is the determination of how a compound was broken down or put together by analyzing for the location of the specific isotope. An example might serve to clarify this statement.

A 3-carbon compound and a 4-carbon compound react to yield a 6-carbon compound plus carbon dioxide.

(1) $C-C-C + C-C-C-C \rightarrow C-C-C-C-C-C + CO_2$

Unless isotopes are utilized, all of the carbon atoms are alike, except for position, and to determine which of the original compounds lost a carbon atom when carbon dioxide was produced is impossible. Reaction (1) could be written:

(2a) $C^1-C^2-C^3 \rightarrow C^2-C^3 + C^1O_2$

(2b) $C^2-C^3 + C^4-C^5-C^6-C^7 \rightarrow C^2-C^3-C^4-C^5-C^6-C^7$

or

(3a) $C^4-C^5-C^6-C^7 \rightarrow C^5-C^6-C^7 + C^4O_2$

(3b) $C^1-C^2-C^3 + C^5-C^6-C^7 \rightarrow C^1-C^2-C^3-C^5-C^6-C^7$

(The superscripts are used to indicate the various carbon atoms of the two compounds.) By allowing the reaction to take place first with isotopes of carbon in the 3-carbon compound, we can determine whether the carbon atom in carbon dioxide originated from this 3-carbon molecule. If the carbon dioxide molecule does not now contain a carbon isotope, the reaction can be repeated with the labeling in the 4-carbon molecule. Actually, since each carbon atom can be labeled separately, we can determine which of the carbon atoms from the original molecules ends up in the carbon dioxide molecule. A similar use of oxygen isotopes has been discussed previously (Section 10.5)

During the last 10 or 20 years, many radioactive atoms have been produced and used in this fashion, and their production is one of the most important applications of the cyclotron for biologists. The replacement within a cell of one protein molecule by another similar protein molecule could not be detected without such labeling. Radioactive materials are detected quite readily with a Geiger-Muller counter or by the fact that the radiations will expose photographic film. By allowing a plant to absorb minerals containing radioactive elements, many steps in the transport and conversion of such minerals into component parts of various complex molecules of the cell have been discovered. Such studies have resulted in tremendous advances in our knowledge of cellular functions and will undoubtedly lead to additional information in the future. However, many difficulties are inherent in this type of investigation—rapid conversions of one material into another, extremely small amounts of materials involved, techniques frequently injurious to cells and tissues—and many processes occurring in cells are still not well understood or explained. In fact, data are frequently hard to interpret because of the difficulties involved in the methods used. As methods improve, more and more valuable information will be obtained.

12.6   Mechanism of energy transfer

Whenever more complex molecules are produced from simpler ones by rearrangements of component atoms and by various types of combinations, energy is utilized. Except in photosynthesis, such energy is obtained from the respiratory activities of the cell involved. It is beyond the scope of an elementary text to delve into the details of respiration and energy transfers, but some few brief comments are pertinent to an understanding of the great importance of this process.

Investigations with many kinds of cells and tissues have revealed that certain organic substances and phosphate groups are involved in making available to the cell that energy which is present in a substrate (food) molecule. The most important such agent is **adenosine triphosphate (ATP).** As the name indicates, it is composed of adenosine plus three phosphate groups, the last two of which are attached by "high-energy bonds." In certain of the oxidative steps of respiration (or fermentation), much of the liberated energy is recovered by the formation of these "high-energy phosphate bonds" of ATP. Inorganic phosphate is used up, and adenosine *di*phosphate (ADP) is converted to adenosine *tri*phosphate (ATP). The curved bond ($\sim$) indicates a high-

$$\boxed{A} - \boxed{P} \smile \boxed{P} + \boxed{P} \rightarrow \boxed{A} - \boxed{P} \smile \boxed{P} \smile \boxed{P}$$

energy condition, ADP having a lower energy value than ATP. The ATP molecule which has been formed can now diffuse throughout the cell to the various areas where energy is required, as in the synthesis of proteins, for example. Energy-requiring processes are accompanied by the breakdown of ATP to ADP. We can think of high-energy phosphate bonds as being capable of stretching molecules out of shape so that the component atoms can snap into new positions, forming new or different molecules.

The formation of ATP allows a slow or gradual utilization of the energy contained in the substrate molecule (usually glucose), in contrast to the rapid energy release of burning or an explosion. The gradual energy release results in the normal functioning of the mechanism. The cell can also build up a backlog of immediately available energy in the form of an ATP reservoir.

One of the best understood syntheses, and one which we can use as an example, is the formation of starch from glucose. Molecules of glucose as such are not utilized. These molecules are first converted to glucose-phosphates which then can be joined to produce starch. The glucose-to-starch reaction is more correctly written in the following manner:

(4)   Glucose + ATP → Glucose—$\boxed{P}$ + ADP

(5)

Glucose—$\boxed{P}$ + Glucose—$\boxed{P}$ + ··· → Starch + n(P) + n(H$_2$O)

The exact number of glucose molecules used is not known, but one water molecule and one phosphate group are liberated whenever two glucose molecules are joined. The letter "n" in reaction (5) represents this unknown number, probably 1,000 units. The ADP produced in reaction (4), as a result of ATP losing one high-energy phosphate, may again be converted to ATP by the respiratory mechanism (utilizing inorganic phosphate).

It is interesting to note the great importance of phosphorylated compounds. Not only must glucose molecules be converted to glucose-phosphates before they can be used in syntheses, but such a conversion must also take place before these molecules can be used in the respiratory reactions. Since ATP is used up during phosphorylations, this means that the initial steps in respiration actually use energy. The later series of reactions then yield energy, and in much more profuse amounts than the quantity required for those first few steps.

In the initial stages of respiration glucose is phosphorylated and then

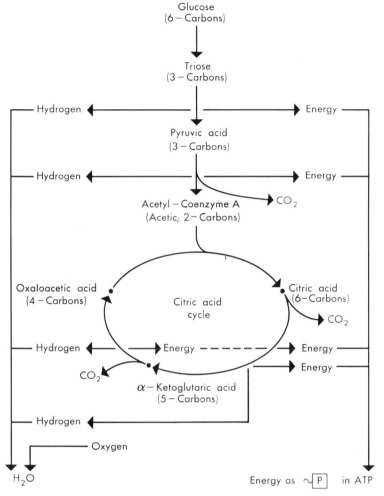

Figure 12-3. Cellular respiration of glucose. (Adapted from Harrington Wells and Patrick Wells, *General Biology*. Copyright 1956 by McGraw-Hill and used with permission.)

converted to fructose, a slightly different six-carbon sugar, which is further phosphorylated:

(6)   Glucose—Ⓟ → Fructose—Ⓟ

(7)   Fructose—Ⓟ + ATP → Fructose-diphosphate + ADP

In this way two high-energy phosphate bonds are used up for every glucose molecule that is converted to fructose-diphosphate, as is shown in reactions (4) and (7) above. This latter compound is next split into two three-carbon fragments, which we may term triose for simplicity.

The first energy-yielding step occurs at this point when the triose is oxidized to phosphoglyceric acid and then on to pyruvic acid. This oxidation takes place by the removal of hydrogen atoms and their acceptance by diphosphopyridine nucleotide (DPN):

$$2\,C_3H_6O_3 + 2\,DPN + 4\,ADP \dashrightarrow 2\,C_3H_4O_3 + 2\,DPNH_2 + 4\,ATP$$

$$\text{triose} \qquad\qquad\qquad\qquad\qquad \text{pyruvic}$$

Two triose molecules are shown in the reaction because each glucose molecule eventually yields two of the triose molecules. The broken arrow indicates that more than one step is involved in this conversion; a total of four high-energy phosphate bonds results and some of the energy of the triose molecule now resides in ATP. There is, thus, a net gain of two high-energy phosphate bonds or ATP for every glucose molecule that is converted to pyruvic acid. In addition to this the reduced DPN (shown as $DPNH_2$) may be oxidized in a complex series of steps, if oxygen is available, to yield additional energy. This terminal oxidation is discussed in a subsequent paragraph. Alternately, the $DPNH_2$ may serve as a hydrogen-donor in various reduction processes, as in the reduction of nitrates (NO_3), the formation of glycerol from triose, or the synthesis of fatty acids.

Figure 12-3 represents a simplified version of cellular respiration. The removal of hydrogens, as in many biological oxidations, makes energy available by the formation of high-energy phosphate bonds, as mentioned in a previous paragraph. In addition to energy, the respiratory process provides intermediates which can be used as building blocks for the synthesis of various complex molecules, as indicated in the following reactions:

(9)
$$
\begin{array}{l}
\text{Triose} \rightleftharpoons \text{Glycerol} \\
\text{Acetic Acid} \rightleftharpoons \text{Fatty Acids}
\end{array}
\Bigg] \rightleftharpoons \text{Fats and Oils}
$$

(10)
$$
\begin{array}{l}
\text{Pyruvic Acid} \rightleftharpoons \text{Amino Acid} \\
\alpha\text{-Ketoglutaric Acid} \rightleftharpoons \text{Amino Acid} \\
\text{Oxaloacetic Acid} \rightleftharpoons \text{Amino Acid}
\end{array}
\Bigg] \rightleftharpoons \text{Proteins}
$$

Nitrogen salts (absorbed by roots)

Each of the compounds at the left of the arrows is a part of the respiratory mechanism, as shown in Figure 12-3. These reactions are reversible, and thus fats (via fatty acids and glycerol) and proteins (via amino acids) are readily converted to respiratory cycle products, which may then be oxidized with a resultant production of high-energy phosphate bonds.

The citric acid cycle, also known as the Krebs cycle, consists of a series of reactions only a few of which have been shown in the diagram (Figure 12-3). Most of the energy which the cell derives from respiration is obtained from these reactions, as the hydrogens unite with oxygen to form water. In these terminal oxidations the hydrogens are actually passed along a series of respiratory enzymes before they eventually combine with oxygen. At each step in this passage, high-energy phosphate bonds are produced as ATP. The 3-carbon pyruvic acid is degraded one carbon atom at a time as carbon dioxide is evolved and is eventually converted to carbon dioxide and water. The 2-carbon fragment (which forms first) attaches to the 4-carbon oxaloacetic,[4] but the resultant 6-carbon compound loses carbon dioxide and hydrogens until the 4-carbon compound is re-formed; thus a cycle exists. The most recent evidence indicates that the conversion of a pyruvic acid molecule to CO_2 and H_2O results in the production of 15 ATP molecules; or a total of 30 for each glucose molecule that is respired. This portion of respiration takes place in the mitochondria, where the enzymes are quite likely oriented in such a fashion as to make possible an efficient step-wise series of reactions. With enzymes arranged in a specific close molecular juxtaposition, substrate molecules, hydrogens, and electrons can readily be passed along from one to the other in this chain of enzymes, much as in a "bucket brigade."

The over-all reaction when pyruvic acid is oxidized may be indicated as follows:

(11) $2 C_3H_4O_3 + 6 H_2O + 10 DPN \dashrightarrow 6 CO_2 + 10 DPNH_2$

The CO_2 is a waste product that diffuses out of the cell. In the terminal oxidation system the hydrogens from $DPNH_2$ are united with oxygen to form water:

(12) $12 DPNH_2 + 6 O_2 \dashrightarrow 12 DPN + 12 H_2O.$

Twelve $DPNH_2$ are shown in reaction #12 because two are produced during glycolysis and ten during the reactions of the citric acid cycle. During the oxidations of $DPNH_2$, 36 ADP molecules are converted to ATP. In the complete respiration of glucose to CO_2 and H_2O, thus, there is a total net gain of 38 high-energy phosphate bonds; the extra two are the gain resulting from glycolysis.

Figure 12-4 summarizes the transformations of glucose that occur in living cells. Some glucose molecules are broken down to carbon dioxide and water, with the concomitant production of energy (in ATP), while other glucose molecules are converted to various complex molecules. The energy necessary to carry out syntheses comes from the ATP reservoir.

[4] Another possibility is that 2-carbon fragments may be used to synthesize fatty acids of varying sizes.

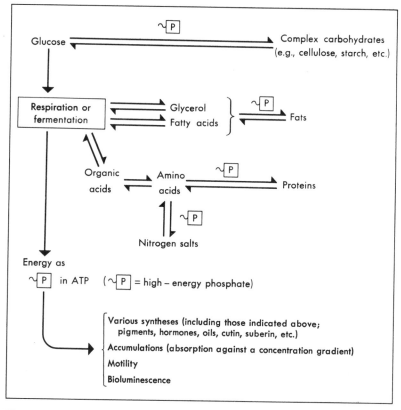

Figure 12-4. Synthetic pathways. (Adapted from George G. Simpson, Colin S. Pittendrigh, and Lewis H. Tiffany, *Life, An Introduction to Biology.* © 1957 by Harcourt, Brace & World and used with permission.)

Summary

1. The energy which the cell expends in carrying out its complex functions (e.g., syntheses of complex materials, maintenance of the living cell, movement, and accumulation of materials) is obtained from the respiratory activities of the cell. In the more advanced types of plants, gaseous oxygen is utilized during respiration, while in many micro-organisms energy is made available by anaerobic fermentation reactions.

2. The initial series of reactions in fermentation (anaerobic) are basically similar to those of respiration (aerobic). Substrates are broken down to pyruvic acid, and the collective steps in this process are termed glycolysis. After the production of pyruvic acid, the two processes diverge. Respiration results in the complete oxidation of the substrate to carbon dioxide and water; fermentation produces a variety of compounds as a result of incomplete oxidation of the substrate.

3. Vitamins are essential to normal growth and development of all organisms, usually by participating in enzyme systems. Green plants are fortunate in that they are capable of synthesizing vitamins. Animals and many non-green plants are not so fortunate and depend upon external sources for vitamins.

4. Most of the energy, which is transported about in the cell and which is transferred from molecule to molecule as various functions of the cell occur, is found as high-energy phosphate bonds attached to carrier molecules, such as ATP.

REVIEW TOPICS AND QUESTIONS

1. Not all of the substances used in aerobic respiration are broken down completely to carbon dioxide and water. Explain fully what is meant by this statement.
2. In what way is the metabolism of a fungus (a non-green plant, such as yeast) more like that of yourself than that of a green plant?
3. A man has two grams of yeast and divides them into two equal portions. He wishes to use one lot (i.e., one gram of yeast plants) for wine production and the other portion as a source of food. (Note: Yeast plants are used in many areas as a food supplement because of their protein and vitamin B content.) His treatment of these two samples of yeast plants would be similar in some ways and different in other ways. Discuss the reasons for each treatment.
4. The rate of respiration is governed by, or influenced by, various factors. Select any one of these, and describe an experiment that would indicate the effect upon respiration of varying this factor.
5. Discuss the various fates which may befall the many sugar molecules that enter the respiratory reactions. (Note: Not all of them end up as carbon dioxide and water.)
6. Discuss the differences among digestion, respiration, and fermentation. Discuss any similarities in these three processes.
7. What becomes of the energy which is liberated during respiration?
8. Compare respiration and photosynthesis.
9. Discuss the importance of adenosine triphosphate (ATP) to living cells.
10. In what way are radioactive atoms or isotopes useful to a study of metabolism?
11. In what ways are the vitamin requirements of plants different from those of animals? In what ways are they similar?

SUGGESTED READINGS

Bonner, J., and A. W. Galston. *Principles of Plant Physiology*. San Francisco: Freeman, 1952.

Green, D. E. "Enzymes in Teams," *Scientific American,* 181 (September 1949), 2–4.

———. "The Metabolism of Fats," *Scientific American,* 190 (January 1954), 32–47.

————. "Biological Oxidation," *Scientific American,* 199 (July 1958), 56–62.

————. "The Synthesis of Fat," *Scientific American,* 202 (February 1960), 46–51.

Lehninger, A. L. "Energy Transformation in the Cell," *Scientific American,* 202 (May 1960), 102–114.

————. "How Cells Transform Energy," *Scientific American,* 205 (September 1961), 62–73.

Rose, A. H. "Yeasts," *Scientific American,* 202 (February 1960), 136–142.

Siekevitz, P. "Powerhouse of the Cell," *Scientific American,* 197 (July 1957), 131–140.

Stumpf, P. K. "ATP," *Scientific American,* 188 (April 1953), 84–93.

CHAPTER 13

Correlation of Processes, Plant Distribution, and Food Chains

IN ATTEMPTING to simplify the situation that exists in the cell, the processes of photosynthesis and respiration have been discussed individually. Obviously any cell which is carrying on photosynthesis is also carrying on respiration, as well as absorption, digestion, syntheses, and the rest of the various processes characteristic of living cells. A discussion of the correlation between photosynthesis and respiration will aid in an understanding of plant distribution and thus, also, of animal distribution.

13.1   Compensation points and plant distribution

The sugars which are produced in photosynthesis may be used in respiration, involved in various syntheses, or stored. If the rate of respiration is equal to the rate of photosynthesis, all of the sugars produced in the latter reaction are used in the former process, and none remain for such syntheses as are necessary to the production of new protoplasm or maintenance of existing protoplasm. That light intensity or temperature at which the rates of photosynthesis and respiration are equal is termed the **compensation point.** A plant cannot grow, or even remain alive for any length of time, under such conditions; it would starve to death.

The growth, or yield, of a plant depends upon food production (photosynthesis) being greater than the food consumption in respiration. If the rate of photosynthesis does not exceed the rate of respiration by a factor of three or more, growth of the plant is not possible. Photosynthesis depends upon light, whereas respiration occurs throughout the 24-hour period. If any sugars are to be available for various syntheses, they must be produced in sufficient amount during daylight hours to provide more than enough substrate for respiration during those hours plus the night hours. Comparative measurements by many investigators indicate that photosynthesis averages 8 to 12 times the rate of respiration under natural conditions.

TEMPERATURE AND COMPENSATION POINTS

Figure 13-1 illustrates the relative rates of photosynthesis and respiration of potato leaves during exposure to different temperatures in shade and in full sunlight. The temperature at which the two curves intersect (32°C. or 40°C.) is the compensation point. Note that the maximum rate of photosynthesis is reached at a lower temperature than the maximum rate of respiration, and that the compensation point is reached at a lower temperature when the light intensity is low. This latter result is due to the lowering of the photosynthetic rate with the decrease in light intensity. Since respiration is not influenced by light, it more rapidly overtakes photosynthesis at this lower intensity as the temperature increases. Survival of the potato plant depends upon the average temperature remaining *below* that at which the compensation point is reached. In fact, the maximum yield of most potato varieties is obtained in areas with cool summers. When Irish potato plants were kept continuously at different temperatures, no tubers were formed on the plants kept at 29°C., while large tubers formed at 20°C. The former temperature is so close to the compensation point that the photosynthetically produced sugars were all used in respiration or in general growth, and no sugars were available for conversion to storage starch. Thus, no tubers. At 20°C., however, the rate of photosynthesis

Figure 13-1. Relative rates of photosynthesis and respiration in potato leaves during 10-minute exposures to different temperatures in shade and in full sunlight. Recalculated from data by H. G. Lundegardh. (From E. N. Transeau, H. C. Sampson, and L. H. Tiffany, *Textbook of Botany*, 1st ed. New York: Harper and Row, 1940.)

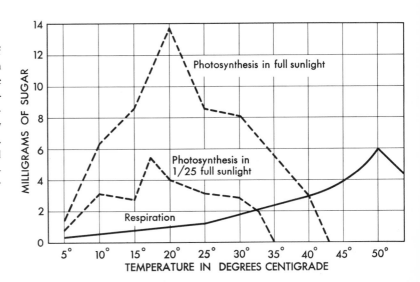

is considerably greater than that of respiration, and excess sugars are stored in the tubers as starch.

The compensation point varies considerably with the kind of plant. In plotting the rates of photosynthesis and respiration versus temperature, one finds that the shape of the curves is basically similar to that shown in Figure 13-1. The maximum rates and the compensation points, however, may occur at higher or lower temperatures. In those plants which grow in warm climates (e.g., sugar cane, date palm) the compensation point is reached at a relatively high temperature, whereas those growing in colder areas reach the compensation point at a much lower temperature. One of the factors involved in plant distributions is this relationship between respiration and photosynthesis. The potato plant would not survive in an area where date palms are grown, and vice versa. (Why the latter?)

LIGHT AND COMPENSATION POINTS

Various investigators have determined the light intensity at which the rates of photosynthesis and respiration are equal. When the compensation point is referred to in terms of light intensity, one should realize that survival depends upon the light intensity being *greater* than that at the compensation point. This, at first, appears to contradict the previous paragraphs, but careful consideration should clarify the situation. In each case the problem is maintaining photosynthesis at a higher rate than respiration. This may be accomplished by lowering the temperature if it is too high or by increasing the light intensity if it is too low.

Table 13-1 indicates the light intensity at which the compensation point is reached in various plants. Note that this light intensity

Table 13-1. Compensation Points (in Terms of Light Intensity) for Various Plants

Plant	Foot Candles *	Plant	Foot Candles
Philodendron	500	Cotton	150
Scotch Pine	400	Tomato	150
Arbor vitae	400	Sunflower	100
Loblolly Pine	300	Bean	100
Tobacco	200	Beech	100–50
Soybean	200	Sugar Maple	100–50
Dryopteris	200	Some herbs, ferns, and mosses	30
Red Oak	200–140	Some algae	1

* Light intensity is measured in terms of foot candles. One foot candle is an arbitrary unit: the light intensity at one foot when the source has the brilliancy of an average candle. Full sunlight has an intensity of approximately 10,000 foot candles.

varies with the kind of plant. This is important in helping to explain plant distribution and plant succession on the basis of light intensities, just as the previous paragraphs utilized similar explanations while dealing with temperature as the environmental factor. For example, the data in this table indicates why a mixed stand of forest trees gradually over a period of years shifts emphases until a climax vegetation is achieved. A **climax vegetation** is one which is stable, the kinds of plants remaining relatively constant as long as no major change in the environment occurs. Such an association, or grouping, of plants may be regarded as consisting of those plants which can compete most advantageously in that environment. For example, if a forest originally consisted of a mixture of pine, red oak, maple, and beech trees, a gradual dying out of the pines and then the red oaks would take place, and the climax forest would consist mainly of beech and maple trees. The pines require the most light, whereas the beeches and maples require the least light, to surpass their respective compensation points, as is shown in Table 13-1. Thus, as seedlings develop and the forest becomes more dense, shading becomes a factor. Eventually the light intensity reaching the seedlings is less than 400 foot candles, and the pines will not survive. When the shading effect of the forest canopy results in the light intensity being reduced to less than 300 foot candles, the oaks will not survive, and the forest soon consists predominantly of beeches and maples.

Man has been a major factor in bringing about changes in natural climax associations by his great carelessness and wasteful practices. Forest fires, over-grazing, wasteful lumbering methods, and excessive destruction of wildlife are examples of man's destruction of natural resources and its concomitant change in climax associations. The gradual disappearance of forest lands in the eastern portion of the United States and the great Dust Bowl of the Midwest are specific examples of human folly. In Spain, much grassland has been ruined by over-grazing with sheep: with the destruction of native grasses, soil erosion occurred at a tremendous rate, and much of the productive topsoil has been lost. As a result, grasses become established with great difficulty, even if grazing is subsequently prevented. Further examples of man's destructive capacity will be discussed in Sections 14.8 and 29.6.

13.2 Root environment and plant distribution

One of the requirements for the normal growth and development of vascular plants is a supply of oxygen, but some plants do not require as much as others. It is not only the above-ground cell which utilizes oxygen, but also the root cell, and here is where difficulties sometimes arise. The solubility of oxygen in water is relatively low. Thus, when soils are water-saturated or flooded, the amount of oxygen available to root cells is greatly curtailed. If this condition prevailed for any length of time, most plants would not survive. Willow (*Salix serissima*) and bald cypress trees (*Taxodium distichum*), cattails (*Typha latifolia*), some sedges (*Carex* spp.), and rice plants (*Oryza sativa*) are examples of plants that can grow quite readily in soils almost devoid of oxygen.

In some of these plants (e.g., *Typha latifolia*), the internal structure is such that large air channels are continuous from the region of the stomata, which is not submerged, to the root tissues themselves. As a result of this structure, oxygen diffuses from the outside atmosphere through the stomata to the various cells that are utilizing oxygen. The root cells are located in an environment with a low external oxygen concentration (wet or flooded soil) but where the internal oxygen concentration is approximately as high as the normal atmosphere. These plants can survive because sufficient oxygen is available to the roots. A similar situation probably exists in bald cypress trees, which have peculiar root projections, called "knees," which grow above the surface of water or saturated soil and seem to provide a pathway through which air can penetrate to the root cells.

Also, the root cells of some plants (e.g., rice) possibly may be capable of existing under anaerobic conditions. This is a physiological type of adaptation and not clearly understood. Two possibilities appear likely: (1) either the anaerobic respiratory reactions (fermentation) produce more energy than those in other plants, or (2) the root cells have lower energy requirements than similar cells of plants which cannot survive in such an anaerobic environment. Rice seeds will germinate in the absence of oxygen almost as well as if oxygen is available; also, the growth of rice seedlings at low oxygen concentrations is much better than that of most other seedlings. This ability of rice seeds to germinate and grow at oxygen concentrations inhibitory to most other seeds is attributed to the more effective fermentation system of rice as compared with other plants. However, sufficient oxygen may diffuse from the emerged leaves to the submerged roots, even though air channels are not present.

13.3 Food chains and energy

Plant distribution influences animal distribution because of the dependence of the latter upon plants for food. Such food is essential as a source of energy (through respiration) and as a supply of basic building material for the synthesis of various components of cells and tissues. The amount of food which is available to humans depends upon the amount made by green plants in excess of what they themselves use and frequently upon what remains after these plants are consumed by other animals and by non-green plants. The term **food chain** is used to designate this feeding of one organism upon another. At the base (bottom) of every food chain is the green plant, the food-producer, and all the other organisms are food consumers. A very simple food chain could be:

Corn → Cattle → Man

Corn, rather than grass, is used in this example in order to emphasize the loss of food value that occurs in such a food chain. Because of the respiratory activity of the "middle-men" in the food chain, man can obtain much more food per acre by eating plants directly than by eating the animals which have consumed these plants. Much more food is utilized in the animal as a source of energy than is utilized in the production of body material. In other words, a relatively large amount of food is eaten in proportion to the gain in weight which results. Consider, for example, the amount of food you—the Reader—consume in a day, a week, or a year, compared to the increase in your weight over the same period of time. Also, much of the body of an animal (a steer in this example) is non-edible as far as man is concerned. The result is that only about ten per cent of the original food value of the plant is available to a human eating the steer—and this is one of the more efficient animals as far as food use is concerned.

If the yield [1] from one acre of corn were utilized by man, approximately 1,000 men could be fed for one day, assuming 3,000 Calories [2] per day as the normal requirement. If this corn is fed to beef cattle, 125 pounds of meat would be available to man, equivalent to the food for 43 men for one day. If the corn is fed to pigs, 273 pounds of pork would be available to man, equivalent to the food for 220 men for one day. Either case results in a tremendous loss of the original energy content of the plant food. In general, the following amounts of energy remain when plant food is first converted to meat and before it is utilized by humans: pork 17 per cent, beef 10 per cent, fowl 7 per cent,

---

[1] These data and calculations are from E. N. Transeau, H. C. Sampson, and L. H. Tiffany, *Textbook of Botany* (New York: Harper and Brothers, 1940).

[2] Calorie (spelled with a capital C) represents the amount of heat (energy) necessary to increase the temperature of 1 kg. of water 1°C. With regard to nutrition, the term Calorie is useful to indicate energy requirements. The Food and Agriculture Organization of the United Nations estimates that the average daily requirement of Calories per person ranges from 2,250 to 2,710. The average individual daily consumption of Calories was more than 3,000 in North America and Western Europe in 1952.

and lamb 3 per cent. A much more efficient utilization of food would result from the direct consumption of plant material. This would eliminate the loss due to respiratory activity of the intermediate organisms in a food chain as well as the loss due to conversion of edible plant products into non-edible animal products.

In those instances where animals feed upon plant material which is not available for human consumption, the conversion to animal products is most advantageous. The supply of food from the great grazing lands of the Midwestern portions of the United States and from many aquatic plants becomes available to humans only after passage through various animals.

13.4 Carbon compounds and energy contents

The interconversion of carbon-containing compounds is an exceedingly important aspect of the study of living organisms. Such compounds constitute the basic structure of all living cells and the energy source for almost all syntheses. The food which an organism consumes consists mainly of carbon-containing compounds of varying degrees of complexity. These are mostly broken down (digested) to simpler molecules which can then be utilized in the synthesis of those complex components of the living organism or cell. As has been mentioned already (see Sections 12.1 and 12.2), all syntheses require energy. The most important factor involved in the change of carbon compounds from one type to another is the energy content of each compound. For example, organic carbon compounds, such as sugar, are considered to have a high available energy content—they can be respired (or oxidized) to yield energy. Carbon dioxide, on the other hand, cannot be oxidized to yield energy; it has zero energy content as far as the cell is concerned.

During respiration, organic carbon compounds are converted to carbon dioxide, water, and available energy:

(1) $\text{Organic carbon} + O_2 \xrightarrow{\text{enzymes}} CO_2 + H_2O + \text{Energy}$

The energy is utilized or lost as heat (waste), and the carbon compound is now in a form which contains no energy (CO_2). Green plants re-charge carbon compounds with energy during photosynthesis:

(2) $CO_2 + H_2O + \text{Energy (light)} \xrightarrow{\text{chloroplast}} \text{Organic carbon} + O_2$

This is the only synthesis occurring in living cells which is not dependent upon respiration for its energy. All syntheses utilize energy, and in this case sunlight supplies the energy. In green plants, then, carbon

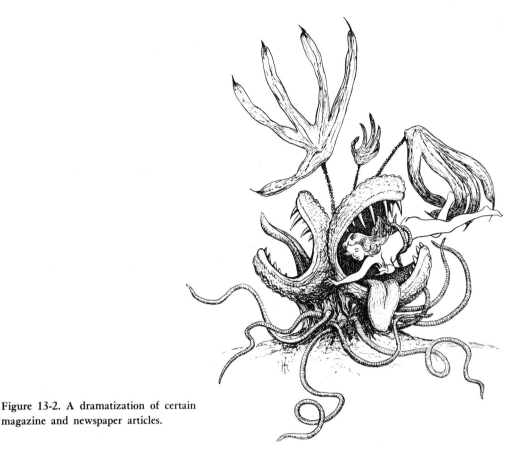

Figure 13-2. A dramatization of certain magazine and newspaper articles.

may be circulated from the air as CO_2, into the green plant as various organic compounds, and back to the air as CO_2 once again.

Carbon can be passed quite readily from one organism to another. Animals eat plants and frequently each other. The passage of carbon from animal to plant is not so direct, however, in spite of the amazing and fantastic stories in magazines about carnivorous or man-eating plants (see Figure 13-2). A few insectivorous plants exist, as well as a few that occasionally feed upon nematodes or eel worms (very tiny soil worms, *not* earthworms), but these are not very important. Carbon present as part of an organic compound in an animal may eventually reach a plant when the animal respires this carbon compound or when the animal dies and decays. The resultant carbon dioxide is available for photosynthesis.

Even though the concentration of carbon dioxide in the atmosphere is low, about 0.03 per cent, the total amount of carbon dioxide is in excess of one million million tons. Wind currents continually bring new supplies of carbon dioxide in contact with green plants; in the case of aquatic plants, the carbon dioxide dissolves in the water, and water currents aid in its distribution.

Of the various sources of the carbon dioxide that is present in the atmosphere, the most important is undoubtedly the decay of organic material. Remember that such decay is due to the activity of microorganisms and, thus, it is actually respiration and fermentation which continually aid in replenishing the supply of atmospheric carbon dioxide. Other sources of carbon dioxide involve: the respiration of any cell or organism even if decay is not involved, burning of fuels (wood, coal, oil), chemical weathering of rocks which contain carbonates, and volcanic action.

Although all organisms eventually die, some of them do not decay completely and, under certain environmental conditions, are converted to peat, coal, or oil. However, this form of carbon is eventually returned to the atmosphere during combustion. One ton of coal produces approximately three tons of carbon dioxide when it is burned, and the amount of coal used by various industries is in the thousands of tons per day. No danger of a lack of carbon dioxide exists; in fact, some scientists fear just the opposite. The Industrial Revolution and the subsequent tremendous increase in fuel consumption may result in an increase in the concentration of carbon dioxide gas in the atmosphere. The suggestion is that such an increase will result in a blanketing effect or a heat trap [3] and that the average temperatures on the earth will rise. This could be very disadvantageous to living organisms. One of the difficulties which could arise would be the melting of the icecaps of Antarctica and Greenland. This would cause a flooding of the earth's coastal lands, where the majority of the world's population now lives. No one is suggesting such a catastrophe in the foreseeable future, but geophysicists are actively studying various phases of the problem in an attempt to determine whether the carbon dioxide blanket is growing thicker and whether this has any effect on air temperature.

An examination of the preceding paragraphs indicates the existence of a carbon cycle, since carbon dioxide is converted to organic carbon (plant and animal structures) and this material is eventually changed back to carbon dioxide, as is represented in Figure 13-3. The important aspect of the carbon cycle is not the transfer or movement of carbon-

[3] Some of the visible light waves, which penetrate through carbon dioxide gas quite readily, are converted to heat when they are absorbed by opaque objects, such as the earth itself, for example. However, heat waves do not penetrate so readily through layers of carbon dioxide. Therefore, when heat is being radiated from the earth to the cooler atmosphere, the carbon dioxide acts as a blanket which decreases the amount of heat lost to the atmosphere; the heat is reflected back to the earth. Whether or not such a heat trap effect will result depends to a great extent upon the amount of carbon dioxide that can be dissolved in the waters of the world.

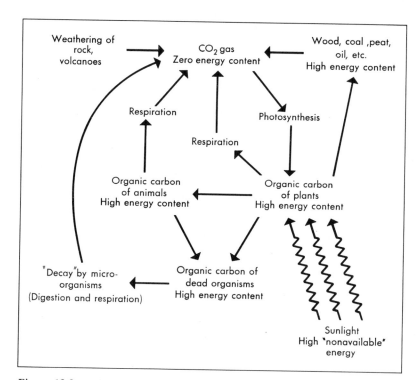

Figure 13-3. Carbon transformations and energy contents.

containing compounds but the energy which is stored or liberated as
the cycle proceeds. However, no corresponding energy cycle takes place,
but a change from zero energy (carbon dioxide) to high available
energy (organic carbon compounds) to zero energy (carbon dioxide
again). In order for such a situation to exist, a continual input of
energy must be maintained, just as a child keeps a hoop rolling by
periodically whacking it with a stick—the thrust given by the stick
imparts energy to the hoop, which responds by rolling along. The
input of energy in the carbon cycle is provided by the sun through
green plants. Photosynthesis converts light energy to chemical energy
and is the thrust which keeps the cycle turning. The radiant energy
of the sun makes life possible; the green plants contribute the means
of utilizing such energy. In this figure, sunlight is indicated as being
high non-available energy. This refers, of course, to the fact that light
energy is available only to green plants; it is non-available insofar as
other organisms are concerned.

Even though we consider carbon dioxide to be on the zero energy
level, this does not imply that energy has been lost. One of the basic
concepts of physics and chemistry is that energy can neither be created

149

nor destroyed **(The First Law of Thermodynamics)**.[4] Energy can be converted from one form to another, however. When gasoline is burned in an automobile, the chemical energy of the gasoline molecules is converted to the kinetic energy of the moving vehicle. As in any process, some of the energy is converted to useless heat, resulting in a loss of available energy **(The Second Law of Thermodynamics)**. This heat is lost to the environment, radiated to outer space, and dissipated. Energy is thus lost for use but not destroyed. Remember that during respiration a similar production of heat (waste) energy occurs.

An understanding of the interconversion of carbon-containing compounds and the energy content of such materials is essential to an understanding of the importance of plants to all forms of life. The green (chlorophyllous) plant provides food and oxygen, while the non-green plant (mainly micro-organisms) brings about decay processes which make carbon dioxide available for further photosynthesis.

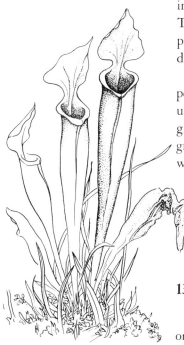

[A]

[B]

Figure 13-4. The pitcher plant (*Sarracenia*). **A:** Habit sketch. **B:** Sectional view to show insects entering and the location of bristles.

13.5 "Carnivorous" plants

In the preceding section, a brief comment was made about insectivorous or carnivorous plants, and a somewhat more detailed discussion might clarify the situation. The pitcher plant (*Sarracenia* spp.) (Figure 13-4) has a funnel-shaped leaf, into which small insects may crawl and then drown in the water which collects at the base of the leaf. Small bristles project downwardly on the inside of the leaf, preventing such insects from crawling out. Digestive enzymes, secreted by the leaf (and possibly bacterial action also), convert the insect body into soluble materials which are then absorbed. A more interesting insectivorous plant is the sundew (*Drosera* spp.) (Figure 13-5), in which the leaves contain tiny projections that secrete a mucilaginous material. Small insects become entangled in these projections and are digested by enzymes which the leaf cells secrete. In this case, also, the digestion products are absorbed.

The most fascinating insectivorous plant, and the one which is probably responsible for the weird magazine articles dealing with carnivorous plants, is the Venus'-flytrap (*Dionaea muscipula*) (Figure 13-6).

[4] Atomic disintegrations result in the conversion of matter to energy. This merely means that matter and energy are really different forms of the same thing, and we should think of the conservation of both energy and matter.

Figure 13-5. The sundew (*Drosera*). At the bottom left, a fly has become entangled in the small projections from a leaf; the mucilaginous drops prevent its escape.

The leaves of this plant are hinged along the mid-line, with the outer margins bearing strong bristles. The upper surface of the leaf contains short "trigger" hairs which are sensitive to contact. When an insect alights on the leaf and brushes against these hairs, the leaf snaps shut and the overlapping marginal bristles effectively imprison the insect. Enzymes are secreted by gland cells on the surface of the blade, and the digested material is absorbed. Such an example of a plant with an actual trapping mechanism easily leads the imagination to conjure up an enlarged version which is capable of enclasping a human. Unfortunately, or fortunately, no carnivorous plants capable of ensnaring even small rodents, much less humans, have ever been found.

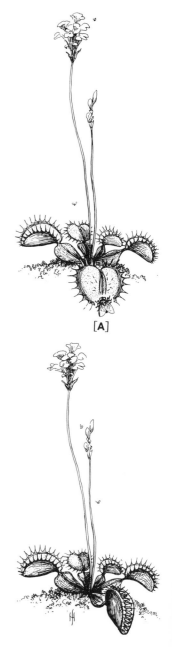

[A]

[B]

Figure 13-6. The Venus'-flytrap (*Dionaea muscipula*). **A:** A fly is landing on the leaf at the bottom. Note the "trigger hairs." **B:** The leaf has shut; the over-lapping marginal bristles have entrapped the fly.

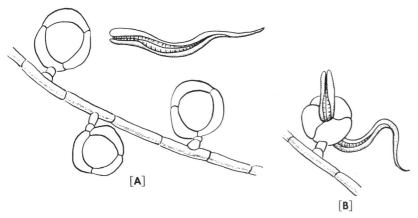
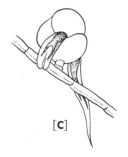

Figure 13-7. Diagram of a nematode (eel worm) being lassoed by a fungus (*Dactylella bembicoides*). **A:** A nematode approaching one of the rings formed by the hyphae of the fungus. **B:** The nematode has entered the ring and has been entrapped by the rapid expansion of the ring cells. **C:** Hyphae of the fungus have entered the body of the nematode. (From Joseph J. Maio, *Scientific American*, July 1958.)

As a point of information, the insectivorous plants are green and quite capable of manufacturing food materials. A possible advantage resulting from the ability to trap and utilize insects is that such plants may be able to survive in a soil that is low in nitrogen content. Nitrogen could be obtained from the proteins and amino acids of the insect.

The only plants that could even remotely be considered to be carnivorous are a few fungi, and even these organisms obtain the majority of their food from dead organic matter in the soil. However, at least one group of fungi can nicely lasso nematodes. Figure 13-7 indicates the manner in which nematodes are trapped or lassoed. The three cells which form the ring structure expand greatly when their inner surfaces are touched. Any nematode so unfortunate as to penetrate within the ring is immediately held fast, since the diameter of the ring is greatly restricted when the cells become swollen. The nematode cannot escape, strands of the fungus penetrate the body of the worm, and digestion of the animal takes place. Even if the nematode is vigorous enough to rip the ring from the rest of the fungus filament, this in no way saves the animal. Additional cellular strands, or filaments, are produced by the ring cells, and the result is the same—the nematode is digested and consumed.

These plants are quite interesting and amazing but not nearly the fantastic organisms of various magazine and newspaper articles, which are at best labeled "science-fiction" with an emphasis on the "fiction."

Summary

1. The compensation point is that light intensity or temperature at which the rates of photosynthesis and respiration are equal. The plant cannot exist under such conditions, since no food materials are available for maintenance and growth. An understanding of compensation points aids in explaining plant distributions; in order for a plant to survive, photosynthesis must greatly exceed respiration. If a plant has a compensation point at a low temperature, it cannot grow in a warm climate. If a plant has a compensation point at a high light intensity, it cannot grow in a shaded area.

2. Certain plants can survive even though their roots are located where the external atmosphere is deficient in oxygen. In most of these plants, structural modifications make possible an internal movement of oxygen to the roots. In others, however, the root cells are capable of obtaining sufficient energy from fermentation reactions.

3. Whenever one organism feeds upon another, the amount of food value in the second organism is always much less than that in the first because of the respiratory losses that always result. The most efficient use of food, therefore, results when the length of a food chain is kept to a minimum.

4. During respiration, a heat (energy) loss always occurs. Without the continual input of energy from the sun, life would soon cease to exist.

5. Some plants can trap certain kinds of small animals as sources of food, but the importance of such plants has been greatly exaggerated in many periodicals.

REVIEW TOPICS AND QUESTIONS

1. A nurseryman in the South obtained a plant from a friend in the North, where this plant produces large edible roots. The nurseryman finds that this plant grows very poorly in his region and produces only tiny, thin roots. Explain this situation on the basis of compensation points.

2. A water molecule taken into the root of a plant from the soil solution is consumed in the production of another material after reaching a palisade mesophyll cell of the leaf. This latter compound in turn appears in the root a few hours after its formation in the leaf and undergoes a number of chemical transformations which result in the production of a new water molecule.

   Describe in detail and in logical sequence the processes, reactions, and the tissues involved, from the uptake of the first water molecule to the formation of the second water molecule in the root, including the forces and energy involved in all movements and transformations.

3. Equal numbers of seeds of pine and oak were planted in a forested area. Ten years later many thriving young oak trees in the forested

area were observed, but only a few stunted pine trees. Give a possible explanation based upon compensation points.

4. (a) Explain what is meant by a food chain, and give an example which includes yourself.

(b) Explain why green plants are always the base of any food chain.

(c) Explain why the last organism gets less and less of the food value of the green plants as the number of organisms involved in the food chain increases.

5. Farmer Muller (in Santa Barbara, California) read that several different varieties of potato were available. In response to his request, friends from all parts of the United States sent him tubers to plant. The tubers were in excellent condition. After mixing them together in a large bin, the tubers were planted, and all plants received the same treatment. Some of these potato plants grew much better than others, and a few plants would not grow at all.

(a) On the basis of an understanding of compensation points, explain the differences in growth.

(b) From what sort of climate did the plants which grew poorest originate?

(c) From what sort of climate did the plants which grew best originate?

(Note: The temperature in Santa Barbara is warm during the summer, but not hot.)

6. You have available a group of young birch trees and a group of young alder trees, and you have been given the following experimental evidence:

(a) At 25°C., the compensation point for birch trees is a light intensity of 100 foot candles.

(b) At 25°C., the compensation point for alder trees is a light intensity of 50 foot candles.

(c) Both trees require approximately the same amounts of minerals and water from the soil for a maximum (and equal) rate of growth.

(d) The area in which these trees are to be planted has plenty of minerals and water, an average temperature of 25°C., and an average light intensity of 150 foot candles.

Explain in detail which group of trees you should plant in order to obtain a dense forest.

7. Explain why approximately seven times as much land is required to produce food in the form of meat as is required to produce food (of similar caloric value) in the form of grains and vegetables.

8. The following statement has been copied from a well-known botany text:

"During the entire life of a plant, the quantity of oxygen released in photosynthesis is approximately equal to the quantity of carbon dioxide released in respiration."

Discuss the fallacy of this statement. (Note: In the photosynthetic production of one gram of sugar, the amount of oxygen released *is* equal to the amount of carbon dioxide released in the respiration of one gram of sugar.)

9. After a favorable sunny summer season over the North Atlantic, fish are more abundant than after a less sunny summer. Explain.

10. If the source of energy by which green plants live is sunlight, how do they remain alive at night?
11. A plant produces large fruits when grown in the garden but produces only small fruits when grown indoors. Indicate how a knowledge of compensation points helps to explain this phenomenon.
12. A marked atom of carbon, as a part of a molecule of carbon dioxide, occurs in the air above a bean field on May 30. On August 28, this same atom of carbon is found to be part of a molecule of cellulose in the wall of a tracheid in the root of a bean plant.

    Trace in proper sequence the movements of this carbon atom, including all tissues (or regions) and organs through which it moves, all forces involved in its movement, all processes in which it becomes involved, and all changes in energy or chemical form taking place in these processes.
13. Discuss the adaptations which enable some kinds of plants to grow with their roots submerged in water; be sure to include the reasons why such adaptations are successful.

SUGGESTED READINGS

Ferry, J. F., and H. S. Ward. *Fundamentals of Plant Physiology.* New York: Macmillan, 1959.

Gerard, R. W. *Unresting Cells.* New York: Harper, 1949.

Plass, G. N. "Carbon Dioxide and Climate," *Scientific American,* 201 (July 1959), 41–47.

Transeau, E. N., et al. *Textbook of Botany.* New York: Harper, 1940.

CHAPTER 14

Transpiration

14.1 Transpiration

The structure of a typical leaf, including the stomata, has already been discussed. When these pores are open, the diffusion of gases into and out of the leaf occurs quite readily, as in the case of carbon dioxide and oxygen during rapid photosynthetic activity. Before either entering or leaving the cell, such molecules dissolve in the water at the cell surfaces. The enormous number of moist surfaces exposed within a leaf cause the intercellular spaces to be continually saturated with water vapor. Since the atmosphere is usually not saturated, a concentration gradient exists, and water molecules diffuse from the leaf (mainly through the stomata) to the external environment, where a lower concentration, and hence a lower vapor pressure of water, exists. The cuticle of the plant is not completely impermeable to water, so such diffusion also takes place from various portions of the plant, though to a much lesser extent than through the stomata. This loss of water vapor from a plant is called **transpiration.**

14.2 Water requirement

The quantities of water lost from a plant may be extremely large (Tables 14-1 and 14-2) and are much greater than the amounts actu-

Table 14-1. Rates of Water Loss per Day in Midsummer

Plant	Water Loss (in quarts) *
A single plant of corn	3–4
A single plant of giant ragweed	6–7
A single young 10-foot apple tree	10–20
A 12-foot columnar cactus	0.02
A coconut palm in moist tropics	70–80
A date palm in a desert oasis	400–500

* One liter is approximately 1.06 liquid quarts.

Source: E. N. Transeau, H. C. Sampson, and L. H. Tiffany, *Textbook of Botany*, 1st. ed. (New York: Harper and Row, 1940), by permission of the publishers.

ally used by the plant in photosynthesis, digestion, and other metabolic processes. Most plants probably use only about 2 to 4 per cent of the water which is absorbed by the plant; over 95 per cent is lost in transpiration. Obviously, this figure is quite different for many xerophytic

Table 14-2. Estimated Water Losses from Single Plants during a Growing Season

Plant	Days	WATER LOSS Gallons *	WATER LOSS Liters
Tomato	100	30	113
Corn	100	50	188
Sunflower	90	125	470
Giant ragweed	90	140	526
Mature apple tree	188	1,800	6,770
Coconut palm, moist tropics	365	4,200	15,800
Date palm, desert oasis	365	35,000	131,600

* One gallon is approximately 3.76 liters

Source: Transeau, Sampson, and Tiffany, *Textbook of Botany*, 1st. ed.

(desert) plants, as will be discussed later. Even though most of the water is not used, this large amount is required or the plant will die of desiccation. The **water requirement** refers to the number of pounds of water absorbed by the plant in producing one pound of solid material. This figure (see Table 14-3) is obtained by dividing the total

Table 14-3. Water Requirements for Certain Plants

Sorghum	250
Corn	350
Red clover	460
Wheat	500
Potato	636
Cucumber	713
Alfalfa	900

Source: Harry J. Fuller and Oswald Tippo, *College Botany*, Rev. ed. (New York: Holt, Rinehart & Winston, 1954), by permission of the publishers.

quantity (pounds) of water absorbed by the total final dry weight (pounds) of the plant in question. Remember that environmental conditions will greatly influence this ratio by their effect on photosynthesis, respiration, and especially transpiration. In spite of this, the determination of the water requirement of a plant gives a fairly good indication of its distribution, in that desert plants tend to have low requirements and mesophytic plants (e.g., sunflower, bean, tomato, etc.) have high requirements. Certain exceptions to this statement will be discussed later in the chapter.

In **mesophytic plants,** those which grow in soils containing moderate amounts of moisture, stomatal transpiration accounts for almost all of the water vapor which is lost. In some **xerophytic plants,** those which grow in soils having a scanty water supply, the number of stomata is greatly reduced, and the relative amount of water lost through these pores is much less than in the first group of plants. In certain desert plants, then, **cuticular transpiration** becomes more significant than it is in plants growing in other environments. Such transpiration refers to the loss of water directly from the epidermal cells through the cuticle layer, a loss which amounts to only 4 to 10 per cent of the total water vapor lost from mesophytes in general. Such great variations among living organisms must be kept in mind, since most of the basic principles of biology continually refer to the majority rather than to the entirety. The concept of variation is frequently evident but will be covered in detail mainly in the discussion of inheritance and evolution (see Chapters 17 and 27).

14.3   Wilting

The water which is used by or lost from a plant is obtained by absorption from the soil. If the root system can absorb 100 grams of water per hour, and if the plant uses 10 grams per hour, the margin of safety is 90 grams. However, if transpiration exceeds 90 grams per hour, the plant **wilts.** This limp or flaccid condition results because the cells lose water, turgor pressure decreases, and the leaf or even the entire plant loses its rigidity. This is especially true of those plants which do not have much woody supporting tissue, the herbaceous plants. Recovery from this wilted condition occurs when the rate of transpiration again falls below 90 grams per hour. Plants in a bean field are frequently seen to wilt or droop near midday and then recover turgor as the sun sets and transpirational losses decrease.

14.4   Environmental factors affecting transpiration

Environmental conditions may vary considerably even over short periods of time, and these changes result in greatly fluctuating water losses. In general, these changes in transpiration rates result from an effect of the environment upon the vapor pressure of water or upon the stomatal openings.

TEMPERATURE

An increase in temperature increases vapor pressure by increasing molecular motion. Since the amount of water vapor within the leaf is

usually greater than the amount in the atmosphere, the water vapor
pressure in the former area is increased to a greater extent, the vapor
pressure gradient steepens, and the rate of diffusion of water molecules
out of the leaf increases. If the temperature is high enough, the rate
of water loss may exceed the rate of water absorption, and the plant
will wilt, as was the case with the bean plants mentioned previously.

LIGHT

When plants are exposed to light as the sun rises, the rate of transpiration increases for two reasons. First, the absorption of light by
green leaves results in an increased temperature of the leaves. As indicated above, this causes an increased vapor pressure of water within
the leaves and an increased water loss. This is an indirect effect of light.

The second reason involves the direct influence of light on stomatal
opening. At night, stomata are partially or wholly closed, and the rate
of transpiration is considerably less than during the day, when the
stomata are open. The opening of stomata is brought about by the
increased turgidity of the two guard cells which form the boundary of
each stoma (see Figure 9-9), but the exact mechanism involved in these
turgor changes is not yet fully understood. Light brings about an increase in the sugar content of the guard cells, probably as a result of
acidity changes[1] and the resultant conversion of starch to sugar. This
increase in osmotic concentration brings about a movement of water
into the guard cells from neighboring leaf cells (Why?), the guard
cells swell, and the thick walls between them are spread apart. The
procedure is reversed as the sun sets.

Light intensity may fluctuate rather rapidly during the day and bring
about many changes in transpiration rates, especially by causing temperature variations in the leaf. Stomata are effective in decreasing vapor
loss only after they have closed to 5 to 10 per cent of their full aperture.

EXTERNAL HUMIDITY

One of the basic principles involved in the diffusion of any material
is the steepness of the concentration gradient between the two areas
in question. Any increase in the atmospheric humidity surrounding a

---

[1] In the dark, respiration occurs, and CO_2 accumulates. The resultant carbonic
acid (H_2CO_3), which forms whenever CO_2 is dissolved in water, causes a
slightly acid condition. The guard cells contain chloroplasts, and photosynthesis,
which occurs in the light, decreases the CO_2 content (and hence decreases the
carbonic acid content), resulting in a decrease in acidity. The starch/sugar
equilibrium shifts to the right, creating more sugar, as the acidity decreases.
The shift is to the left when acidity increases. This is the most probable explanation for the increased osmotic concentration of guard cells in the light.

plant would decrease this gradient and thus decrease transpiration. If the atmosphere is saturated with water vapor, transpiration will usually cease. In many greenhouses the common practice is to water the walls and floors to insure a high degree of humidity surrounding the plants.

AIR CIRCULATION

As water molecules diffuse out through the stomata, they tend to accumulate above these openings, effectively decreasing the concentration gradient by increasing the external humidity. Air movements prevent such accumulation and bring drier air masses in contact with the leaves, thus maintaining high rates of transpiration.

SOIL MOISTURE

If water is not readily available in the soil, the rate of transpiration may exceed the rate of absorption. Such a condition cannot exist for any length of time without wilting of the plant. As was indicated previously, this flaccid (limp) condition is a result of a decrease in turgor pressure of cells as water is lost more rapidly than it is replaced. The stomata, therefore, close when the plant wilts, and transpiration decreases.

14.5 Structural features which reduce water requirements

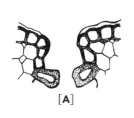

[A]

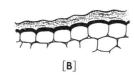

[B]

A plant which transpires readily must obviously have available to it a considerably greater supply of water than is necessary for a similar plant transpiring at a lower rate. For example, if two plants each utilize 1 gram of water per hour, but the first plant transpires 99 grams per hour while the second transpires 9 grams per hour, the first plant requires ten times as much water as the second: 100 grams per hour vs. 10 grams per hour. Therefore, a low rate of transpiration is advantageous for desert plants. Remember, however, that modifications which result in low rates of transpiration enable plants to exist in the desert, but that such modifications did not arise in order that the plant could survive in the desert; they are chance occurrences.

A thick cuticle is found on many cacti and other succulent plants. In fact, the cuticle of such plants (i.e., the century plant, *Agave*) can

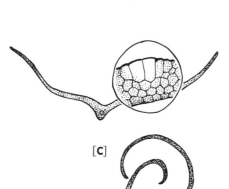

[C]

Figure 14-1. Examples of structural features which reduce water requirements. **A:** A sunken stoma. **B:** A very thick cuticle. **C:** At the top, a leaf in its normal position; the enlargement shows the bulliform cells of the epidermis. At the bottom, the leaf is shown after water loss has caused the bulliform cells to lose turgor; the leaf rolls up.

sometimes be peeled off like a layer of cellophane. Since the transpiration which takes place through the epidermis is usually a rather high proportion of total transpiration in xerophytes, such a thick and continuous cuticle aids in water retention (Figure 14-1B).

Any features which result in a decrease of evaporating surfaces will, of course, bring about a lowering of transpiration rates. Such structures are readily found in an examination of desert floras: (1) a reduction in the number of stomata (cacti); (2) reduction in the size (creosote bush, *Larrea tridentata*) or absence (prickly pear, *Opuntia*) of leaves; (3) small leaves that last for only short periods. Ocotillo, or Jacob's Staff (*Fouquieria splendens*), has the appearance, until the rainy season starts, of a dead piece of driftwood stuck upright in the desert soil. Then in a period of days, hundreds of tiny green leaves appear as if by magic. As soil moisture disappears, these leaves wither, die, and drop off readily. In such a plant, the relatively large evaporating surface, which the leaves represent, is present only during those periods when moisture is available.

Compared to mesophytic plants, many desert plants are found to have few stomata. In others the stomata are sunken in pits which greatly retard the removal of accumulated water vapor by wind currents (Figure 14-1A). Many of the grasses have rows of specialized bulliform cells in the epidermis. These cells are large and have thin walls. As a result, the bulliform cells lose water, and consequently turgor, more rapidly than other epidermal cells, and the leaf rolls up, a situation which is diagrammed in Figure 14-1C. The external humidity of the area enclosed by the rolled leaf soon increases, as transpiration continues and water vapor accumulates. The water vapor pressure gradient between the leaf and this external area decreases. Transpiration, at least from that portion of the leaf surface, decreases.

The root systems of certain desert plants are also important in enabling such plants to survive in dry areas. The deep-penetrating roots of the acacia and the mesquite (*Prosopis*) reach submerged water supplies, and these trees survive in spite of relatively high rates of transpiration. Many cacti, on the other hand, have extensive, shallow, fibrous (many-branched) root systems. When correlated with succulent water-storage tissues in which the cells usually contain much colloidal material, this system becomes very advantageous for life in the desert. The rains which occur moisten the upper few inches of soil, where the majority of roots are located, resulting in extremely rapid absorption of water before the soil dries out. This water is then retained within the succulent leaves (as in the ice plant, *Mesembryanthemum*) or stems (many cacti) because of the hydrophilic colloids. Water is adsorbed very strongly to such colloids and evaporates only with great difficulty. If a drop of water is placed in bright sunlight next to a drop of cell sap from the century plant (*Agave*), the drop of water will have evaporated within ten minutes or so, while the drop of cell sap will scarcely have changed due to the hygroscopic colloidal mucilages and gums present in the latter.

14.6 Significance of transpiration

Many and varied beneficial and harmful effects have been attributed to transpiration. The difficulty in distinguishing between the opposing aspects of this process appear to arise mainly from a misunderstanding of the term, and the student would do well to refer to Section 14.1 at this time.

LOWERING OF LEAF TEMPERATURE

Evaporation of water from a surface lowers the temperature at that surface because of the loss of water molecules of a relatively high kinetic energy—the decrease in over-all kinetic energy of molecules at the surface appears as a decrease in temperature, which is really a measure of kinetic energy. This basic principle has resulted in the statement that transpiration is not only beneficial but actually essential in preventing leaf temperatures in bright sunlight from rising so high as to injure the cells. Calculations based upon known rapid rates of transpiration, however, indicate that this lowering of temperature would amount to probably no more than 2 to 3°C.—not a very substantial decrease. Also, those plants in which such a lowering of temperature would be most effective are the desert plants, and the rate of transpiration in the cactus is so slow as to result in a mere fraction of a degree decrease in temperature. On the other hand, the loss of heat by radiation, conduction, and convection undoubtedly is the major reason which prevents leaf temperatures from greatly exceeding air temperatures.

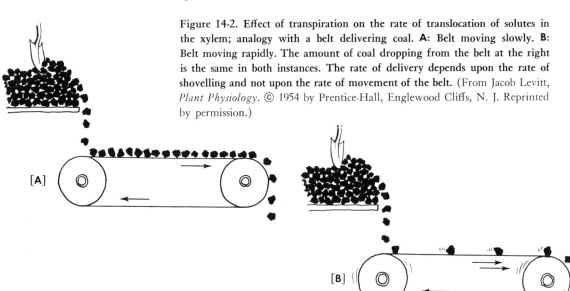

Figure 14-2. Effect of transpiration on the rate of translocation of solutes in the xylem; analogy with a belt delivering coal. **A**: Belt moving slowly. **B**: Belt moving rapidly. The amount of coal dropping from the belt at the right is the same in both instances. The rate of delivery depends upon the rate of shovelling and not upon the rate of movement of the belt. (From Jacob Levitt, *Plant Physiology*. © 1954 by Prentice-Hall, Englewood Cliffs, N. J. Reprinted by permission.)

[A]

[B]

Frequently, high rates of transpiration are said to result in high rates of mineral absorption. While most of the minerals are transported in the xylem along with water, our understanding of diffusion and differentially permeable membranes emphasizes the independent absorption of these two materials. Even the transport of minerals through the xylem is not directly related to rates of transpiration. One might think of the transpiration stream as a rapidly moving belt between the supplying area (the roots) and the receiving area (the leaves), as is indicated in Figure 14-2. In this figure, the amount of coal reaching the bucket at the right depends upon the speed of addition of coal to the belt and not upon the speed of the belt. Also, movements of minerals tend to follow concentration gradients.

WATER SUPPLY

Another misconception concerning the importance of transpiration is embodied in the statement that this process is essential in bringing water to the top of tall trees, that without transpiration water would not be pulled to the tops of trees by the "transpiration stream" and the tree would die. Herein lies a simple basic misunderstanding. Transpiration is the *loss* of water from a plant, and a loss of water can never increase the moisture content of anything. The fallacy involved in the statement arises from correlating unrelated facts. In other words, while high rates of transpiration will result in the absorption and movement of large amounts of water into and through the plant, it is *not* true that these large amounts of water result in an increase of moisture in the leaves. After all, such water merely replaces that which was lost due to transpiration. Even if transpiration could be stopped entirely, water would still be absorbed by and transported through the plant. Why?

HARMFUL

The significant factor, then, about transpiration is that it is harmful. It is a loss of water, a loss of one of the essentials of life and one of the substrates of an exceedingly important process. (What process?) Because a process occurs in a plant does not insure that it must be beneficial. With wet cell walls within a leaf and open stomata (both essential for photosynthesis), transpiration must of a necessity occur. It is simply a matter of diffusion of water vapor from an area of high concentration (the leaf) to an area of lower concentration (the atmosphere). Danger arises only when the amount of water diffusing out in this fashion exceeds the amount entering the roots. The resultant

163

wilting usually greatly reduces the yield of the plant and may result in death.

Many of the practices employed by nurserymen and farmers are efforts to reduce transpiration rates and water losses. One of the most important procedures is to remove weeds from any close proximity to the desired plants. Such weeds transpire a vast quantity of water which is thus unavailable to other plants. The undesirable plants also remove minerals from the soil. The result if weeds are not removed is stunted growth of the crop plants. Nurserymen whitewash greenhouses during the summer as an effective way to reduce light intensity, temperature, and thus transpiration. Frequently, a fine spray of water is used to saturate the atmosphere in the greenhouse and in this way decrease transpiration rates. The resultant saving in time and effort of watering is considerable.

In propagating plants by cuttings or in transplanting from one location to another, every effort must be made to maintain as low a loss of water as possible because of the low rates of absorption which result from the lack of roots or from damaged roots. For this reason, some of the leaves are removed, the plants are frequently covered with glass jars, and they are always carefully and thoroughly watered. Until a root system is well-established in the new area, even fairly low rates of transpiration may result in wilting because of the poor absorption of water. Flaccid (wilted or plasmolyzed) cells are not capable of growth or division. Certainly, a good supply of water is essential for the normal development of the cutting or transplant.

14.7   Plant distribution and water relations

One of the basic concepts in an understanding of plant distribution concerns the interaction of water supply and transpiration. Rainfall, temperature, and light are of primary consideration when discussing regional plant distribution, while soil, topography, and light (again) enter the picture on a more local basis. The influence of temperature and light on compensation points and the resultant effect on plant distribution have already been discussed (see Chapter 13). We should mention at this point that many areas in the world have temperatures too low to sustain any great development of the more complex plants. In fact, unusually early or severe frosts may result in considerable damage to young plants and greatly decreased yields of those plants which survive.

As an indication of the effect of transpiration on plant distribution, one might examine the areas in which apple trees, corn plants, and cactus plants are growing, and compare this with the amount of water necessary to sustain each plant. The average loss of water during a single summer day is approximately as follows:

Apple tree, 10 feet tall	10–20 liters
Corn plant	3–4 liters
Cactus, columnar, 12 feet	0.02 liters

The apple tree, thus, requires the most water, and the cactus plant requires the least. An examination of the structures of these three plants explains the significant differences in transpiration rates. The leaf of the apple tree is not greatly modified (i.e., it has a thin cuticle, no mucins, many stomata), water losses are high, and thus the tree grows only in those areas where relatively large amounts of moisture are available, that is, in regions of good rainfall, along streams and rivers, or in irrigated areas. The leaf of the corn plant, on the other hand, is somewhat modified and typically grass-like. Fewer stomata, a thicker cuticle, and bulliform (or motor) cells are present in the epidermis. Because of the lower rate of transpiration, the corn plant quite readily survives in drier areas than does the apple. The cactus plant is, of course, the most modified of the three: the evaporating or transpiring surface is greatly decreased by the absence of leaves, it has a thick cuticle and few stomata (which are sunken), and the fibrous root system is near the surface and correlated with water storage tissue. The result is that the cactus is found in the dry uplands of the desert where there is very little water supply and where neither the apple tree nor the corn plant could survive.

Of course, some exceptions to this correlation between transpiration-rainfall-plant distribution do exist. For example, some desert annuals transpire quite rapidly and yet exist readily in these relatively dry areas. An examination of the life cycles of such plants furnishes an explanation. These small, flowering plants germinate and produce flowers and seeds all within the span of the few weeks when desert showers provide the necessary moisture. Such plants actually escape desiccation as a result of a very short growing season. Another example would be the date palm, which frequently loses 400 to 500 liters of water in a single day while growing in a desert. The factor involved in this case is the extensive water supply of the desert oasis (or the irrigation canal). However, apple trees could not grow in this location, even though a sufficient water supply is available. (Review the concept of compensation points for an explanation.)

Figure 14-3 indicates the average annual inches of rainfall for the United States. Note the gradual decrease in rainfall across the eastern two-thirds of the nation as one proceeds from east to west. The greater complexity of the rainfall lines in the western third of the country is

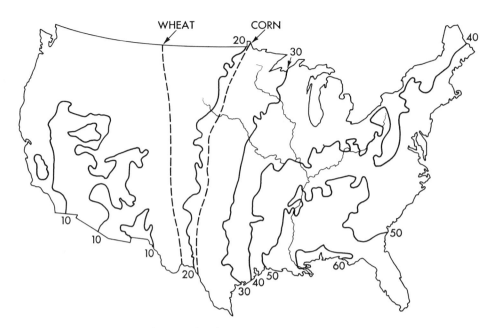

Figure 14-3. The solid lines indicate average annual inches of rainfall in the United States. The westernmost boundaries for wheat growth and for corn growth are shown by dashed lines.

due to the vast mountain ranges, which influence rainfall. This effect will be discussed later. The companion Figure 14-4 indicates the very general type of plant growth found in these regions. Plant distribution follows the rainfall belts in a general way.

In the eastern third, one finds broad-leaved plants and deciduous trees (e.g., truck crops, fruit trees, beech, maple) which have but few modifications that result in decreased transpiration, since the rainfall in this area is sufficient to support such plants.

In the central area are located the vast grasslands of the United States. The farther west one travels, the less the rainfall, and broad-leaved plants are found only near rivers and streams. The grassland itself changes gradually from the tall (6–10 ft.) native grasses in the east to moderately tall bunch grasses further west to the short grasses (less than 2 ft.) of the west: the farther west, the shorter the grass. As mentioned previously, grass leaves have lower rates of transpiration than broad leaves; the short grasses have less leaf surface and transpire less than the tall grasses. Consequently, tall grasses require less rainfall than broad-leaved plants but more than short grasses. The grasses are, however, less modified with regard to transpiration than are desert plants.

In the arid regions (the deserts) are found those plants which have the lowest rates of transpiration or which escape desiccation by one means or another. The various cacti, creosote bush (*Larrea tridentata*), Jacob's Staff (*Fouquieria splendens*), and desert annuals are examples of this flora.

The rainfall lines in the western third of the United States are more complex because of the vast mountain ranges in this area (the Rocky Mountains, the Sierra Nevada range, and the coastal mountain range). The moisture-carrying winds blowing in from the Pacific Ocean rise along the slopes of these ranges, moisture condenses as the air is cooled, and rain falls mainly on the western slopes, leaving a rain-shadow to the east. By the time the winds reach and pass the Rockies, they are devoid of moisture. In general, then, rainfall is much heavier on the windward side of a mountain range than it is on the leeward side. In fact, if the mountains are relatively high, almost no rain may fall on the leeward side.

Temperature fluctuations run at right angles to rainfall belts, temperatures in the northern hemisphere being higher in the south than in the north. Since temperature greatly influences transpiration, a rainfall which would support certain plants in the north would be insufficient for these plants in the south. For example, in some parts of Mexico, 35 inches of rainfall is insufficient to support anything but desert vegetation, due to high transpiration rates. In the southern part of the United States, this is sufficient for grassland, while trees readily grow with this amount of moisture in the northern part of the country. Mountain areas again complicate the picture because of the influence of altitude on temperature and thus on transpiration.

As discussed more thoroughly in Chapter 16, soil types cause variations in the kinds of plants which can be supported by a specific

Figure 14-4. The shaded areas indicate general types of plant growth. For further discussion see the text.

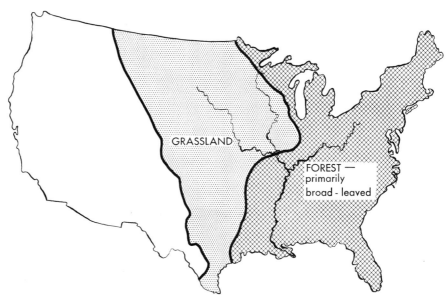

amount of rainfall. In general, more effective water penetration and aeration occurs in sandy soils than in clay soils. Therefore, a rainfall which would make possible the growth of trees in a sandy soil would be sufficient only for grasses in a clay soil.

Irrigation systems provided by man can, and do, enable crop plants to be grown in areas not having a suitable rainfall. This situation exists in the Imperial Valley of California, which receives a meager 10 inches of rainfall per year and develops some of the best crops of lettuce, tomato, and cotton in the country. This is an example of the results that man can achieve; it also emphasizes the importance of a water

Table 14-4. The Response of Cotton to Irrigation: Athens, Ga.

YEAR	RAINFALL (June, July, Aug.)	IRRIGATION	SEED COTTON YIELDS (lbs./acre)	
			Unirrigated	Irrigated
1949	12.05 in.	3.00 in.	1,155	1,286
1950	9.93 in.	1.50 in.	1,087	1,430
1951	12.37 in.	4.00 in.	2,165	2,528
1952	8.82 in.	9.44 in.	742	2,534
1953	6.25 in.	9.91 in.	934	1,731

Source: Water, The Yearbook of Agriculture, 1955 (Washington, D. C.: United States Department of Agriculture), p. 257.

supply. Table 14-4 indicates the type of response which can be achieved by supplementing rainfall with irrigation even in the more humid regions of the United States. The increases in yield resulting from irrigation are especially noticeable during relatively dry seasons, but even in wet seasons an increased yield does result. The answer to the economic question of whether the additional output will raise farm incomes enough to justify the higher cost frequently depends upon the farmer himself. Benefits and costs vary greatly from farm to farm, and each farmer needs to appraise his own situation. In general, however, the advantages outweigh the disadvantages, and irrigation is continuing to expand. In relatively dry areas, of course, irrigation is necessary if crops are to be grown successfully.

An understanding of the relationship between transpiration rate, water requirement, and rainfall is important to a knowledge of plant distribution, including both native plants and cultivated plants. Figure 14-3 indicates the distribution of two important crop plants in the United States. In general, the corn belt is limited to those areas receiving 25 to 50 inches of rain per year, whereas wheat can be grown with as little as 15 inches of rain. The latter transpires less than the former and thus has a lower water requirement. The effect of a north-south temperature fluctuation is quite distinctly shown in the slant of the line representing the western boundary of wheat growth: about 13 inches of rainfall is sufficient in the north, while 17 inches is required by similar wheat growing in the southern states. An understanding of the reasons for such plant distribution should enable us to decide upon the type of crops to plant in a particular region. Unfortunately, we don't always take advantage of available information.

14.8 The Dust Bowl

An enormous area of the central portion of the United States is now known as the "Dust Bowl" because of the tremendous dust storms prevalent throughout that location. Its size was approximately 12,000,000 acres as of 1958, including large portions of Nebraska, Kansas, Colorado, Oklahoma, New Mexico, and Texas, an area greater than that of Massachusetts and Vermont combined. Dust clouds frequently rise to 20,000 feet, carrying soil as far as the Atlantic Coast, where muddy rain sometimes results. This is a recent development; the seriousness of the situation was first emphasized by the Dust Bowl of the 1930's. This entire area had for generations been lush grazing land. Never had a Dust Bowl existed before the advent of farming, and it never should have developed. It has been created entirely by man through his disregard of an understanding of plant distribution. Even more frightening is the fact that the Dust Bowl of the 1950's was almost twice as large as that of the 1930's, and that the former Dust Bowl was predicted 10 to 15 years beforehand. Let us now examine the causes of this situation.

To grow crops like beans or tomato in the wheat belt is obviously impossible. The same reasoning indicates the impossibility of growing wheat in the short grass regions of the midwest. However, the figures for annual rainfall refer to average amounts over a period of many years. Seasonal fluctuations occur, so that the wheat frontier may be pushed farther west during the wet cycles, and then the dry seasons wipe back this frontier. Poor range land with a low rainfall average and low prices tease the farmer into buying such land and growing wheat during the wet years. One drought season, which is bound to come, will wipe out his crop. The danger zone, wherein rainfall fluctuations can ruin crops, includes almost the whole western half of the wheat belt. Corn may also be involved in some cases.

This attempt to grow crop plants in unsuitable areas was the cause of dust storms and gave rise to the Dust Bowl. The climate in this area has not changed appreciably for generations. The high winds of the Great Plains have existed for ages without creating dust storms, because the soil has been held in place by the roots of the native short

Figure 14-5. An approaching dust storm. Dry topsoil, devoid of vegetation, is being blown about by winds. (Courtesy United States Department of Agriculture, Soil Conservation Service.)

Figure 14-6. The aftermath of dust storms. Plants are almost completely covered by drifting soil. If such plants are not first destroyed by the abrasive action of blown soil particles, they will be smothered and die. (Courtesy United States Department of Agriculture, Soil Conservation Service.)

Figure 14-7. Dust storm damage. The field in the background has been severely damaged by wind erosion of its topsoil. The small grassy area in the foreground is gradually being covered by wind-blown soil. (Courtesy United States Department of Agriculture, Soil Conservation Service.)

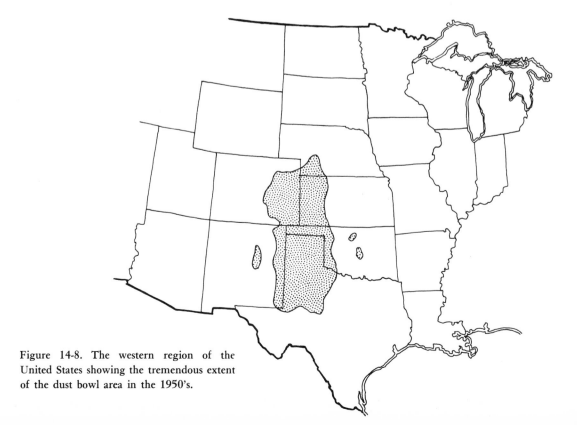

Figure 14-8. The western region of the United States showing the tremendous extent of the dust bowl area in the 1950's.

grasses. This native vegetation is plowed under in preparing the soil for wheat and corn production. The failure of these crop plants results in the soil being devoid of vegetation; it dries out and blows away in any heavy wind (see Figures 14-5, 6, 7, 8).

The wind erosion, which was made possible by man's disregard of known facts about plant distribution, has resulted in the loss of millions of tons of topsoil. Such damage is almost irreparable, since it took 100 to 200 years to create each inch of topsoil. This damage has an exceedingly far-reaching effect, besides the more immediate problem of poverty and migration of the farmers from the dust bowl area; it creates a social problem in regions not directly a part of the Dust Bowl, as the West Coast states discovered during the 1930's. At this time, many farmers in the midwest lost everything and moved to the coast in search of a livelihood. With jobs few and no means of support, they were a further drain on the national economy. All this, of course, was unnecessary.

The solution of the dust bowl problem is simple, though drastic, and consists basically of returning most of this area to grazing land. In many areas crops such as sorghum, rather than wheat, also may be planted. The real difficulty involved is to convince people not to plant wheat, which gives them a greater financial return for a short period, but to plant the more stable sorghums and grasses which are more suited to the area. Obviously, over-grazing would have the same deleterious effect upon the soil as is achieved by attempting to grow wheat.

Some areas have adopted land-use ordinances which have been very successful in combating the dust bowl. Experts of the Soil Conservation Districts indicate the most suitable use of land (e.g., grazing, sorghum, wheat, etc.), and the land owner is eligible for crop insurance and price supports only if he follows these suggestions. In other words, he is not forced to conform with proper land-use practices; he is just not rewarded for ruining his land if he wants to disregard the suggestions. Many areas throughout the dust bowl region already have been at least partially reclaimed by proper land use, and much more should be done to remedy a disgraceful situation.

Summary

1. Transpiration is the loss of water vapor from a plant. Most of this loss occurs through the stomata, although some water vapor is lost directly from the epidermal cells. This process is what is really responsible for the tremendous water requirements of most plants, since relatively little of the water which is absorbed is actually utilized by the plant. Without the losses through transpiration, plants would require relatively little water.

2. The rate of transpiration is influenced by those environmental factors which influence evaporation in general: temperature, external humidity, and air circulation. In addition to these factors, soil moisture and structural features are important.

3. Transpiration is harmful to the plant. It is a loss of water, and such a loss is always detrimental.

4. The rate at which a plant transpires is the main factor determining the amount of rainfall necessary for that plant to survive. Of course, minor variations due to soil conditions and to the proximity of bodies of water do occur. Irrigation systems enable plants to grow in areas that do not have a sufficient rainfall.

5. The "Dust Bowl" of the central portion of the United States is a result of man's disregard for proper land use. Such a situation need never have occurred, and it can still be remedied with appropriate agricultural procedures.

REVIEW TOPICS AND QUESTIONS

1. When plants are transplanted, some of the leaves are usually removed (pruning). Explain in detail the advantage of this practice.
2. Explain the functioning of four different structural or physiological features which enable certain plants to exist in desert areas.
3. Explain in detail how humans have been responsible for the development of the midwestern (U. S.) Dust Bowl. In what ways have fluctuations in annual rainfall been influential? Indicate why such a situation is a nation-wide problem and not just a local one.
4. Briefly describe the east-west distribution of apple, corn, and wheat plants in the United States. Explain in detail for each plant the correlation between structure, water requirement, and rainfall.
5. Describe an experiment which would enable you to determine the effect of air temperature on the rate of transpiration.
6. Explain why a plant could wilt even though the soil in which it has been growing is thoroughly watered.
7. A healthy, potted plant is thoroughly watered and then placed in a warm dark room. After three hours, a bright light is turned on for another three-hour interval. Draw a curve plotting the relative rate of transpiration versus time for the 6-hour period, assuming that sufficient water was present in the soil at all times. Explain each change in the curve, and discuss the factors which are limiting or retarding during the experiment.
8. Explain the fallacy involved in each of the following statements, and indicate the correct interpretation where pertinent:
    (a) Transpiration supplies the plant with water.
    (b) Transpiration keeps the cell walls moist.
    (c) Transpiration draws water to the leaves for use in photosynthesis.

(d) Transpiration must be beneficial, for otherwise, through evolution and natural selection, the process would have been eliminated.

(e) An increase in transpiration results in an increased absorption of water and therefore increases the turgor of the plant.

9. List those factors which influence transpiration, and discuss the effect upon transpiration of varying each factor individually.

10. Describe in detail an experiment that would demonstrate whether stomata are the main pathways through which water is lost from a leaf.

SUGGESTED READINGS

Ellison, W. D. "Erosion by Raindrop," *Scientific American,* 179 (November 1948), 40–45.

Greulach, V. A. "The Rise of Water in Plants," *Scientific American,* 187 (October 1952), 78–82.

Hudson, J. P. "Plants and Their Water Supplies," *Endeavor,* 16 (1957), 84–89.

Meyer, B. S., et al. *Introduction to Plant Physiology.* Princeton: Van Nostrand, 1960.

Sayre, A. N. "Ground Water," *Scientific American,* 183 (November 1950), 14–19.

Syrett, P. I. "Transpiration," *New Biology,* 25 (January 1958), 27–46.

Went, F. W. "The Ecology of Desert Plants," *Scientific American,* 192 (April 1955), 68–76.

———. "Climate and Agriculture," *Scientific American,* 196 (June 1957), 82–98.

Mineral Nutrition

15.1 Essential elements

While plant material can be chemically analyzed for the elements that are present, this does not, however, prove the essentiality of the particular elements that are found, because root cells will absorb any soluble minerals from the soil, whether or not they are essential to the plant. Even toxic materials will be absorbed if they are soluble. The cell membranes are differentially permeable but not selective between two molecules of equal size and solubility, only one of which is toxic. If the material is soluble and the molecules are not too large, it will be absorbed. At least sixty different elements have been found in various kinds of plants, including demonstrable amounts of gold (in *Equisetum* spp.) and silver. Almost all the elements which occur on earth probably can be found in some plant or other. In most instances, no significance can be attributed to the presence of elements which have not been shown to be essential. However, the absorption of the element selenium by plants may be important—not to the plants, but to the animals grazing upon those plants. In certain grassland areas of the western United States (South Dakota and Wyoming), selenium is quite prevalent, and cattle grazing in those regions are sometimes poisoned. The disease is known as "blind staggers" and frequently results in death. Soils containing more than 0.5 parts per million of selenium are considered to be potentially dangerous when used for grazing land.

In order to determine the essentiality of an element, one must show that the plant develops abnormally in the absence of that element, that no other element can replace the one in question, and that normal development is obtained when the element is provided to the plant. This is not necessarily the simple task that it may seem. Many elements that are now known to be essential have been discovered only very recently. They are necessary in minute amounts (1 to 10 parts per million) and are frequently found as contaminants in other chemicals, in the glassware, or in the water used for experimental purposes. Technical advances, as in the purification of chemicals, for example, have made possible the compilation of a list of at least fifteen essential elements (see Section 15.4):

C HOPKNS CaFe Mg MoB CuMnZn

Chemical symbols (see Table 3-1) have been utilized, and the list has been arranged in a special way for ease of remembering. The symbols can be translated into phrases:

"See Hopkin's cafe? Mighty good. Mob comes in."

Such associations (i.e., chemical symbols with phrases) are useful tools for memorization.

The last twelve of the elements listed in the preceding paragraph are absorbed as minerals from the soil. (Carbon, hydrogen, and oxygen are obtained mainly from carbon dioxide and water.) Iron, molybdenum, boron, copper, manganese, and zinc are frequently called **trace elements,** because they are required in much smaller amounts than are the others. This does not mean that any of these elements is "less essential" than others; without any one of the fifteen, growth of the plant is abnormal, and death eventually results. Again, let us emphasize that these are the *known* essential elements; the history of mineral nutrition experiments makes plant physiologists realize that other elements may be required in such small amounts that they are almost invariably present as minor contaminants during experimental procedures.

15.2 Functions of essential elements

The reasons for the essentiality of several elements becomes quite obvious when one examines the molecular structure of the various compounds found in living cells. The main structural components of protoplasm are the protein molecules, which contain carbon, oxygen, hydrogen, nitrogen, and frequently sulfur and phosphorus. Most of the rather complex molecules within a cell contain carbon, hydrogen, and oxygen atoms, but in addition to these atoms, the chlorophyll molecule contains magnesium, the middle lamella consists primarily of calcium pectate, and certain respiratory enzymes contain iron or copper as part of their prosthetic groups. Without any one of these component atoms, gross abnormalities result.

Only ten elements (C, H, O, N, S, P, Mg, Ca, Fe, Cu) have been shown to be component parts of cellular molecules. However, recent evidence has shown that certain minerals are essential for the normal development of a plant because the ions concerned (e.g., Mg^{++}, Mn^{++}) are necessary for the functioning of various enzyme systems. The activity of some enzymes of the glycolytic reactions (Section 12.3) is dependent upon the presence of magnesium ions, but magnesium may not actually be a part of the enzyme molecule. In other words, magnesium may be functioning quite differently from the iron atom mentioned in the previous paragraph. Ions which are necessary for enzyme activity, but which have not been shown to be part of the enzyme molecule, are termed **activators.** The trace elements appear to function mainly in this way.

15.3   Absorption of minerals

As has been indicated previously (Sections 4.4 and 8.3), absorption of minerals may occur as a result of diffusion, accumulation, or ionic exchange. Recent evidence indicates that the latter two mechanisms are by far the more important. Remember, too, that the growth of roots through the soil continually brings the absorbing surfaces of the plant in contact with additional soil particles and soil solution. Diffusion and associated phenomena were discussed in considerable detail in Chapter 4, so absorption of minerals will now be discussed more from the viewpoint of accumulation.

ACCUMULATION OF SALTS

Many plant cells are capable of building up concentrations of salts which are greater than the concentrations of the same salts in the external solution. This was first demonstrated with fresh-water algae but has also been shown to occur in root cells. These accumulated salts are present within the cell in a dissolved state, so this phenomenon is truly an absorption *against* a concentration gradient (i.e., from an area of lower concentration to an area of higher concentration). This is similar to a stone rolling uphill. Work is required to accomplish such a difficult task, which means that energy is expended. Such energy is derived from respiratory reactions.

Salt accumulation is restricted to cells which are capable of cell division and growth—cells which are relatively active metabolically. Meristematic cells and cells in the early stages of enlargement are especially active. Thus we find greatest accumulation near the root apex and decreasing accumulation in those cells farther from the root tip. Respiratory activity of the cells decreases as the distance from the apex increases. Since salt accumulation is dependent upon respiration, various conditions conducive to respiration must prevail: adequate aeration (oxygen), sufficient food (sugar, or other substrates), and a favorable temperature. A deficiency of any of these factors has been shown to result in little or no accumulation.

15.4 Hydroponics

Because of newspaper and magazine articles (some rather fantastic ones, at that), the average person is aware that plants can be grown in water culture and that soil is not essential. Such soilless agriculture is frequently termed **hydroponics.** This has been a well-established practice with botanists since at least 1865, when Knop and Sachs published the results of their investigations. In essence the "test-tube farmer" is merely providing water and minerals to the plant—the same materials which the plant would obtain from the soil. Obviously, any plant grown in water culture must be supported in some manner because of the lack of a solid soil foundation.

The physiology of the plant is the same whether it is grown in soil or in a nutrient solution. Care must be taken that the solution contains all of the essential elements in prescribed amounts and that the total salt concentration is not so high as to be injurious. Soil-grown plants have the same requirements. Irrespective of their location, these plants require light if photosynthesis is to occur and the plants are to grow.

The foregoing paragraph should make clear the fact that many of the claims made for hydroponics are great exaggerations, misrepresentations, or actual falsehoods. Plants cannot be grown in a basement, an attic, or a closet unless light is available in addition to minerals and water. Artificial light can be used instead of sunlight, but to do so at present is certainly not economically feasible. The tremendous yields attributed to plants grown by the water-culture method are based upon results from a limited number of plants grown under ideal conditions of light, spacing, temperature, and support. To expand such results to an acre basis without adequate correction for natural shading and other facets of competition is erroneous. When soil-grown and solution-grown plants are maintained under similar conditions, no significant difference in yield or quality is apparent between the two groups.

Mineral-nutrient solution techniques have been used satisfactorily for a wide variety of purposes since their inception in the mid-1800's. One of the most important uses is in determining the essential character of various mineral elements. The chemical composition of such solutions can be arranged quite readily, whereas a soil solution may contain ions which become adsorbed to soil colloids and thus not easily detected. The growth of two similar groups of plants, one growing in a nutrient solution containing mineral X, the other lot growing in a nutrient solution devoid of X, can thus be compared. If the growth of the first lot is better than that of the second, then mineral X can be added to lot number two. If this elicits an increased growth, and no other elements cause similar results, one may consider X to be an essential mineral. Additional precautionary measures should be taken, but a discussion of them is beyond the scope of this text. This is, however, the general method which has been used to prove that at least twelve minerals are essential. Newer techniques may extend this list. For example, some scientists claim that sodium and chlorine are essential in minute amounts and that these small amounts are almost universally present as contaminants in chemicals or in glassware which are used. Therefore, to arrange a mineral solution which does not contain sufficient sodium and chlorine would be extremely difficult.

15.5 "Organic farming"

We might at this time mention the foolishness of the controversy (amounting almost to a feud in some localities) of "organic farming" versus the use of chemical fertilizers in the growth of crop plants. The "organic farmer" usually maintains that chemicals should not be added to the soil and that compost (partially decomposed organic material), manure, or plowed-under plant parts should be used. The reasoning behind this firm stand appears to be based upon the fact that chemical fertilizers are poisonous when eaten or will at least make a person rather ill. I wonder if steer manure is not in the same category. In actuality, the addition of chemical fertilizers or compost material results from the same basic requirement of the plant—the need for minerals.

In most soils, nitrogen is the element which is most often deficient. As plants grow, they absorb nitrogen salts (in the form of ammonium ions or nitrate ions) from the soil. The harvesting of a part or all of the plant results in the removal of nitrogen from the soil. After continued cultivation, the lack of nitrogen becomes evident through the characteristic symptoms which appear in plants subsequently grown in that soil. A reduced yield always results, and the solution to the problem is merely to add nitrogen. The only difference between "organic farming" and any other method is the *form* in which nitrogen is added. Chemical fertilizers usually contain nitrate or ammonium salts, whereas manures contain organic nitrogen compounds (e.g., proteins, amino acids, urea). Nitrogen in this latter form is *not* available to the crop plant. Various micro-organisms in the soil convert such organic nitrogen compounds to ammonium salts and nitrate salts (Section 20.5), which are then readily absorbed by the plants growing in that soil. In effect, then, the organic material added to the soil supplies minerals which can be added more rapidly and more easily by the judicious [1] use of chemical fertilizers.

The amount and kind of minerals absorbed from the soil varies considerably with the kind of plant. This is one of the reasons that rotation of crops is a good idea. However, some minerals are removed and not returned to the soil, since they are in the product (e.g., fruit, tuber) which is sent to market. At intervals, at least nitrogen, phosphorus, and potassium must be added to the soil. Most of the other essential minerals are present in such large amounts that they need not be replenished.

The only real advantage of using organic material rather than chemical fertilizers accrues from the beneficial effects on soil structures which result from adding the former. Water-holding capacity, aeration, and mineral-holding capacity of soils will be discussed in Chapter 16. It is sufficient to say at this time that the addition of organic matter to the soil greatly enhances the advantageous physical characteristics of the soil.

Summary

1. Fifteen elements are known to be essential to the normal growth of green plants, some of these being required in minute amounts. Additional elements may be added to the list as investigations progress.

2. The essential elements may be required because they are the component atoms of structural molecules of the cell, or they may be activators of enzyme systems. In some cases the function of the element is unknown.

3. Although minerals diffuse into plant cells, most absorption of minerals is a result of accumulation or ionic exchange.

4. Most plants can be grown quite readily if their roots are immersed in a mineral nutrient solution. Such solutions are valuable tools in mineral nutrient investigations. They do not, however, have any real advantages over soil if the plants are treated similarly and if no mineral deficiency exists in the soil.

5. If crop plants are to be grown for any length of time on a given area, fertilizer will have to be added to that soil. As the plants are harvested, some of the minerals which they have absorbed will be removed with them. Eventually plant growth will be poor unless such minerals are replaced, as by fertilizing.

[1] The directions given on a bag of fertilizer should be followed rather carefully. The old idea that "if one pound is good, two pounds will be twice as good" is dangerous. Review plasmolysis, Section 4.4.

1. Describe in detail an experiment which would enable you to determine whether silicon is essential for the growth of bean plants.
2. Describe in detail an experiment which would enable you to determine whether roses are able to absorb nitrate salts through their leaves.
3. If plants in general could absorb minerals through leaf epidermal cells, would this ability be of any value?
4. Plant growth is better when ammonium sulfate, NH_4SO_4, is added to a soil. Give three possible explanations for this increased growth.
5. The following statement appears in a newspaper: "Garden vegetables can be grown quite readily in a kitchen closet by using mineral nutrient solutions."

    Discuss this statement critically.
6. Plants in a field show abnormal growth. Describe in detail what you should do to determine whether this abnormal growth results from a mineral deficiency.
7. List the essential elements. Indicate, as far as is known, the function of each essential element.
8. Explain why the root system is poorly developed when a plant is grown in a mineral nutrient solution. What could be done to obtain a better root system in such a situation?

SUGGESTED READINGS

Anderson, A. J., and E. J. Underwood. "Trace Element Deserts," *Scientific American*, 200 (January 1959), 97–106.

Gericke, W. F. *The Complete Guide to Soilless Gardening*. Englewood Cliffs, N. J.: Prentice-Hall, 1940.

Gilbert, F. A. *Mineral Nutrition and the Balance of Life*. Norman, Okla.: Univ. of Oklahoma, 1957.

Hambidge, G. (ed.) *Hunger Signs in Crops*. Washington, D. C.: National Fertilizer Assoc., 1941.

Larson, J. D. "The Story of Nature's Soil," *Nature Magazine*, 46 (April 1953), 209–212.

McElroy, W. D., and C. P. Swanson. "Trace Elements," *Scientific American*, 188 (January 1953), 22–25.

Osborn, F. *Our Plundered Planet*. Boston: Little, Brown, 1948.

Wallace, T. "Mineral Deficiencies in Plants," *Endeavour*, 5 (1946), 58–62.

CHAPTER 16

Soils

16.1 Soil

The preceding chapter stated that plants obtain essential minerals from the soil, and this indicates that at least a brief discussion of soils would be of benefit to an understanding of plant growth. Few people do not know what is meant when the word "soil" is used, and yet hardly anyone can give a definition of the word, since all of the connotations implied by such a small word are difficult to put into words. Possibly we can think of **soil** as the very thin uppermost part of the earth's crust, which has developed from the weathering of minerals and contains living organisms and the products of their decay. Such a structure consists of an intimate mixture of mineral materials, organic matter, water, and air in varying proportions. The water and air are in the pore spaces which are between and within the solid particles. The basic framework of the soil consists, then, mainly of small fragments of mineral matter derived from solid rock (bedrock) by long periods of weathering.

16.2 Origin of soil material

The weathering processes may be considered as mechanical disintegrations or as chemical decompositions, and the soil materials which result are designated as sedentary or transported.

MECHANICAL FORCES OF WEATHERING

Within this category we should first consider the effects of temperature fluctuations. Mineral aggregates (the rocks) expand and contract irregularly with increases and decreases in temperature, setting up differential stresses which eventually produce cracks and crevices. In addition to such physical strains must be added the enormous forces of expansion resulting from water freezing in such cracks. Growing roots also frequently exert a prying effect on rock and may aid in some disintegration. Water, ice (glaciers), and wind are additional agents which bring about abrasive action of rock particles upon each other, with smaller and smaller particles resulting from such grinding action. As a result of these physical or mechanical forces, large solid bedrock material is gradually converted to small rock particles.

CHEMICAL PROCESSES OF WEATHERING

Scarcely has the disintegration of rock material begun than its decomposition takes place. Various hydrolyses result in the formation of soluble materials and frequently the slow development of colloidal clays. If organic matter is present, the carbon dioxide and carbonic acid which result greatly increase the rate at which materials dissolve. Through decay and carbon dioxide production, plant and animal residues may exert a much greater influence on soil production than the mechanical effects of growth and burrowing of the organisms themselves. Oxidations, especially of iron-containing rock, result in the weakening and crumbling of the rock. Again, the result of all these forces is to convert bedrock into smaller particles.

SEDENTARY OR RESIDUAL SOIL MATERIAL

These soils have developed from the disintegration and decomposition of parent material (bedrock) in place, with little or no transportation. There tends to be a rather uniform gradation, with the finer particles on top and the coarser ones below. Most residual soils have undergone long periods of intense weathering and may be thoroughly oxidized and leached, especially in warm humid climates. In cooler, drier climates, weathering is less drastic—the Great Plains of the United States would be a good example of this type.

TRANSPORTED SOIL MATERIAL

Those soils which have been moved to new positions by the mechanical forces of nature are frequently subdivided according to the agencies of transportation and deposition.

Colluvial. In soils of this type, the movement has been caused by **gravity;** talus at the foot of slopes, landslides, and mud flows are examples. The soil material formed in this way is usually coarse, has unfavorable physical and chemical characteristics, and is of little importance agriculturally.

Alluvial. When the agent of transport is running water, deposition occurs when the water slows down; such soils are alluvial deposits. The flood plains along the Mississippi River and the delta formed at the mouth of this river are excellent examples of this type of soil; so also are the deltas and flood plains of the Ganges (India), Po (Italy), and Nile (Egypt) Rivers. These deposits are frequently extremely fertile.

Glacial till. Ages ago northern North America, northern and central Europe, and northern Asia were invaded by a succession of great ice sheets, during which time immense **glaciers** pushed outwardly (especially southward), receded, and pushed out again several times. Hills were rounded, valleys were filled, and great masses of rock particles were ground and carried about. When the ice melted away (and the glaciers receded), a mantle of glacial drift remained. Since the interglacial periods were considerably longer than the time during which ice actually overlay the country, plants and animals existed in many areas that were subsequently covered. This resulted in organic debris being mixed in the glacial drift.

Glacial soils are thus quite variable because of the diverse ways by which the debris was laid down (including streams of water issuing from the glaciers), differences in the composition of the original materials, and fluctuations in the grinding action of the ice. In the United States a large area of the northern portions of the Midwest and the Northeast consists of soil deposits associated with glacial ice. Most of these soils are of rather recent development, not much leaching has occurred, and they are quite well suited for agriculture.

Aeolian deposits. The most important **wind-blown** material is termed **loess.** Such soils are found in the central and northwestern United States, in northern France, in northern Argentina, and in the great plains of China. They are generally silty in nature and vary considerably with regard to fertility and productivity, depending upon the climatic conditions existent in different parts of the loessial area.

Many kinds of soil may develop from quite similar parent material because of differences in weathering and transport, in topography (e.g., slope, drainage), in organic accumulation, and in climate. Over long periods of time, even slight differences may have profound effects.

16.3 Soil formation

The disruption of the original silicate minerals paves the way for clay formation. The colloidal clay particles are plate-like and composed of sheet-like molecules held loosely together. The result is a cohesive, porous structure with a tremendously large surface area to which positively charged particles are adsorbed—characteristics which are exceedingly important in relation to soil fertility.

Living organisms bring about an accumulation of organic matter which gradually blends with the mineral matter. The resulting complex mixture with its colloidal properties can now be termed soil. A true soil, then, cannot be formed without the presence and decay of some organic matter; mere physical and chemical weathering is only part of soil formation. The colloidal particles, both clay and organic matter, are quite gelatinous and add much to soil structure, as will be discussed later. Basically, soils are porous aggregates of inorganic particles with an admixture of decaying organic matter in varying amounts.

16.4 Soil texture

The mineral particles of the soil vary greatly in size and quantity, with the larger fragments imbedded in and coated over with colloidal materials of a rather gelatinous nature. The **texture** of a soil refers to the sizes (e.g., coarse, medium, or fine) of the particles that dominate, and soil particles are arbitrarily classified on the basis of their diameter as follows:

Coarse Gravel	Over 5.0 mm.	Fine Sand	0.2–0.02 mm.
Fine Gravel	5.0–2.0 mm.	Silt	0.02–0.002 mm.
Coarse Sand	2.0–0.2 mm.	Clay	Below 0.002 mm.

Soils are named on the basis of a mechanical analysis of the percentage of sand, silt, and clay that they contain. In **sandy soils** the silt and clay particles comprise less than 20 per cent of the material by weight, whereas a **clay soil** contains at least 30 per cent clay particles. The third basic soil group, the **loam** class, is the most important one agriculturally and contains about 50 per cent sand and 50 per cent silt plus clay. For example, a typical loam soil would contain 46 per cent sand, 36 per cent silt, and 18 per cent clay. Various kinds of sandy, loamy, and clayey soils occur in the field, and these groups grade into each other. This results in such terminology as loamy sands, sandy loams, silty clay loams, sandy clays, and silty clays. For our purpose, however, we will consider only the three broad categories first listed and discuss the importance of soil texture to plants. Remember, for our limited discussion, as far as size of particles is concerned, sand is the largest and clay the smallest.

PENETRATION OF AIR AND WATER INTO THE SOIL

The particles which form a soil are not solidly packed together; spaces or channels exist between the individual particles. The larger

Figure 16-1. Soil particles indicating the variations in space between the particles of different sizes, and the development of a crumb structure. **A**: Large particles with large spaces. **B**: Small particles with small spaces. **C**: Small particles grouped into large aggregates forming a crumb structure.

[A]

[B]

[C]

the particles, the larger the spaces between them, and through such channels penetrate air and water. Sandy soils have excellent penetration characteristics, whereas such movements in clayey soils would occur with difficulty because of the extremely tiny channels that exist (Figure 16-1A, B). Rain falling upon a clay soil is mainly lost as runoff, while the rapid penetration in a coarse (sandy) soil might result in water sinking too rapidly to depths below that occupied by roots. All too frequently, the pounding effect of raindrops packs clay particles so tightly together that it is virtually impossible for water to penetrate. This emphasizes the importance of a loam soil with its mixture of sand and clay. Root growth and penetration are also much easier in sandy soils or loams than in clays.

WATER-HOLDING CAPACITY

Water is adsorbed on the surfaces of soil particles as well as being held in small channels as a result of capillary action. Besides having a porous structure, most clays are of colloidal size, and this results in a tremendously large surface-to-volume ratio. One gram of clay probably has at least 500 square feet of surface, which is thousands of times greater than an equivalent weight of sand. Because of this enormous surface, much more water is held in a clay soil, once it is penetrated, than in a sandy soil. Capillary water and a great deal of the adsorbed water is available to plants by absorption through root systems. Clays, then, act as a reservoir of water, greatly decreasing percolation (permeation) losses and retaining water which is later available to plants. The water-holding capacity is lowest in sandy soils, while loams of course are in an intermediate position. Too much water may sometimes be retained in the soil. If a high concentration of clay is present, such a large quantity of water may be held by the soil particles as to saturate the tiny channels of the soil. If this condition persisted for any extended length of time, it would be injurious to plant growth, since it would cause a deficiency of oxygen in the root environment. This is similar to what happens when a soil is flooded. Roots would then grow poorly, if at all, and eventually the tops would suffer.

FERTILITY

186

This term as applied to soils refers to the mineral content of the soil. Just as water is adsorbed to the surfaces of soil particles, so also are

mineral ions (e.g., K^+, Mg^{++}, Ca^{++}, etc.) held to these surfaces. In
this case, clays also act as storehouses of mineral nutrients, greatly retarding the leaching of minerals out of the soil with the water that
drains through. The finer the texture, the greater the general fertility
of that soil. Permanent agriculture on sandy soils is possible only with
constant application of fertilizers, usually in the form of chemicals, to
replenish the supply of minerals. This is especially important when
sandy soils are located in relatively dry areas where irrigation is necessary. The resultant leaching may make necessary the use of such frequent addition of fertilizers that the cost of agriculture becomes pro-
hibitive.

16.5 Soil structure

The general characteristics of a soil are determined not only by the
texture but also by the **structure,** which refers to the arrangement or
grouping of soil particles into aggregates. When the aggregates are
rather porous and relatively small, the soil is considered to have a
granular, or **crumb, structure** which is characteristic of many soils
high in organic matter and is particularly important in land under
cultivation. The soil granule actually consists of a rounded porous mass
of mineral particles of varying sizes bound together by the colloidal
clays and organic matter contained within them. In effect, small soil
particles are lumped together to form larger ones with the result that
a crumb soil has many of the advantageous characteristics of a light
sandy soil plus those of a heavy clayey soil (Figure 16-1C).

IMPORTANCE OF STRUCTURE

The relatively low amounts of inorganic colloidal materials in sandy
soils results in the looseness, good aeration, good drainage, and easy
tillage of such soils. However, they have a very low capacity to hold
water and minerals, which in turn means low soil moisture and a
general lack of fertility. Organic matter will act as a binding material,
will greatly increase the water-holding and mineral-holding capacity,
and will supply minerals as it decays. Heavy clayey soils, on the other
hand, tend to puddle, especially if cultivated when wet. When such
plastic and cohesive soils are cultivated, the spaces between particles
become greatly reduced; when dry, the soil is hard and dense. Though
such soils have excellent water-holding and mineral-holding capacity,
they are very difficult to work and may become almost impervious to
air and water and even roots. As should now be clear, loam soils with
their mixtures of sand, silt (intermediate in characteristics between
sand and clay), and clay have the advantageous characteristics of both

sandy and clayey soils and fewer of the disadvantageous characteristics. The addition of a crumb structure enhances the advantages.

The most important factor in the encouragement of granulation is organic matter, especially humus. It not only binds but also expands, making possible the porosity which is characteristic of soil granules. Decaying plant roots are important sources of organic matter, and the maintenance of a soil in sod is an effective means of promoting granulation. The slimes and other viscous products of micro-organisms, the filaments of fungi—all serve to establish a crumb structure.

HUMUS

All organic matter in the soil is eventually decayed by the activity of various micro-organisms, the bacteria, fungi, and actinomycetes. Cellulose, starch, sugars, proteins, and such compounds are decomposed quite readily, while lignin, oils, fats, resins, mucins, and others are decomposed with difficulty. As a result, the organic material is gradually converted to carbon dioxide, water, simple minerals (e.g., nitrates, sulfates, calcium compounds, phosphates, etc.), and a colloidal complex called **humus.** This last product is a result of enzymatic dissolution of the more resistant organic materials, which then tend to unite with proteins and other nitrogenous compounds.

The complex, amorphous, colloidal condition of humus produces a material whose adsorptive characteristics are far in excess of those exhibited by clay. All of the advantageous aspects of clays are greatly magnified in this converted organic material. The high porosity and low plasticity of humus tends to alleviate the puddling tendency of clays when the two are mixed. A small amount of humus has physical effects on the soil in excess of its proportionate amount. The addition of organic material to the soil, then, has tremendous advantages: it increases granulation, water-holding capacity, and mineral-holding capacity, and it is a source of minerals.

Because organic material is so extremely important in a soil, plowing under of grass is much preferred to burning. To utilize grass clippings and leaves in forming a **compost pile** is also advisable. A compost is commonly made of alternate layers of vegetable matter, soil, and manure. The pile should be kept moist, and the addition of phosphate will aid in the formation of an effective fertilizer. Bacterial action rapidly decomposes the mass, but occasional turning aids decomposition. After some months, compost may be spread over the surface or, preferably, disced into the ground. Manures, of course, also are excellent as soil additives. Organic increments are the major sources of nitrogen and phosphates, in addition to improving the physical characteristics of the soil.

SOIL ORGANISMS

The source of the organic material which is converted to humus is the great variety of living organisms found in the soil—their secretions and excretions while living, and their tissues when they die. In some instances portions of the organism, but not the entire individual, may die. The sloughing off of root cap cells, the sloughing off of bark, and the dropping of leaves, fruits, and twigs are good examples of this. Most of the organic matter consists of plants and their products, with a much smaller proportion contributed by animals.

In addition to the roots and underground stems of the vascular plants, many other kinds of plants live in the soil. The most important are the bacteria, followed in importance by the molds. Enormous numbers of bacteria may be present, as many as five billion per gram of soil, but they are so small (seldom exceeding 4 to 5 microns in diameter, or about $\frac{1}{5000}$ of an inch) that their presence is not apparent except through their activity. Further discussion of bacterial decay processes will be encountered in Chapter 20; mold decay activity is discussed in Chapter 21.

Many animals contribute to the humus of a soil when they die, but in addition to this, many of them are more actively involved in the formation of soil structure. Ants, beetles, millipedes, sowbugs, slugs, and snails utilize much undecomposed plant tissue as food, and their feces contribute to humus; further decomposition is carried on by bacteria and molds. Burrowing animals (e.g., gophers, ground squirrels, prairie dogs, moles) may be undesirable as far as agricultural practices are concerned, but their burrows serve to aerate and drain the land, and they may transfer considerable quantities of soil. One of the most important animals in the soil is the earthworm. The number of earthworms varies with the amount of organic material available to them for food; some soils may have over one million per acre. Several tons of earth may pass through their bodies during the year, and such turning and passage greatly influences soil structure. The mucus secretions and the grinding action within the digestive tract of the earthworm result in the familiar "casts" which surround the earthworm holes. These are examples of the granular condition that results from earthworm activity. The holes left in the soil serve to increase aeration and drainage.

While any one group of animals is probably unimportant in organic transfers or humus formation, the total mass becomes highly significant even if considered only on the basis of contributing at death to the accumulation of decomposable tissue.

189

Summary

1. The soils in which plants grow consist of mixtures of mineral materials, organic matter, water, and air in varying proportions. The small fragments of mineral materials are derived from solid rock by long periods of mechanical and chemical weathering. The organic matter consists of living organisms, their secretions and excretions, and their decay products. Mixing of the various soil components is a result of the activity of wind, water, glaciers, gravity, and the vertical shiftings of the earth's crust.

2. The texture of a soil refers to the sizes of the particles which predominate, and soils are classified on the basis of an arbitrary scale of particle sizes. Since particle sizes vary gradually from one extreme to another, no sharp line of distinction can be drawn; thus a great variety of soil types exists. However, the texture of a soil determines the qualities of air and water penetration, water-holding capacity, and fertility. In general, penetration of air, water, and roots occurs much more readily through soils in which large particles (sand) dominate. On the other hand, water-holding capacity and fertility characteristics are mainly a result of the small particles (silt and clay).

3. Soil structure refers to the arrangement or grouping of soil particles into aggregates as a result of the binding characteristics of colloidal clays and organic matter. A soil with a granular or crumb structure has many of the advantages of both sandy and clayey soils.

4. When organic matter is added to a soil, it is gradually converted by micro-organisms to carbon dioxide, water, minerals, and a colloidal complex called humus. A small amount of humus has advantageous physical effects on the soil far in excess of its proportionate amount.

5. Basically, a soil which is conducive to the good growth of plants consists of a mixture of sand, silt, clay, and organic matter that exhibits the advantages, and not the disadvantages, of each particle.

REVIEW TOPICS AND QUESTIONS

1. Explain why soil B is more productive than soils A and C, even though they all receive the same amount of rainfall, light, and temperature.

Particles	Soil A	Soil B	Soil C
Sand	80%	50%	5%
Clay	5%	20%	90%
Organic matter	1%	4%	4%

2. Briefly discuss the development of a loam soil.
3. Soil is composed of mineral particles (ranging in size from coarse sand to colloidal) and organic matter in process of decomposition. Discuss how variation in amounts of these constituents affects each of the following: (a) fertility, (b) water-holding capacity, and (c) aeration.

4. What are the advantages of using compost or manures rather than chemical fertilizers? What are the advantages of using the latter rather than the former?
5. List the agencies which may be involved in transporting soils from place to place.
6. List five animals that contribute to soil formation, and indicate how each functions.

SUGGESTED READINGS

Fuller, H. J., and O. Tippo. *College Botany.* New York: Holt, 1954.

Kellog, C. E. "Soil," *Scientific American,* 183 (July 1950), 30–39.

Lyon, T. L., and H. O. Buckman. *The Nature and Properties of Soils.* New York: Macmillan, 1946.

Swanson, C. L. W. "Soil Conditioners," *Scientific American,* 189 (July 1953), 36–38.

CHAPTER 17 ❧

Inheritance

and Variation

THE basic vegetative structures and nutritional aspects of the flow-ering plant have been discussed in previous chapters. Now, before discussing reproduction of any plant group, we will attempt to arrive at an understanding of inheritance and the importance of sexual repro-duction in general. Then we will delve into the plant kingdom, cover-ing reproduction in the various groups as we encounter them. This seems to be an advisable means of approaching the plant groups, since reproductive structures form the basis for all modern systems of classi-fication and can also be used to demonstrate evolutionary advances.

17.1 Meiosis

During sexual reproduction, when **gametes** (sex cells: egg and sperm in flowering plants) unite, two sets of chromosomes are combined, thus doubling the chromosome number of the fertilized egg over that of the unfertilized egg. Without any mechanism for reducing the chro-mosome number, a doubling would occur each generation. This does not happen; the number of chromosomes is usually constant for each type or species of plant or animal: corn, 20; pine tree, 24; housefly, 12; fruit fly, 8; man, 46.[1] Every corn plant has 20 chromosomes, no matter how many generations are examined. Therefore, at some time after fertilization and before the next fertilization, or once each gen-eration, a reduction in chromosome number is accomplished. The rather interesting type of cell division which accomplishes this reduc-tion is **meiosis.**

[1] Until recently, man was thought to have 48 chromosomes. More delicate techniques have shown that the number is actually 46.

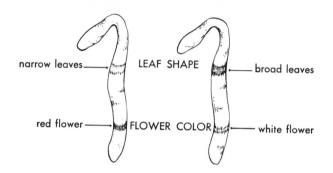

narrow leaves — LEAF SHAPE — broad leaves

red flower — FLOWER COLOR — white flower

Figure 17-1. Homologous chromosomes. They are alike in size, shape, and in the characteristics which are controlled. They may be unlike, as in the diagram, in the way in which these characteristics are controlled.

Note that each example listed in the foregoing paragraph had an even number of chromosomes. This is not a coincidence. Chromosomes occur in pairs in most organisms, and the members of a pair are **homologous chromosomes,** or **homologs.** Such homologous chromosomes are both alike *and* different. As indicated in Figure 17-1, they are alike in size, shape, and in the characteristics which are controlled, but they may be unlike in the way in which these characteristics are controlled. For example, leaves may be broad or narrow; the characteristic is leaf shape, which is governed by a **gene** at a specific location on the chromosome. In general, one member of a pair of chromosomes comes from the female parent (egg), and the other homolog comes from the male parent (sperm). The organism thus is **diploid** (has two sets of chromosomes). Some organisms (such as many algae and fungi) have only one set and are **haploid.** All organisms that reproduce sexually have both haploid and diploid phases, but the emphasis (i.e., the majority of cells of an organism) is usually haploid *or* diploid, most often diploid. All of the more complex plants and animals are diploid: trees, man, ferns, fish, flowering plants, cats, dogs, etc. In these organisms the haploid condition occurs in only a few cells or structures.

Meiosis (Figure 17-2) is similar to mitosis (Section 2.3) but differs in some important respects. Much of prophase occurs as during mitosis,

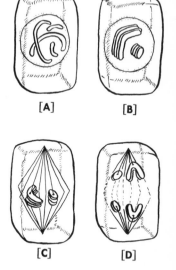

[A]   [B]

[C]   [D]

Figure 17-2. Meiosis. **A:** Early prophase I. **B:** Late prophase I; synapsis has occurred and tetrads of chromatids are present. **C:** Metaphase I. **D:** Anaphase I; the homologous chromosomes are separating, but not the chromatids. **E:** Telophase I. **F:** Metaphase II. **G:** Anaphase II; chromatids are separating. **H:** Haploid spores resulting from meiosis.

      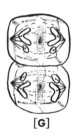   

[E]   [F]   [G]   [H]

but the homologous chromosomes pair in meiosis. This pairing, or **synapsis,** which takes place much like closing a zipper, is quite precise along the entire length of the chromosomes. If part of a chromo-

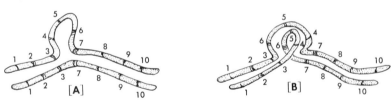

Figure 17-3. Loop formation during synapsis. Double chromatids are not shown. **A:** The type when part of one chromosome is missing. **B:** The type when part of one chromosome is inverted.

some is missing, the homolog forms a loop (Figure 17-3A); if one part is inverted, the homolog forms a different kind of loop (Figure 17-3B). This indicates that the genes must be strongly attracted to one another. As in mitosis, the chromosomes double, and four chromatids are actually present during synapsis; this is sometimes called the **tetrad** stage (Figure 17-2B).

The chromosomes migrate to the central region of the cell (metaphase I), and then the *homologous chromosomes separate* (anaphase I). The centromeres (kinetochores) have not yet duplicated, and the chromatids do *not* separate. This is very different from mitosis, and the result is that different kinds of chromosomes occur in the two groups, which are moving to the opposite poles of the cells (Figure 17-2D). In mitosis the two groups are duplicates of one another. Telophase I is the same as telophase in mitosis, although the second cellular division may occur with only a short interphase or no interphase. In some cases cytokinesis may not take place until both nuclear divisions have occurred.

During metaphase II (Figure 17-2F) the chromosomes usually line up at right angles to that of the first division. The centromeres have now duplicated, and the *chromatids separate* during anaphase II. The second division of meiosis results in four haploid cells, called spores (Figure 17-2H). These spores are quantitatively and qualitatively *different* from the original cell. They have half the number of chromosomes as the original cell, and the spores are not all genetically alike.

Figure 17-4 represents a more diagrammatic view of meiosis to emphasize the way in which the two pairs of chromosomes may line up at metaphase I. The letters on the chromosomes represent genes; **A** and **a** govern the same characteristic but in contrasting ways (e.g., broad vs. narrow leaves), and the same is true of **B** and **b** (red vs. white flower color). The alignment of chromosomes is determined purely by chance and may be as in the diagram at the left or as in that at the right. The haploid spores, then, will have a genetic component which is also determined by this chance arrangement. The spores may contain large **A**'s and **B**'s, or small **a**'s and **b**'s, as diagrammed at the bottom left. The other arrangement results in spores which contain large **A** and small **b**, or small **a** and large **B**. Since quite a few cells are undergoing meiosis at the same time, the four possible kinds of spores (**AB, ab, Ab,** and **aB**) occur at about equal frequency—like the results of flipping a coin. If three pairs of chromosomes are present, they can line up in four different ways (Figure 17-5), and eight kinds

Figure 17-4. The possible alignments of two pairs of chromosomes during meiosis, and the haploid conditions that result. Only chromosomes are shown; no other structures are represented. In this situation there are two possible alignments at metaphase I—the left and right arrangements in the diagram. If the alignment is as at the left, the haploid condition shown in the two lower-left bracketed diagrams is the result. The haploid condition shown in the two groups at the lower-right result if the alignment happens to be as indicated at the right in metaphase I. The four possible kinds of haploid cells are produced in approximately equal numbers.

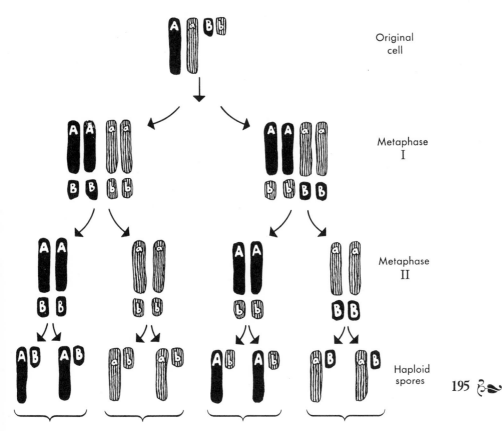

195

(1)   A A a a   A A a a   a a A A   a a A A
      B B b b   B B b b   B B b b   B B b b
      C C c c   c c C C   C C c c   c c C C

(2)   A B C   A B c   a B C   a B c
      and   and   and   and
      a b c   a b C   A b c   A b C

Figure 17-5. Possible alignment of three pairs of chromosomes and the haploid conditions which result. In (1) the letters represent the chromatids at metaphase I; in (2) the letters represent chromosomes after telophase II. There are eight possible kinds of haploid combinations.

of spores can be produced (**ABC, abc, ABc, abC, aBC, Abc, aBc,** and **AbC**). With each additional pair of chromosomes, the number of ways of lining up is doubled. Thus, the number of possible haploid cells is 2^n, where n = the number of pairs of chromosomes.[2] Human cells have 46 chromosomes, or 23 pairs, resulting in 2^{23}, or approximately 10,000,000, kinds of haploid cells (2 multiplied by itself 23 times). Remember that, even with all the different ways of lining up, each haploid cell has a complete set of chromosomes containing one of every kind of gene (one of each letter). Eventually in plants the spores develop into sex cells (egg or sperm), which are haploid. In humans and other animals, meiosis results directly in the production of egg or sperm, by-passing the spore stage.

17.2   Significance of Meiosis

During this type of division, the cell divides twice, while the chromosomes double only once. In the first division of the cell the homologous pairs of chromosomes separate. The chromatids separate in the second division. The products are quite different from the original cell. When the many different kinds of haploid gametes re-combine during fertilization, the resultant diploid cells may vary greatly from each other and from the originals. This is one of the most important features of sexual reproduction—the production of variants. These variations depend upon random alignments of chromosomes during meiosis.

17.3   Chromosome duplication

Although we are certain that chromosomes, and thus genes, are duplicated when a cell divides, the exact mechanism involved in such

[2] Actually, n = the number of *heterozygous* pairs, but this will be discussed later (Section 17.9).

duplication is not known. Recent investigations, however, have suggested a possible answer based upon the molecular components of chromosomes.

The principal constituents of chromosomes are **proteins** and **nucleic acids,** combined as **nucleoproteins,** the nucleic acid fraction being the key in the transmission of hereditary characteristics from cell to succeeding cells. Nucleic acids are long sequences of **nucleotides,** just as proteins are long sequences of amino acids, and have two forms: **ribose nucleic acid (RNA),** which occurs mainly in the cytoplasm, although it is apparently synthesized in the nucleus, and **deoxyribose nucleic acid (DNA),** found in the chromosomes. The nucleotides of DNA consist of a phosphoric acid group, P, tied to the sugar, ribose, S, which is bound to one of four different nitrogenous bases, designated by the numerals 1 through 4. Figure 17-6 represents a portion of the DNA molecule. This molecule is very long and has an enormously great number of possible sequences of nucleotides, even though they differ only in which of the four nitrogenous bases are involved. The molecule consists of two parallel portions, formed of phosphate and sugar groups, which are held together by weak hydrogen bonds between bases 1 and 4 or 2 and 3; no bonds form between 1 and 2, 1 and 3, 2 and 4, or 3 and 4. The parallel portions actually twist around in a spiral fashion, or a helix, but they have been shown untwisted for clarity. The pattern of 1—4 and 2—3 bonds apparently determines the characteristics of an organism.

DNA has been extracted from one bacterial type and used to change the hereditary characteristics of a second bacterial type; the second type

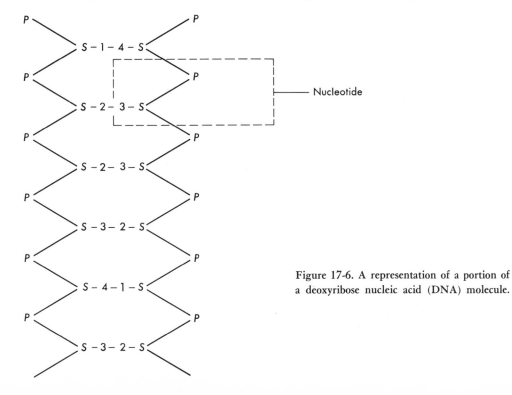

Figure 17-6. A representation of a portion of a deoxyribose nucleic acid (DNA) molecule.

was converted to the first type. This experiment, plus the structural determination of DNA, has opened the door to tremendous advances in the study of inheritance—advances which geneticists are now pursuing with great eagerness.

With this knowledge of DNA structure and its importance in governing the development of organisms, a very interesting suggestion has been made as to the possible mechanism of chromosome duplication. The bonds between the nitrogenous bases are weak and easily broken, as represented in Figure 17-7, giving rise to "half-chains" of DNA. Present within the cell, floating around in the cell "soup," are many nucleotide building blocks which are synthesized by enzymes within the cell. Whenever nucleotide P-S-1 collides with the P-S-4 nucleotide portion of the half-chain, a bond forms; the same thing occurs when P-S-4 collides with P-S-1, P-S-3 with P-S-2, or P-S-2 with P-S-3. No other bonds form; if P-S-1 collides with the P-S-2 portion, no reaction takes place. Each half-chain gradually accumulates an exact replica of the half-chain from which it separated, and, as a result, two DNA molecules—exactly alike and the same as the original—are formed and replace the original one.

A "mistake" in copying as DNA duplicates could cause the resultant cells to be quite different from the original cell, because the DNA would be different. For example, if a P-S-4 ends up next to a P-S-2, no bond will form, but the half-chains may be kept together by all of the *other* bonds between them. In this case the mistake is not sufficiently great so as to result in death. When the next duplication occurs, the "mistake" is perpetuated, and differences in subsequent cells may sometimes be apparent as variations in basic characteristics. (See Section 27.11 for a discussion of mutations.)

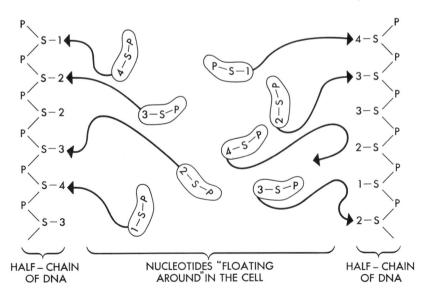

HALF–CHAIN
OF DNA

NUCLEOTIDES "FLOATING
AROUND" IN THE CELL

HALF–CHAIN
OF DNA

Figure 17-7. Possible mechanism of DNA duplication. The bonds between the nitrogenous bases (designated by numbers 1 through 4) have broken, giving rise to "half-chains" of DNA. The nucleotide building blocks are shown attaching to these half-chains. Exact duplicates accumulate, and two DNA molecules result.

17.4 Gene function

Specific locations on chromosomes have long been known to govern certain characteristics of organisms. These loci are termed **genes,** and as the chromosome duplicates, so also are each of the genes duplicated. We are not yet certain whether a chromosome consists of a single exceedingly long DNA molecule (combined with a protein to form a nucleoprotein), in which case the gene is a small portion of this complex molecule, or whether the genes are DNA molecules linked together to form the chromosome. (In either case DNA is what determines development.)

From the experimental data available, the most logical explanation concerning gene function involves the influence of genes (and DNA) on protein synthesis. The enzymes, which govern all of the metabolic reactions of the cells are proteins; thus, the kinds of proteins which are produced determine the activities and development of an organism. Genes govern the activities which can occur in a cell, but remember that the environment many times influences what actually does occur. For example, a green plant is capable of carrying on photosynthesis, provided that carbon dioxide and other essentials are available to it, but, as indicated in the chapter on mineral nutrition, if certain minerals are not available, chlorophyll will not develop. When one speaks of genes governing the development of an organism, one really means the potential development—for such development to occur, the environment must also be suitable.

In recent years more and more evidence has accumulated which indicates that the DNA molecules of the nucleus act as templates which determine the order in which the nucleotides of RNA are arranged. The smaller **soluble RNA** molecules accumulate mainly in the nucleolus, while the larger **messenger RNA** molecules migrate from the nucleus to the ribosomes on the endoplasmic reticulum. Eventually the soluble RNA molecules move to the cytoplasm and form combinations with amino acids; the coding of the soluble RNA, which was established by the nuclear DNA, determines which amino acid will combine with a particular RNA molecule.[3] The soluble RNA portion of this complex will fit only one portion of the larger messenger RNA, in which the coding is a duplication of the nucleotide arrangement of the chromosomal DNA. As a result, the various soluble RNA molecules, each carrying a specific kind of amino acid, line up along the messenger RNA molecule in an order determined by the coding of the latter. Once assembled in this specific orientation, the amino acids

---

[3] Before such a combination can occur, the amino acid must react with ATP. This is another example of the importance of the ubiquitous ATP molecules.

become linked and then separate from the RNA molecules. Various additional cross-linkages, spirals, and cyclic arrangements of the amino acids may take place in the formation of a complex protein molecule.

To summarize: The DNA of the genes (or chromosomes) determines the coding of the soluble RNA molecules. This in turn determines which amino acids will combine with the soluble RNA. The coding of the messenger RNA determines the order of alignment of the soluble RNA molecules with their attached amino acids and thus determines the orientation of amino acids with respect to one another. The alignment of amino acids determines the specific protein (enzyme) which is formed. Since enzymes govern the metabolic activities of the cell, the genes effectively determine what these activities will be. The actual appearance of an organism results from the cooperative activity of individual cells.

17.5 Sexual and asexual reproduction

Sexual reproduction involves both meiosis and fusion of gametes. Due to meiosis, the gametes and offspring are highly variable. This is very desirable as a survival factor. Some of the offspring may be better suited to the environment than are the parental types, the environment may change and then be more favorable for the offspring, or the offspring may be more capable of existing in a new environment to which they may have migrated. Our whole concept of evolutionary change has, as part of its foundation, the occurrence of variations as a result of sexual reproduction.

Asexual reproduction by-passes both meiosis and fusion of gametes. The new plant is formed directly from a fragment or an extension of the old plant. The rooting of stem cuttings, the production of new plants by Bermuda grass (*Cynodon dactylon*) and strawberry (*Fragaria virginiana*) from runners, and new plants developing from bulbs and corms—all are examples of asexual (non-sexual) reproduction. The resultant plants are genetically like the original, and no variations are possible. In the long run—in terms of evolutionary ages—asexual reproduction alone would be detrimental to most plants under natural conditions, because the biggest source of variations is eliminated. Often, of course, desirable varieties of cultivated plants are propagated vegetatively (asexually) to maintain uniformity (e.g., citrus, avocado, roses, etc.), but this is an artificial situation.

17.6 Genetics

Prior to 1900 nothing was known about chromosomes and genes. Really scientific, carefully devised experiments were not carried out, and this led to the general impression that inheritance worked in a "blending" fashion—that is, that the traits of the parents are blended together in the offspring, like mixing colors of paint. Casual observation would indicate that this is true. However, the work of Gregor Mendel, published in 1866, was to blaze a path away from this idea of blending and toward the concept of "particulate inheritance." Interestingly enough, this work was almost completely ignored until about 1900, when the study of chromosomes and genes presented a mechanism which clarified Mendel's ideas. Thus, though Mendel is conceded to have established the foundations of **genetics,** this study of inheritance and variation can be considered to be a new science, because most of the enormous amount of investigations included in this term have been carried on since only about 1900.

MENDEL'S EXPERIMENTS

Gregor Mendel (1822–1884) was an Augustinian monk who had actually trained to be a biology teacher. He was interested in growing plants and seeing how hereditary characteristics were transmitted. Others had had this interest also, but Mendel made several fantastically shrewd decisions. First of all, he thought of studying the inheritance of one character at a time—one variable. This had not been done before. Also he had allowed plants to self-pollinate and observed that each produced offspring of its own kind. For example, in the garden pea plant with which he worked, Mendel found that one strain grew to a height of six to seven feet, while the plants of another strain grew only to one or two feet in height.

Mendel crossed a tall plant, which was a descendant of a long line of tall plants, with a short plant, which was a descendant of a long line of short plants. This was easily accomplished by transferring the pollen from one plant to another. The egg and sperm are from different plants and unite during fertilization, to produce the **zygote,** or fertilized egg. The offspring, therefore, will receive genes from both parents by way of the gametes. If the blending idea of inheritance was accurate, the progeny of this mating would all be intermediate in height. In the next section we shall discuss in detail the results which Mendel obtained.

17.7 Monohybrid cross

When the mating, or cross, is made between parents differing in a single character, it is termed a **monohybrid cross.** One such cross is that under discussion, as originally performed by Mendel. The first generation offspring, commonly termed the F_1 or First Filial Generation (filial: pertaining to son or daughter), were *all* tall plants. No intermediate or short plants were produced. Mendel continued by self-fertilizing or self-pollinating the F_1 (most plants have bi-sexual flowers) and discovered that the F_2 (second generation) contained both tall and short plants but again no plants of intermediate height.

From his results Mendel deduced that both the tall and the short trait must have been present in the F_1, since the F_2 consisted of both types. He also counted the large number of offspring and realized that he was getting approximately three-fourths tall plants and one-fourth short plants in the F_2 (Figure 17-8). Mendel suggested that these

Figure 17-8

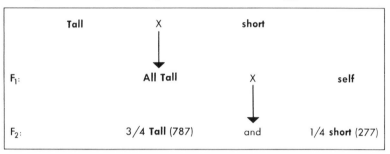

observations could be explained by making two simple assumptions. First, he assumed that each trait (e.g., plant height) is determined by a "factor" and that these factors occur in pairs (e.g., tall vs. short). Second, when gametes are formed, the two factors are separated from one another. These conclusions were based upon observations of the results of his experiments plus sound reasoning. Remember that he knew nothing of meiosis, genes, or chromosomes—no one did at that time. We now call these factors **genes,** and they are usually symbolized by the use of letters. **T** can represent Tallness, while the contrasting, but related, characteristic of shortness can be indicated by **t.**

Because the original tall plants always gave rise to tall plants when self-pollinated, they must have contained genes **TT.** Similar reasoning indicates that the short plants should be designated as **tt.** These genes are on homologous chromosomes, which separate during meiosis (Section 17.1), and the haploid gametes each contains only one of the genes (Figure 17-9). The F_1 tall plants must have both tall and short

Figure 17-9

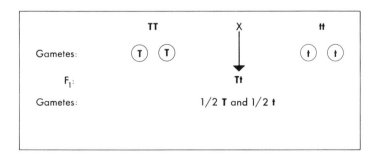

factors, or **Tt,** and the F_1 gametes are of two kinds, because the homologous chromosomes would again separate during meiosis. Since only the tall characteristic shows up when both tall and short factors are present, tallness is said to be *dominant* over short, and the gene for shortness is *recessive.*

When the F_1 plants are self-fertilized, the eggs and sperm combine at *random,* like flipping two coins at the same time and counting how many times the various combinations appear—two heads, two tails, or one head plus one tail. Each coin will come down heads one-half of the time and tails one-half of the time; the probability is that for each coin heads (or tails) will show up one chance out of every two. The larger the total number of tosses, the closer one gets to the theoretical 1:1 ratio. If a coin were tossed only four times, three heads and one tail or even four of one kind would not be too surprising. However, for 1,000 tosses to result in 900 heads and 100 tails, or even 700 to 300, is extremely unlikely. More probably, the 1,000 tosses would come close to a 500:500 ratio—one actual count resulted in a 497:503 ratio. This is, of course, one reason that it was important for Mendel to count large numbers of progeny.

In the foregoing paragraph only one coin at a time was considered. Suppose the two coins are tossed together? What is the probability of *both* landing heads? When two events take place, each having a similar possible result, and if one doesn't influence the other, the two separate probabilities are multiplied together to find the probability that both will happen simultaneously. In other words each coin will land heads one-half of the times; they will both land heads ½ × ½, or one-fourth of the times. Also, they will both turn up tails one-fourth of the times, and one tail plus one head will occur two-fourths (or one-half) of the times.[4]

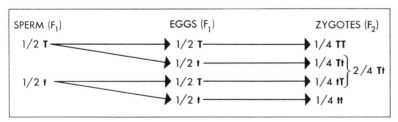

Figure 17-10

Now let us return to the F_1 tall plants which Mendel caused to be self-fertilized. One-half of the sperm contain **T** and one-half contain **t,** one-half of the eggs contain **T** and one-half contain **t,** and the fusion

[4] To verify this figure of one-half, toss a penny and a nickel, so that one coin can be distinguished from the other. One-fourth of the times, the penny will be heads and the nickel will be tails; another one-fourth of the times, the penny will be tails and the nickel will be heads (½ × ½ = ¼). In each of these cases there is one head and one tail: ¼ + ¼ = 2/4, or ½.

of egg and sperm occurs at random. Either one of the two kinds of sperm may fuse with either one of the two kinds of eggs (Figure 17-10). As was indicated by the appearance of the F_1 progeny, tallness is dominant to shortness, and any plant containing at least one **T** would be tall. The F_2 zygotes in the above would give rise to plants three-fourths of which would be tall and one-fourth of which would be short. This is exactly what Mendel observed. His actual count in one experiment was 787 tall and 277 short, whereas 798:266 would be an exact ¾ : ¼ (or 3:1) ratio. However, a 3:1 ratio fits these and many other experimental results more accurately than does any other simple ratio. Also, the more offspring, the closer the figures are to the theoretical ratio.

We can now diagram the complete series of crosses—as shown in Figure 17-11. All of the tall plants in the F_2 looked alike, but Mendel

Figure 17-11

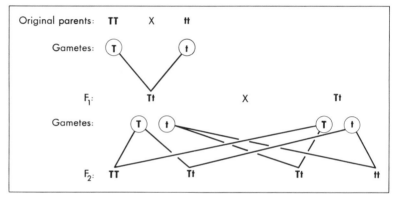

found that one-third of them (**TT**) produced only tall progeny when self-fertilized, while two-thirds of them (**Tt**) produced three-fourths tall plants and one-fourth short plants (just as had the F_1). The short plants produced only short plants when self-fertilized.

Frequent use is made of the Punnett square, or checkerboard, in diagramming crosses between individuals. In this method the kinds of eggs are written across the top line and the kinds of sperm down the first column. The squares are then filled in by carrying the letter symbols down each column and across each row. The two letters in each square thus represent the possible kinds of progeny (F_2) that may result from self-pollinating the F_1 (Figure 17-12).

Figure 17-12

SPERM \ EGG	T	t
T	TT	Tt
t	Tt	tt

In order to understand fully the inheritance of characteristics, one must be completely familiar with meiosis. The following diagrams represent the diploid condition and the important phases of meiosis which result in the formation of haploid structures in the aforementioned monohybrid cross. Remember that Mendel started with pure strains. The plants were **true-breeders;** tall plants always gave rise to tall plants, and short plants always gave rise to short plants. Therefore, one parent plant had **T** on both homologous chromosomes, and the other parent plant had **t** on both homologous chromosomes (Figure 17-13).

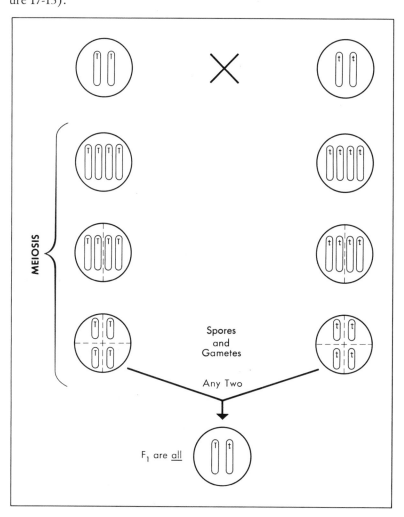

Figure 17-13

In plants, meiosis results in the production of haploid spores which eventually give rise to gametes by mitotic divisions. The gametes and the spores from which they arose are thus genetically alike.

The F₁ plants are then self-pollinated or self-fertilized. Actually, since all of the F₁ plants are alike in this case, they could be cross-pollinated. The F₂ should be the same in either case (Figure 17-14).

Figure 17-14

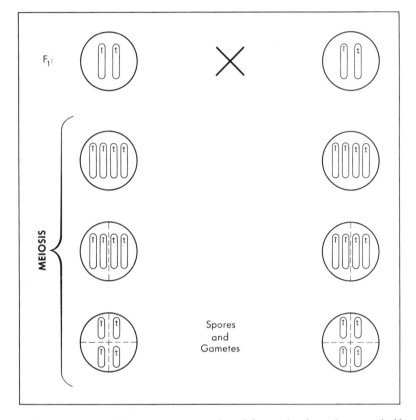

Many spores and gametes are produced by each plant, but one-half are **T** and one-half are **t.** As mentioned previously, either one of the two kinds of sperm may fuse with either one of the two kinds of eggs, and this fusion occurs at random (Figure 17-15).

Figure 17-15

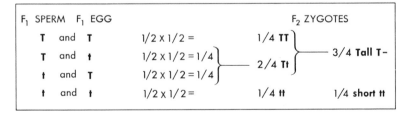

Three-fourths of the F₂ generation have at least one **T** gene and are tall (**T** is dominant), while one-fourth have both recessive factors (**tt**) and are short. The larger the number of offspring, the closer the actual ratio is to the theoretical one.

17.8 Test cross

In appearance a **TT** plant is the same as a **Tt** one. In order to determine the gene make-up, a test cross is frequently made. One of the F_2 tall individuals is crossed with (fertilized by) a short plant. The latter is selected because both genes of the pair must be **t** for the recessive short characteristic to appear; the short plant must be **tt.**

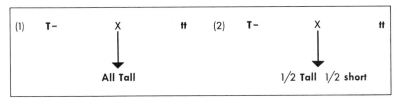

In the first instance the tall plant must have had two **T** genes. (Why?) In the second instance the tall plant must have had one **T** gene and one **t** gene. (Why?)

When such a test cross is made utilizing the tall F_2 plants under discussion, one-third of them are shown to be **TT** and two-thirds are **Tt**. The same result is obtained, of course, if we self-pollinate (self-fertilize) the F_2 plants. All those that breed true (i.e., produce only tall offspring) must have been **TT**. Again one finds that one-third of all the tall F_2 plants are **TT**.

17.9 Useful terms

In discussing inheritance and variations, several terms are quite useful. Some of these have already been mentioned. An individual is **homozygous** if the genes in any given pair are alike (**TT** or **tt**), and **heterozygous** if they are not alike (**Tt**). The term **allele** refers to one of a pair of unlike genes, **T** or **t**. Every organism has more than one pair of genes and may be homozygous for some characteristics and heterozygous for others. The common practice is to term an individual heterozygous (or a **hybrid**) if even only one pair of genes is not alike.

A **dominant** factor is the one of a contrasting pair of genes which is expressed and masks the other when both are present. A **recessive** factor, then, is masked and not expressed when both are present. A **Tt** pea plant is tall because the dominant factor, **T**, masks the recessive factor, **t**. The external appearance (tall or short, for example) of an individual is its **phenotype;** the genetic make-up of an individual is termed its **genotype.** Thus, two plants may have the same phenotype (e.g., tall) but different genotypes (**TT** and **Tt**). Of course, many examples show no dominance. For example, some four o'clock plants (*Mirabilis jalapa*) have white flowers and others have red flowers. If these two plants are crossed, the F_1 all has pink flowers; the F_2 consists of all three types of individuals (i.e., white-flowered, pink-flowered, and red-flowered). This situation, where the F_1 is intermediate in the characteristic, is termed **incomplete dominance, partial dominance,** or **lack of dominance.** However, most cases in which the progeny are intermediate between the parents are due to multiple genes (Section 17.15).

17.10 Dihybrid cross

Two or more independently inherited traits may occur in various combinations in an organism. Again we may turn to an experiment by Mendel to discover whether two pairs of contrasting characteristics are inherited independently and whether Mendel's ideas of factors and simple ratios are suitable explanations.

Mendel crossed a pea plant that always produced dominant yellow round seeds **(YYRR)** with one which produced recessive green wrinkled seeds **(yyrr).** The resultant seeds were all yellow round; the F_1 were heterozygous for both pairs of genes **(YyRr),** or dihybrids, with the dominant characteristics masking the recessive ones (Figure 17-16).

Figure 17-16

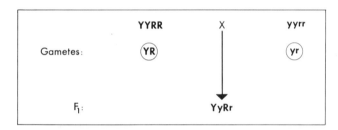

The F_1 were allowed to self-pollinate, and Mendel found that four kinds of seeds were produced: approximately $\frac{9}{16}$ yellow round, $\frac{3}{16}$ yellow wrinkled, $\frac{3}{16}$ green round, and $\frac{1}{16}$ green wrinkled.[5] In examining each trait by itself, one finds that there are $\frac{12}{16}$ yellow and $\frac{4}{16}$ green, $\frac{12}{16}$ round and $\frac{4}{16}$ wrinkled. In both cases the results (really $\frac{3}{4}$ to $\frac{1}{4}$) are what could be expected from a monohybrid cross (see Section 17.7), which demonstrates that single-factor ratios are maintained during such a dihybrid cross. Obviously, then, the two pairs of genes segregate independently of one another. This is termed **independent segregation,** or **random assortment** of genes. The way the **Y**'s separate has nothing to do with the way the **R**'s separate, because they are on different chromosomes. However, since homologous chromosomes do separate, the haploid cell (gamete in this case) cannot

---

[5] The exact figures in one of Mendel's experiments were 315, 101, 108, and 32 (total 556). This is very nearly a 9:3:3:1 ratio.

contain two **Y**'s or two **R**'s, but only *one of each*. Whether the capital letters or small letters are present in a gamete (i.e., **YR**, **Yr**, **yR**, or **yr**) depends upon the alignment of chromosomes during metaphase I of meiosis. (See Section 17.1 and Figure 17-4 for a more complete explanation.)

F₁: YyRr   X   YyRr

Gametes: (YR) (Yr) (yR) (yr)   (YR) (Yr) (yR) (yr)

Figure 17-17

SPERM \ EGG	YR	Yr	yR	yr
YR	YYRR	YYRr	YyRR	YyRr
Yr	YYRr	YYrr	YyRr	Yyrr
yR	YyRR	YyRr	yyRR	yyRr
yr	YyRr	Yyrr	yyRr	yyrr

Although only four kinds of gametes are involved, they combine entirely at random. (See Figure 17-17.) The four-letter symbols in the checkerboard thus represent the possible kinds of progeny that could be expected in the F₂. The larger the number of progeny, the closer the ratio approaches 9:3:3:1. This is the phenotypic ratio, whereas the symbols in the Punnett square represent the genotypes. A difference between phenotype and genotype merely means that dominance is involved.

Because the pairs of genes segregate independently, the computation is made simpler by considering each characteristic alone and then combining the ratios. Refer to Section 17.7, and treat each trait as a monohybrid cross. The heterozygous yellow-seeded individual will produce three-fourths yellow seeds and one-fourth green seeds when self-pollinated; the heterozygous round-seeded individual will produce three-fourths round seeds and one-fourth wrinkled seeds. This is considering the F₂ in terms of one trait at a time (Figure 17-18).

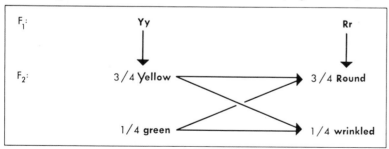

Figure 17-18

Now, to determine how many of the F₂ seeds will be *both* yellow *and* round, the two ratios are combined as indicated: ¾ yellow × ¾ round equals $\frac{9}{16}$ yellow round seeds. Other possible combinations are also indicated in Figure 17-19.

Figure 17-19

F_2:

$3/4 \times 3/4 = 9/16$ **Yellow Round**
$3/4 \times 1/4 = 3/16$ **Yellow wrinkled**
$1/4 \times 3/4 = 3/16$ **green Round**
$1/4 \times 1/4 = 1/16$ **green wrinkled**

$\Big\}$ 9:3:3:1

In the foregoing, only the phenotypes are considered. The genotypes can be determined in a similar fashion by indicating the heterozygous condition of some of the round seeds and yellow seeds. The heterozygous yellow-seeded individual will produce one-fourth homozygous yellow-seeded, two-fourths (or one-half) heterozygous yellow-seeded, and one-fourth homozygous green-seeded individuals when self-pollinated. Similar reasoning is used for the heterozygous round-seeded individual (Figure 17-20). In order to determine how many of the

Figure 17-20

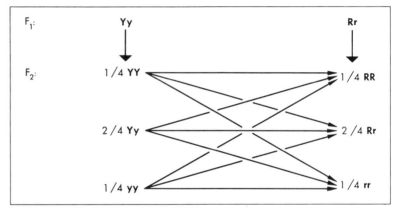

F_1: Yy   Rr

F_2: 1/4 YY   1/4 RR

2/4 Yy   2/4 Rr

1/4 yy   1/4 rr

F_2 progeny will be homozygous for both traits, one must again combine ratios; $\frac{1}{4}$ **YY** $\times \frac{1}{4}$ **RR** $= \frac{1}{16}$ **YYRR**. Other possible combinations (e.g., $\frac{2}{4}$ **Yy** $\times \frac{2}{4}$ **Rr** $= \frac{4}{16}$ **YyRr**; $\frac{2}{4}$ **Yy** $\times \frac{1}{4}$ **rr** $= \frac{2}{16}$ **Yyrr**) are also indicated in Figure 17-21. The results shown are the same as

Figure 17-21

F_2:

$1/4 \times 1/4 = 1/16$ **YYRR** $2/4 \times 1/4 = 2/16$ **YyRR**
$1/4 \times 2/4 = 2/16$ **YYRr** $2/4 \times 2/4 = 4/16$ **YyRr**
$1/4 \times 1/4 = 1/16$ **YYrr** $2/4 \times 1/4 = 2/16$ **Yyrr**

$1/4 \times 1/4 = 1/16$ **yyRR**
$1/4 \times 2/4 = 2/16$ **yyRr**
$1/4 \times 1/4 = 1/16$ **yyrr**

those obtained by using the Punnett square or checkerboard, which was shown previously.

17.11 Another test cross

To show that the F_1 individuals of the previous section are actually heterozygous is easily done by crossing them with the recessive parent **(yyrr)**. The resulting progeny (Figure 17-22) are of all four possible

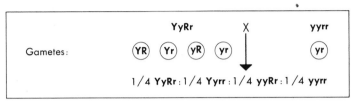

Figure 17-22

combinations of yellow, green, round, and wrinkled. This indicates that all four traits were present in the individual being tested and that the pairs of genes segregate independently (note the four kinds of gametes produced by the heterozygote).

This test cross can also be treated one trait at a time. The heterozygous individual produces gametes one-half of which carry the factor for yellow seed, the other half carrying the factor for green seed. Similarly, in the heterozygous individual, one-half of the gametes will have a gene governing round seed formation, while the other half will have the gene which results in the production of wrinkled seeds. All of the gametes are alike in the recessive individual (Figure 17-23). One-half

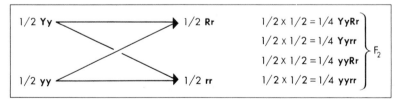

Figure 17-23

of the progeny are yellow-seeded, one-half are green-seeded; one-half are round-seeded, one-half are wrinkle-seeded. However, we are interested in both characteristics.

The possible characteristics are indicated (Figure 17-24) and are, of

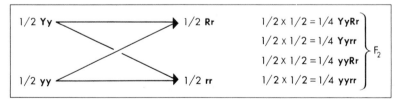

Figure 17-24

course, the same as were obtained previously. Whether the Punnett-square method or the proportion method is utilized depends upon personal preference. Genetics is basically mathematical in approach, and complete understanding comes with practice in working problems. The reader is strongly urged to attempt all the problems available at the end of this chapter.

17.12   Self-pollination and homozygosity

Continued self-pollination increases the proportion of offspring which are homozygous. Assuming that all parents have an equal number of progeny, with each generation of inbreeding (self-pollination), the proportion of heterozygous individuals is reduced by half. Remember that when a monohybrid is self-pollinated, only one-half of the progeny are heterozygous. As our example (Figure 17-25), we shall use one

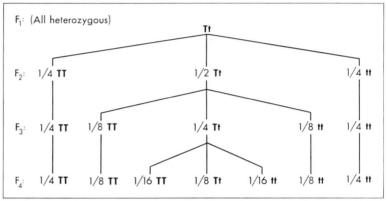

Figure 17-25

of the original characteristics with which Mendel worked. The F_1 is all heterozygous as a result of crossing a homozygous tall **(TT)** with a homozygous short **(tt)** pea plant. When all of the individuals from the F_1 on are allowed to self-pollinate, the heterozygotes form a smaller and smaller proportion of the population. In the F_2, only half of the individuals are heterozygotes. This drops to one-fourth in the F_3, and to one-eighth in the F_4. Subsequent proportions would be one-sixteenth, one-thirty-second, one-sixty-fourth, and so on.

Application of this principle of increased homozygosity is the fundamental reason why brother and sister matings in humans is frowned upon. Everyone carries a few recessive harmful genes. In matings of close relatives, the probability is high that these harmful genes are the same and the homozygous condition is quite likely to occur.[6] In plant and animal breeding, however, desirable recessive genes are brought out in this way.

17.13   Mendelian principles

As a result of the preceding discussions, it is possible to list four basic principles of genetics. These are a direct result of Mendel's work

---

[6] Of course such matings of brother-sister or cousin-cousin were forbidden, or at least looked at askance, before there was any real knowledge of heredity. Such prohibitions were, however, probably a result of observations that these matings resulted in abnormally high numbers of defective children.

in the middle 1800's and verified repeatedly by many other investigators.

1. The principle of unit characters. The inherited characteristics of an organism are controlled by factors, or genes, and these genes occur in pairs.

2. The principle of dominance. One gene in a pair may mask, hide, or inhibit the expression of the other gene. Dominance does not occur between all gene-pairs.

3. The principle of segregation. The members of pairs of genes separate prior to gamete formation (i.e., during meiosis), and only one gene of each pair is present in a gamete.

4. The principle of independent assortment. The members of different pairs of genes are distributed to the gametes independently of one another and are combined at random during fertilization.

17.14   Lack of dominance

One instance in which the F_1 is intermediate in a characteristic, as compared with the parents, has already been mentioned (Section 17.9). The diagrams of a one-factor cross (in Figure 17-26) and a two-factor cross may help to clarify this situation. In this example the phenotypic

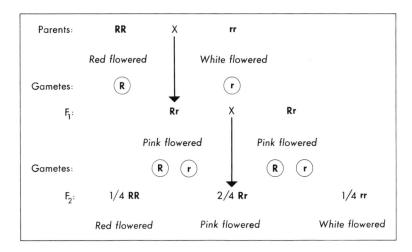

Figure 17-26

and genotypic ratios are identical, because every genotype is expressed in the phenotype.

In the example shown in Figure 17-27A, dominance is expressed in one pair of genes but not in the other. Each characteristic can be treated separately, and then the various combinations of both traits can be determined (Figure 17-27B). The results are the same as were obtained with the Punnett-square method.

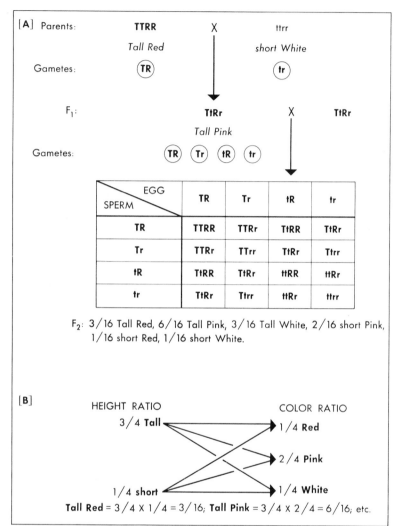

F₂: 3/16 Tall Red, 6/16 Tall Pink, 3/16 Tall White, 2/16 short Pink, 1/16 short Red, 1/16 short White.

Figure 17-27

[B]

HEIGHT RATIO ... COLOR RATIO
3/4 Tall ... 1/4 Red
... 2/4 Pink
1/4 short ... 1/4 White

Tall Red = 3/4 X 1/4 = 3/16; **Tall Pink** = 3/4 X 2/4 = 6/16; etc.

17.15 Multiple genes

Up to this point, all of the characters which have been discussed are those which can be sharply or distinctly divided into clearly differentiated classes (e.g., the pea plant was tall or short, with no in-between sizes). However, many characters vary quantitatively in that gradations are continuous from one extreme to the other. Such characteristics are somewhat difficult to study and are beyond the scope of this text. They will be given a very brief discussion at this time to alert the student to the complexities of genetical studies.

Mendel's genius lay in the choosing of sharply distinguished contrasting characters. Before this, various individuals had found that the F_1 was more or less intermediate between two extreme parents and that the F_2 was composed of all gradations from one extreme to the other. This was the basis of the old idea of "blending." Not until after simple Mendelian inheritance was understood was an explanation of this quantitative gradation possible. If several sets of genes are involved in the expression of a single characteristic, and if no dominance exists between the alleles, then they will be cumulative in their effect. We speak of **multiple genes** or **factors** when several sets of alleles produce more or less equal and cumulative effects on the same character.

In this type of heredity no obvious ratios may be found. This is quite different from the incomplete dominance discussed in the previous section. For example, one investigator found in a cross between a plant having very large flowers and one having very small flowers that the flowers of the F_1 were medium in size and that the F_2 had flowers varying in size from very small to very large. Moreover, about one out of sixteen of the F_2 was as small as the one original parent and one out of sixteen was as large as the other original parent plant. To a geneticist this immediately suggests that two factors are involved, in which the double dominant and double recessive each occur about once in every sixteen individuals (refer to a dihybrid cross, Section 17.10). If we assume two pairs of genes, **A** and **a,** **B** and **b,** the cross may be diagrammed as in Figure 17-28. Thus, even where "blending" appears to occur, Mendel's basic principles are upheld.

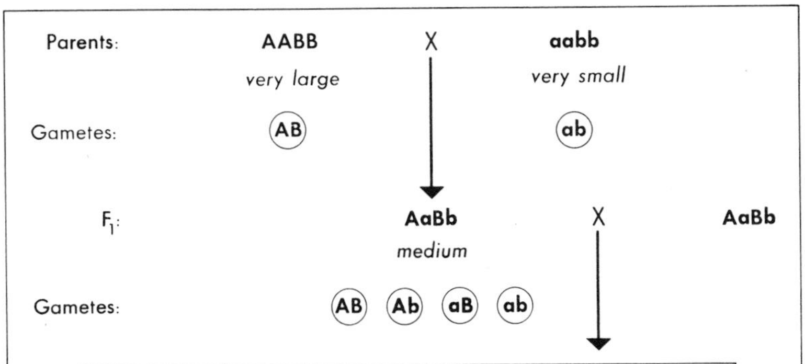

SPERM \ EGG	AB	Ab	aB	ab
AB	**AABB** *very large*	**AABb** *large*	**AaBB** *large*	**AaBb** *medium*
Ab	**AABb** *large*	**AAbb** *medium*	**AaBb** *medium*	**Aabb** *small*
aB	**AaBB** *large*	**AaBb** *medium*	**aaBB** *medium*	**aaBb** *small*
ab	**AaBb** *medium*	**Aabb** *small*	**aaBb** *small*	**aabb** *very small*

Figure 17-28

Other such examples of multiple genes involve more than two pairs. The complexity increases, but the basic principles remain the same.

17.16   Linkage

Mendel experimented with characteristics which were governed by genes located on separate chromosomes, and this made possible the independent assortment of genes at meiosis. However, all genes are not on different chromosomes; many chromosomes include hundreds or thousands of genes. Two genes on the same chromosome are said to be linked. They do not separate independently but remain together during meiosis.

If two pairs of genes on different chromosomes are involved, four possible kinds of gametes are produced by a dihybrid individual (see Section 17.10). If these genes are linked, a similar dihybrid individual can produce only two possible kinds of gametes (Figure 17-29).

Figure 17-29

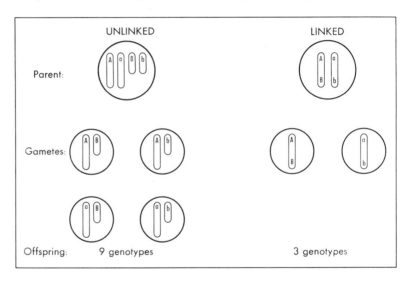

If genes are linked, their number and importance is unchanged, but the number of chromosomes involved is reduced. The variety of gametes (independent assortment) is also reduced, because this depends upon the number of chromosomes.

CROSSING-OVER

Many investigators noticed that linked genes sometimes become unlinked, and the frequency with which this occurs depends upon the distance separating the two genes on a chromosome. The explanation for this behavior was found upon careful examination of meiosis (Section 17.1). In prophase I, during synapsis, the chromatids of homologous chromosomes become intertwined and frequently exchange parts.

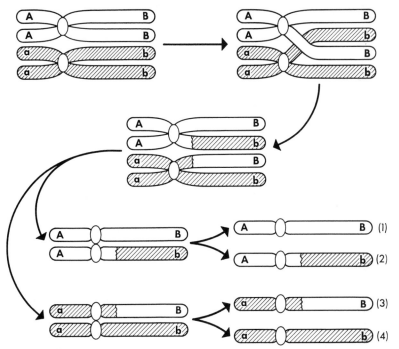

Figure 17-30. Crossing-over during meiosis. In the first division of meiosis
the kinetochores have not doubled and thus the chromatids do not separate;
the homologous chromosomes separate. In the second division the chromatids
separate. The numbers indicate the four types of haploid cells that result.

Figure 17-30 represents this exchange, or **crossing-over,** at one location.
As a result, all four chromatids of the tetrad are different, and the
resultant haploid cells will be of four kinds, instead of two as would
be true if crossing-over did not occur. Without crossing-over, chromosomes (1) and (2) of Figure 17-30 would be alike, and chromosomes
(3) and (4) would be alike. Just one pair of chromatids crossing-over
doubles the possible kinds of haploid cells (i.e., gametes). The letters
represent genes located at opposite ends of the chromosome. In the
four chromosomes located in the four haploid cells which are produced
as a result of meiosis, genes **AB** are still linked in one gamete but not
linked in others. In one of the latter, genes **A** and **b** are now linked.

Crossing-over is a normal occurrence during synapsis, and breakage
may occur at any point on the chromosome where two chromatids
happen to be overlapping. As a result, crossing-over may occur simultaneously at several locations on a single chromosome, resulting in an
almost infinite variety of gene combinations. The longer the chromosome, the greater the possibility of more than one cross-over taking
place. Also, the farther apart that two genes are on a chromosome, the
more likely that crossing-over will occur, separating them. Variations
in gametes, and thus in progeny, result from crossing-over as well as

from the random alignment of chromosomes during meiosis. The possibilities for variations are thus enormous; such variations in living organisms provide the material for evolutionary change.

The student should diagram a dihybrid cross (utilizing the letters **AaBb**) in three ways: (1) with the genes on different pairs of chromosomes (2N = 4 chromosomes), (2) with the genes linked (2N = 2 chromosomes) and no crossing-over, and (3) with linkage plus crossing-over.

17.17   Reflection on gene action

The phenotypic response of gene action is a result of the coordinated effect of the entire set of genes: a single gene may affect many characteristics, or each expressed characteristic may be influenced by many genes. Each gene probably governs one basic reaction, but the characteristics which are expressed as the phenotype result from many such reactions. Therefore, to state that each characteristic of an organism is governed by one gene is incorrect. In some cases we are fortunate enough to find that one gene has an obvious effect on the mature organism and, thus, is studied readily. This is not, however, the situation that always exists.

Summary

1. Meiosis is a cellular division which occurs prior to gamete formation and results in a diploid cell giving rise to haploid cells. Not only does a reduction in chromosome number occur, but also a separation of the homologous pairs of chromosomes. The number of different kinds of haploid cells which are produced depends upon the random alignment of chromosomes at metaphase of meiosis.

2. The principal constituents of chromosomes are nucleoproteins, the nucleic acid portion of which is involved in the transmission of hereditary characteristics from cell to cell. The deoxyribose nucleic acid (DNA) molecule consists of two parallel portions which separate when the chromosome duplicates. Each half accumulates material from the cell contents until exact copies of the chromosomes are produced.

3. The DNA molecules act as templates which determine the configuration of the ribose nucleic acid (RNA) molecules. The latter are involved in protein synthesis.

4. Four basic principles are involved in genetical studies: (a) unit characters, (b) dominance, (c) segregation, and (d) independent assortment. Dominance, however, does not occur between all gene-pairs.

5. Genes which are located on the same chromosome are said to be linked. Such genes may become unlinked by a process known as crossing-over in which chromatids exchange parts.

1. Briefly define the following: diploid, haploid, allele, synapsis, homozygous, heterozygous, hybrid, phenotype, genotype, linkage, and crossing-over.
2. Assuming that the diploid number is four, diagram a cell in the following stages of division:

    (a) Early prophase of meiosis.
    (b) Metaphase of mitosis.
    (c) Metaphase I of meiosis.
    (d) Metaphase II of meiosis.

3. Describe the manner in which genes are presumed to function.
4. Briefly explain the meaning of each of the four basic Mendelian principles: (a) unit characters, (b) dominance, (c) segregation, and (d) independent assortment.
5. Genes **A, B,** and **C** are located on the same long chromosome; their alleles are similarly located on the homologous chromosome. Assuming that the diploid cell is heterozygous for all factors, list the types of gametes that may be produced (a) if crossing-over occurs between genes **A** and **B,** (b) if crossing-over occurs between genes **b** and **c,** and (c) if crossing-over does not occur.
6. Why does linkage present a problem to plant breeders who are trying to develop new kinds of plants?
7. Explain the significance in the life of plants of each of the following: (a) synapsis, (b) mitosis, (c) sexual fusion, and (d) meiosis.
8. You have a red-flowered snapdragon that is resistant to a rust disease, and a white-flowered snapdragon that is susceptible to this rust disease.

    If white flowers and disease resistance are both recessive characters, describe step by step what you would have to do to produce a true-breeding strain which is white-flowered and disease resistant.
9. Prior to the time of Mendel, crosses between phenotypically different organisms had been performed with the result that the progeny were intermediate between the two parents. The conclusion was that the progeny resulted from a blending of the characteristics of the two parents.

    Mendel came to the conclusion that each parent contributed factors to the progeny and that the factors from one parent were inherited independently of the factors from the other parent. He did not agree that any blending occurred. Discuss the type of information which led Mendel to this conclusion.
10. In Jimson weeds purple flower color **(P)** is dominant over white **(p)** and spiny pods **(S)** over smooth **(s).** These pairs of alleles are not linked.

    (a) A Jimson weed of genotype **PPss** is crossed with one of genotype **ppSS.** What will be the genotype and phenotype of the F_1 generation? If the plants of the F_1 generation are self-fertilized, what will be the phenotypes of the F_2, and in what ratio will these phenotypes occur?

    (b) Two Jimson weeds with white flowers and smooth pods are crossed with one another. What will be the genotype and phenotype of the F_1 generation?

11. In corn plants one gene controls the height of the plant. Normal height **(N)** is dominant over dwarf **(n)**. A normal corn plant is crossed with a dwarf plant. Of the progeny 247 are normal and 264 are dwarf. What are the genotypes of the two parent plants?

12. Briefly explain how the following influence the possible number of different kinds of gametes produced by an individual: (a) linkage and (b) crossing-over.

13. Plant *Y* is always self-pollinated (self-fertilized) and bears red flowers; flower color is governed or controlled by one gene-pair. In one fertilized egg a single gene changed, by chance, to a recessive white flower characteristic.
    (a) What kind (color) of flowers will be found on the plant *Z* developing from this fertilized egg?
    (b) If this plant *Z* is self-fertilized, what will be the genotypes and phenotypes of its progeny? Be sure to include ratios.

14. In peas red flowers **(R)** are dominant over white flowers **(r)**. A pea plant with white flowers is crossed with one that has red flowers. Of the progeny 147 have white flowers and 161 have red flowers. What are the genotypes of each parent and of each type of progeny?

15. A strain (*X*) of tomato characterized by the ability to grow at low temperatures carries a gene **(t)** for this character which is recessive. Strain *X*, however, has no resistance to a serious wilt disease. A second strain (*Y*) is characterized by resistance to the wilt disease; this resistance is the result of a recessive gene **(r)**. A certain area in Wyoming is characterized by low temperatures during the growing season and also by the prevalence of the wilt disease; the common tomato cannot be grown there for both reasons.

    You are given (1) strain *X*, homozygous for ability to grow at low temperature and for lack of resistance to wilt, and (2) strain *Y*, homozygous for resistance to wilt and for lack of ability to grow at low temperature. You wish to produce strain *Z*, which will grow successfully in the Wyoming area. By means of diagrams (or checkerboards), indicate the necessary crosses and point out the genotype of strain *Z*.

16. A flower grower finds in his nursery a plant with white flowers (recessive to the usual red) which he wishes to propagate from seed. However, the plant carries on the opposite end of the same long chromosome a recessive gene for dwarfness, which is undesirable.

    Explain how the grower can obtain a tall, white-flowered plant which will breed true for both of these characters. Describe all steps in the process.

17. A plant-breeding program in one of our agricultural experiment stations resulted in the production of two varieties of melon. Variety *X* is homozygous for disease susceptibility **(S)**, for large fruit **(L)**, and for smooth fruit **(w)**. Variety *Y* is homozygous for disease resistance **(s)**, for large fruit **(L)**, and for wrinkled fruit **(W)**. The genes governing disease resistance (or susceptibility) and size of fruit have been determined to be at opposite ends of the same long chromosome.

    Explain how the plant breeder should continue his program in order to obtain a plant which is homozygous for disease resistance, for large fruit, and for smooth fruit.

18. Starting with one plant that is homozygous for smooth leaves **(M)**

and heterozygous for fused petals **(F),** and a second plant which is heterozygous for smooth leaves and homozygous for fused petals, explain how a plant breeder could obtain a plant which has hairy leaves (the recessive allele of smooth) and separate petals (the recessive allele of fused).

19. A tall, red-flowered plant (heterozygous for both characters) is crossed with a dwarf, white-flowered plant (both characters recessive). The F_1 consisted of 1,008 tall, red-flowered plants and 988 dwarf, white-flowered plants. Explain these results.

20. A rancher had one peach tree which produced much larger fruit than the others but had such a poor root system that the tree did not grow very well. His other trees, which had excellent root systems, produced small fruit. Since fruit size and root system each is dependent upon a single factor respectively, and since small size and poor root system are dominant, explain how the rancher would (or could) produce trees with large fruit and a good root system.

21. On one long chromosome of a potato occurs a dominant gene **(G)** which causes giant tubers but which is lethal (causes death of the plant) if it is homozygous. On the same individual chromosome (but at the other end) is a second dominant gene **(B)** which causes a bitter flavor and is undesirable.

    You wish a strain of potato with giant tubers and a pleasant flavor. Explain how you can obtain the desired strain, assuming that the strain which is presently available is heterozygous for flavor.

22. An onion has, on opposite ends of a long chromosome, gene **(w)** (recessive) for white bulbs and gene **(s)** (recessive) for small bulbs. Another plant of the same species carries the corresponding genes **(W)** (dominant) for non-white bulbs and **(S)** (dominant) for large bulbs. Both of these plants are homozygous.

    How can we obtain from these plants a true-breeding strain of onion with large white bulbs? Describe the steps and processes necessary to arrive at such a strain.

23. In violets the gene which bears the potentiality for blue petals is dominant over that for yellow petals, and the gene which bears the potentiality for large flowers is dominant over that for small flowers.

    A plant with yellow petals and large flowers was crossed with one which had blue petals and small flowers. The F_1 generation was composed of:

    > 47 plants with yellow petals and large flowers
    > 45 plants with yellow petals and small flowers
    > 50 plants with blue petals and large flowers
    > 46 plants with blue petals and small flowers

    What were the genotypes of the parents? Show the method you used to determine these genotypes.

24. A plant is heterozygous for yellow flowers (red is recessive) and for hairy leaves (smooth is recessive). This plant is self-fertilized, and the offspring (or progeny) consist of:

    > 72 plants with yellow flowers and smooth leaves
    > 143 plants with yellow flowers and hairy leaves
    > 68 plants with red flowers and hairy leaves

Explain the genetical basis for such results, including the reason why no red-flowered, smooth-leaved individuals were produced.

25. By adjusting the environment, an ordinarily late-flowering, rust-resistant plant was crossed with an early-flowering, rust-susceptible plant. All of the 200 plants of the F_1 generation were early-flowering and rust-resistant. In the F_2 generation the progeny were as follows:

302 early-flowering, rust-susceptible
584 early-flowering, rust-resistant
287 late-flowering, rust-resistant

Let **E** = early-flowering, **e** = late-flowering, **R** = rust-resistant, and **r** = rust-susceptible.

(a) Diagram, showing only the chromosomes and genes concerned, a diploid cell of each of the plants crossed initially and a diploid cell of the F_1 generation. Show as many chromosomes as necessary to indicate the distribution of the genes.

(b) Give the phenotypic ratio that would be expected if the early-flowering, rust-resistant plants of the F_2 were self-fertilized.

SUGGESTED READINGS

Beadle, G. W. "The Genes of Men and Molds," *Scientific American,* 179 (September 1948), 30–39.

Bonner, D. *Heredity.* Englewood Cliffs, N. J.: Prentice-Hall, 1961.

Crick, F. H. C. "The Structure of the Hereditary Material," *Scientific American,* 191 (October 1954), 54–61

Dobzhansky, T. "Genetics," *Scientific American,* 191 (September 1954), 55–61.

Hoagland, M. B. "Nucleic Acids and Proteins," *Scientific American,* 201 (December 1959), 55–61.

Horowitz, N. H. "The Gene," *Scientific American,* 195 (October 1956), 78–90.

Hotchkiss, R. D., and E. Weiss. "Transformed Bacteria," *Scientific American,* 195 (November 1956), 48–53.

Ingram, V. M. "How Do Genes Act?" *Scientific American,* 198 (January 1958), 68–74.

Jacob, F., and E. L. Wollman. "Viruses and Genes," *Scientific American,* 204 (June 1961), 92–107.

Mirsky, A. E. "The Chemistry of Heredity," *Scientific American,* 188 (February 1953), 47–57.

Sinott, E. W., et al. *Principles of Genetics.* New York: McGraw-Hill, 1958.

Snyder, L. H., and P. R. David. *The Principles of Heredity.* Boston: Heath, 1957.

Sonneborn, T. M. "Partner of the Genes," *Scientific American,* 183 (November 1950), 30–39.

Srb, A. M., and R. D. Owen. *General Genetics.* San Francisco: Freeman, 1952.

Taylor, J. H. "The Duplication of Chromosomes," *Scientific American,* 198 (June 1958), 36–42

Winchester, A. M. *Genetics.* Boston: Houghton-Mifflin, 1958.

CHAPTER 18

Plant Taxonomy

18.1 Classification

The plants and animals of the world have been of interest to mankind for many thousands of years. During that time much information has been accumulated, and gradually man realized that disseminating such knowledge is vital to a thorough understanding of living organisms. The more data that was accumulated, the more important became the need to apprise others of the work done by various individuals. In order to discuss plants and animals, they must be given names, preferably in some logical way, or else the 350,000 species of plants known today would just be a gigantic hodge-podge of confusion.

With this in mind, **taxonomists** (those biologists especially interested in plant classification and relationships) have developed a system of categories within which any plant may be placed and given a name. Many such systems have been developed, with many changes being made as botanists learned more about plants, and with many changes undoubtedly yet to come. The system used in this text is one which has been adopted by a large majority of botanists, but one which is subject to change, just as are all systems of classification. The general recommendations and procedures of The International Rules of Botanical Nomenclature have been adopted.

In general, the higher the category, the more individuals in it and the fewer the number of categories at the same level. Conversely, the lower the category, the fewer individuals in it and the larger the number of categories at that level. The following outline of the position of the "redwood tree" will serve to illustrate the method of grouping organisms.

Kingdom Plantae
Division Tracheo*phyta*
Subdivision Pter*opsida*
Class Gymnosperm*ae*
Order Conifer*ales*
Family Taxodi*aceae*
Genus *Sequoia*
Species *sempervirens*

The **scientific name** consists of the genus and species, *Sequoia sempervirens* in this case, and the other groupings need not be used. A number of species are combined into a larger unit, the genus; a number of genera likewise are combined to form a family; families combine to form order; and so on to the all-inclusive kingdom. It is recommended that division names end in the suffix-*phyta,* sub-divisions end in -*opsida,* classes end in -*ae* or -*eae,* orders in -*ales,* and families in -*aceae.* The names of genera and species have diverse endings, and in some cases long-time usage has prevented the complete adoption of the endings here suggested for the other groupings.

These taxonomic groupings are devices which enable one to identify more readily a specific organism, much in the manner of the geographical identification of a specific locality. If I may be forgiven the use of my own working area, the following may serve to illustrate my meaning.

Hemisphere Western
Country United States of America
State California
County Santa Barbara
Town Goleta
Locality University Campus

The largest grouping, hemisphere, contains the greatest number of specific areas, while the county or town contain fewer such areas.

18.2 Scientific name

As mentioned in the previous section, the smallest two categories to which a plant belongs, the genus and species, constitute its **scientific name** and is usually followed by the name or initial of the person who first described the species fully. All scientific names are **binomials** (i.e., a name consisting of two parts) in which both terms are underlined or italicized and the genus is capitalized, for example *Sequoia sempervirens* (D. Don) Endl. The abbreviated names following the scientific name of the redwood refer to the man who first described the species, David Don, and the man who revised that classification, Stephen Endlicher. We are indebted to the great Swedish naturalist Linnaeus (Karl von Linné) for establishing the binomial system of classification in his monumental work *Species Plantarum,* published in 1753. Until that time, plants were referred to by a short descriptive phrase, a polynomial, which was cumbersome, to say the least. Such phrases made no attempt at indicating relationships, which is the basis for all modern classification.

Beginning students frequently want to know why a redwood cannot be called a redwood, and why it must be called *Sequoia sempervirens.* This is certainly a logical question and deserves an answer. A standardized name of international recognition is necessary so that each interested individual knows which plant is being discussed and the relationship of this plant to others. This accord would be difficult to achieve if common names were used, because the same common name is frequently used for entirely different plants, depending upon the locality. No difficulty arises with the redwoods, but, as an example, the word "corn" refers to "maize" in the United States, "wheat" in England, and "oats" in Scotland. The name *Zea mays* refers to one specific plant in all three countries, that which many of us are fond of as corn-on-the-cob. In this case the "us" refers to people in the United States. Different common names are also often applied to the same species in different areas. For example, *Pseudotsuga menziesii* is called Douglas Fir, Douglas Spruce, Red Spruce, Yellow Spruce, and Oregon Pine—it is *not* a fir or a spruce or a pine; the name derivation is *pseudos,* false, and *tsuga,* hemlock. Consider also the confusion arising from "Poison Sumac," "Poison Ivy," and "Poison Oak." These are actually closely related species within the genus *Rhus* (respectively *R. vernix, R. toxicodendron,* and *R. diversiloba*), although the common names would not indicate this. The confusion engendered by the use of common names is quickly clarified when scientific names are utilized. Also, it might be pointed out that no common names exist for many genera or species: Chrysanthemum, Fuchsia, Aster, and Asparagus are examples.

The terms used to name plants are derived mostly from either Latin or Greek and are selected for various reasons. In many cases the term reflects a specific characteristic, such as *Lupinus horizontalis,* in which the lower branches are prostrate, or *Trifolium* spp., which has leaves divided into three leaflets (palmately trifoliate). In other cases the name reflects a location, such as *Pyrus americana* (American mountain ash), or it may refer to a famous person, as in the genus *Erwinia,* which was named after Erwin F. Smith, a noted authority in the field of bacterial plant pathogens. Once a plant has been named and de-

225

scribed fully, that name cannot be used again. The correct name is that which first appears in the literature, although changes must sometimes be made as classifications are revised. Under these conditions, however, the species name is maintained if at all possible, even if the plant is placed in a new genus, family, etc.

18.3 What is a species?

Much controversy still exists concerning the definition of a **species,** but it may be regarded as a group containing all of the individuals of a particular kind of plant and excluding all those that are different. One may say that two groups are different species if reasonably consistent differences exist between them and if they maintain these differences under natural conditions. Usually, but not always, species are incapable of interbreeding. In any case, the species is considered to be a biological unit delimited primarily by genetical criteria and containing similar individuals.

No exact definition is possible, because species are not really stable but are by-products of the dynamic evolutionary process and are constantly changing. The exact range of such terms as "similarities" and "differences" is also extremely difficult to determine. However, the species concept is an exceedingly important one in taxonomy and accepted by all biologists in spite of the difficulties involved in defining the term. The comment made by a competent botanist may be most applicable: "A species is whatever a qualified taxonomist says it is."

IDENTIFICATION OF A SPECIES

How does one identify a plant or find out its name? The simplest method is to ask someone who knows. This does *not* mean "ask any botanist." A plant anatomist, plant physiologist, or plant cytologist would undoubtedly know some of the more common plants, but his specialty is not taxonomy; the taxonomist should be consulted.[1] If no taxonomist is available, a local manual should be utilized. This is a

---

[1] The layman usually assumes that all botanists are taxonomists and/or horticulturists. The two most frequent questions asked of a botanist are: (1) "What plant is this?"; (2) "What is the matter with my ———? It has spots all over it." And yet the same individuals would not think of asking a zoologist to diagnose illness in their children, pets, or livestock. They might, of course, ask a zoologist to identify such diverse items as insects, spiders, snakes, and birds—with about the same results as obtained with botanists identifying plants.

Those fields covered by the term "botany" are so diverse, and include such a tremendous amount of data, that no individual is competent in all phases of the subject. See Chapter 1 for a discussion of the various aspects of botany.

book which contains "keys" as an aid to identification. In most instances one finds a **dichotomous key;** one in which two choices are available at each step, such as:

1a. Leaves parallel-veined; flower parts in 3's 2
1b. Leaves net-veined; flower parts in 4's or 5's 10
    2a. Flowers without sepals or petals   3
    2b. Flowers with sepals and petals   8

Each choice leads to another choice of two until the final choice indicates the species. Unfortunately, some groups are not easily "keyed out." A further possibility is to compare the plant with specimens in an **herbarium,** which is an orderly collection of dried, pressed, and labeled plant specimens.

Actually, identifying plants can be a fascinating hobby as well as a profession. Many people find that collecting, preserving, and identifying plants is an excellent outlet for their energy; it is instructive and rewarding. Taxonomy is probable that phase of botany which first interests the beginner.

18.4 Natural and artificial systems of classification

The early systems of classification tended to be **artificial,** in that they were based upon arbitrary criteria without regard for evolutionary relationships and emphasized differences such as flower color, leaf shape, or type of bark. The natural systems of today have almost completely replaced those of an artificial nature. A **natural system** is one which attempts to classify organisms according to their genetic relationship and reflects the results of evolution. Such a system is based upon both similarities and differences, with the most similar organisms grouped together.

Because natural systems are based upon man's knowledge of plants, they must constantly be revised to keep up with new knowledge. Even when knowledge appears to be complete, the system will be imperfect, because a vast number of changing, evolving organisms cannot conform to a man-made system of a few categories. And if enough categories could be created, the main purpose of classification would be defeated.

An excellent example of an organism that does not quite fit is *Euglena.* This is a one-celled organism, motile by means of a single hair-like appendage (a flagellum), flexible, capable of ingesting food through a gullet, and containing chloroplasts. All except the last characteristic would indicate that it is an animal; the presence of chloroplasts indicates that it is a plant. Then what *is* it? The difficulty arises in the question which is asked. The question *should* be: "What shall we *call* this organism?" *Euglena* can fit into either kingdom. In fact, zoologists usually study *Euglena* as a member of the Class Mastigophora in the Phylum Protozoa, whereas botanists place this organism in the Division Euglenophyta in the Sub-kingdom Thallophyta. This is merely indicative of the fact that man-made rules do not regulate the activity of living organisms. How we classify such an organism is not important so long as it is given a name so that it can be studied and discussed by interested biologists. A suggestion has been made that such organisms belong in a third kingdom, termed Protista; this suggestion has not been adopted by most biologists.

In even our modern natural system of plant classification we are forced to accept at least some artificiality. The Class Deuteromycetes (or Fungi Imperfecti) in the Division Eumycophyta consists of an artificial group of fungi in which the existence of sexual reproduction has not been determined. This is strictly a grouping of convenience, and the only relationship involved is to indicate the similarity of these organisms to other true fungi of this division. If a closer relationship is determined by investigation, a member of this class is transferred to its more logical position in one of the other classes in the Division Eumycophyta. Some fungi without known sexual stages are placed in classes other than Deuteromycetes because of the obvious relationships indicated by various structural characteristics.

18.5 Types of reproduction in plants

Modern systems of classification are based mainly upon reproductive structures, because these are the most stable morphological characteristics. The environment has considerable influence on the general size and shape of the plant; a lack of water or certain minerals, for example, will result in stunted and abnormal development, but the reproductive parts will remain unchanged, provided the plant is capable of reproducing at all. Although plants manifest various kinds of reproduction, it may be thought of as being comprised of two basic types, asexual and sexual, with certain modifications depending upon the plant.

ASEXUAL REPRODUCTION

This type of reproduction is accomplished by cell division and growth, and no fusion of protoplasts (or gametes) occurs.

Vegetative reproduction involves only the ordinary processes of cell division and growth, no special forms of cells being produced. This type of reproduction is accomplished by a variety of methods: the production of runners by strawberry plants, the sprouting of tubers and corms, and the fragmentation of a multicellular plant body into segments each of which is capable of developing into a new plant, as in many algae, are common examples. The rooting of woody cuttings and the grafting of plant parts are methods of vegetative propagation utilized by many individuals, but these do not usually occur under natural conditions. Two methods of vegetative reproduction are sufficiently important to be named and defined separately: fission and budding. **Fission** is the division of a unicellular organism into two new unicellular organisms of approximately equal size and is the method by which bacteria and various other thallophytes [2] reproduce. **Budding** is the production of small individuals as outgrowths from the mature organism, which then develop into mature individuals of full size. In the unicellular yeast plant a small protuberance develops and enlarges, a wall forms between the "bud" and the parent cell, and separation of the two structures results in two cells or plants.

Spore formation is that type of asexual reproduction in which are produced specialized reproductive cells or groups of cells which are capable by themselves of producing new plants by cell division and growth. The many different kinds of spores are designated by a variety of names. If the spores are motile, by means of hairlike appendages, they are called **zoospores.** The structure in which spores are produced is a **sporangium** (*-angium* means case or container), although such a structure is sometimes given a more specific name, such as the sporangium in the mosses, which is called a capsule.

SEXUAL REPRODUCTION

This type of reproduction involves three principal features:

1. The fusion of two protoplasts (or gametes) followed by the fusion of their nuclei. The chromosomes, now twice the original number in the gametes, mingle but do not fuse.

2. The subsequent separation of two sets of chromosomes, each with the original number (haploid), into separate cells. This process is meiosis (see Section 17.1).

3. Cell division and growth, which may occur entirely between fusion and meiosis (reduction), or entirely between meiosis and fusion, or at both places in the cycle.

In some of the primitive organisms, the motile gametes are structurally alike, **isogametes,** and their fusion is termed **isogamy.** The term **heterogamy** is used when referring to the fusion of motile gametes which are structurally dissimilar, **heterogametes.** In the more advanced

[2] Thallophytes = members of the sub-kingdom Thallophyta, which will be discussed in Chapters 19 and 20.

229

organisms, the non-motile female gametes, **eggs,** are usually larger than the male gametes, **sperm,** which may be motile. The fusion of egg and sperm, as in such diverse plants as *Oedogonium* (one of the Chlorophyta [3]) and *Lilium* (one of the Tracheophyta [3]), is termed **oögamy.** The cell resulting from the fusion of two gametes is termed a **zygote,** and it is diploid.

18.6 Alternation of phases

As mentioned in the previous section, cell division and growth may occur between fusion and meiosis and also between meiosis and fusion. This is the common situation in most plants, except for some of the lower forms, and is referred to as **alternation of phases** or **alternation of generations.**[4] In the complete life cycle of a plant, the zygote develops into a multicellular, diploid, asexual body, the **sporophyte,** which produces spores as a result of meiosis. These spores develop into a multicellular, haploid, sexual phase, the **gametophyte,** which produces gametes. Thus, two distinct structures are involved in the generalized plant life cycle as diagrammed in Figure 18-1. This life cycle with various modifications and embellishments will be used throughout the discussion of representative members of the plant kingdom.

As various plant groups are discussed, the similarities as well as the differences will be emphasized, and the fact will become obvious that the life cycle representative of a particular group can be superimposed upon the word-diagram of Figure 18-1. In some the gametophyte is the dominant portion, consisting of a relatively large multicellular plant body, while the sporophyte is relegated to an almost insignificant portion of the total life cycle. A few of the algae, for example, produce no multicellular sporophyte, and the zygote is the only diploid structure. The other extreme, where the gametophyte is tiny and inconspicuous, occurs in other algae (e.g., *Laminaria*) and in the flowering plants. Different as these two extremes may appear to be, one is quickly impressed with many basic similarities upon close examination of the structures involved. The basic sequence of events and the basic functions remain the same, even though the structures may be of various sorts:

zygote → sporophyte → spores by meiosis → gametophyte → gametes → zygote by fusion

The various structural modifications are examples of evolutionary

[3] The Tracheophyta and the Chlorophyta are discussed in subsequent chapters.

[4] The student should be able to determine why the first phrase is preferable to the second.

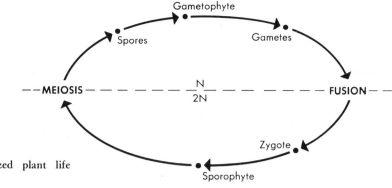

Figure 18-1. Generalized plant life cycle (word diagram).

adaptations, and in some cases one or more portions of the generalized life cycle may be by-passed or lost (e.g., the sporophyte in the alga *Ulothrix*).

18.7 Classification of the plant kingdom followed in this text

In subsequent chapters representative individuals from various plant groups will be considered in more detail. No attempt will be made to include all of the major groups; rather, selected groups will be utilized to emphasize evolutionary advances and the importance of plants to all life. The following is a brief descriptive account of most of the major plant groups, some of which will be discussed later (a few in more detail than others):

SUB-KINGDOM THALLOPHYTA [5]

These plants do not form embryos. They lack true roots, stems, and leaves; they have no vascular tissue; and the sex organs and sporangia are typically one-celled or at least without sterile wall cells.

DIVISION CHLOROPHYTA

Green algae. The plant body is unicellular, colonial, or multicellular, with the cells containing organized and delimited nuclei and plastids. Chlorophylls "a" and "b" and carotenoids are present, as in the higher green plants. Food reserves are mostly starch and fats. Asexual reproduction occurs by cell division and zoospores; sexual reproduction is isogamous, heterogamous, and oögamous. Motile

[5] The two sub-kingdoms are of questionable status (artificial groupings) and have been removed from some systems. The various divisions then stand separately and are not divided into two groupings.

cells usually bear two or four equal flagella anteriorly placed. Genera: *Chlamydomonas, Ulothrix, Oedogonium, Ulva*, etc.

DIVISION EUGLENOPHYTA

Euglenoids. These are unwalled, unicellular, and typically uniflagellate, with definite nuclei and plastids. Chlorophylls "a" and "b" and carotenoids as in Chlorophyta. Food reserves are paramylum (similar to starch) and fats. Asexual reproduction is by cell division. A gullet, which functions to ingest food, is present in some genera. Genera: *Euglena, Colacium*, etc.

DIVISION CHRYSOPHYTA

Yellow-green and golden-brown algae and the diatoms. The plant body is unicellular, colonial, or multicellular, with organized nuclei and plastids. Chlorophylls "a" and "c" or "e" are present but may be masked by various yellow or brown pigments. Food reserves are oils and leucosin or volutin, both complex carbohydrates. Asexual reproduction is by cell division, motile and non-motile spores; sexual reproduction is isogamous or heterogamous. The wall of each cell is composed of two overlapping halves, either in the metabolic or cyst stages; silica frequently composes part of the wall. Flagella, when present, are of unequal size and anteriorly placed. Genera: *Vaucheria, Pinnularia, Navicula*, etc.

DIVISION PYRROPHYTA

Dinoflagellates. These are typically unicellular, with a wall composed of interlocking plates and containing two grooves, one encircling the cell transversely while the other runs longitudinally along one side. They have two flagella, one lying in the transverse groove, the other extending out from the longitudinal groove. Genera: *Ceratium, Goniaulax*, etc.

DIVISION PHAEOPHYTA

Brown algae. The plant body is a filamentous to complex parenchymatous structure with considerable differentiation. Chlorophylls "a" and "c" are usually masked by a brown pigment, fucoxanthin. Food reserves are sugars and fats. Asexual reproduction is usually by motile spores; sexual reproduction is isogamous or oögamous. Motile reproductive cells are pear-shaped and have two lateral, unequal flagella. General: *Ectocarpus, Laminaria, Fucus*, etc.

DIVISION RHODOPHYTA

Red algae. These plants are essentially branching filamentous structures, which may build up a relatively complex body. Chlorophylls "a" and "d" are usually masked by a red pigment, phycoerythrin; a blue pigment, phycocyanin, may also be present. Food reserve is "floridean" starch. Asexual reproduction is by non-motile spores; sexual reproduction is oögamous. No flagellated cells are produced. Genera: *Nemalion, Polysiphonia, Porphyra, Gelidium*, etc.

DIVISION SCHIZOPHYTA

Blue-green algae and bacteria. The plant body is unicellular or colonial, with the cells containing a poorly organized nucleus and no plastids. Chromatin is always present, and possibly chromosomes in some. Pigmentation is variable. Reproduction is by fission; sexual reproduction is very rare. The outer wall layer is frequently mucilaginous.

Class Cyanophyceae

Blue-green algae. Chlorophyll "a" is usually masked by a blue pigment, phycocyanin, or a red pigment, phycoerythrin. Food reserve is glycogen, a type of starch. Genera: *Oscillatoria, Nostoc, Gleocapsa*, etc.

Class Schizomycetes

Bacteria. Chlorophylls are lacking. They are largely heterotrophic, although a few are chemosynthetic autotrophic. Genera: *Nitrosomonas, Clostridium, Erwinia, Vibrio, Pasteurella*, etc.

DIVISION MYXOMYÇOPHYTA

Slime molds. The body is a naked, multinucleate, non-septate, amorphous mass of protoplasm. They are heterotrophic. Asexual reproduction is by non-motile spores; sexual reproduction is by fusion of amoeboid gametes. Genera: *Plasmodiophora, Spongospora, Physarium*, etc.

DIVISION EUMYCOPHYTA

True fungi. The plant body is unicellular, unbranched or branched filamentous, or pseudoparenchymatous. They are heterotrophic. The reserve food is glycogen. Asexual reproduction is by many kinds of spores, some of which are produced in definite sporangia; sexual reproduction is varied. Certain spores are produced only after sexual reproduction and form immediately following meiosis.

Class Phycomycetes

Algal fungi. The plant consists of non-septate (coenocytic), branching filaments not organized into compact bodies of definite

233 ﴾﴿

form. Asexual reproduction is by means of spores produced in a sporangium; sexual reproduction is similar to Chlorophyta. Genera: *Rhizopus, Saprolegnia, Phytophthora, Pythium,* etc.

Class Ascomycetes

Sac fungi. The members of this group are unicellular to multicellular. In most of the latter the septate filaments combine to form a definite macroscopic reproductive body, the ascocarp. Asexual reproduction is usually by chains of spores produced at the tips of filaments, although sometimes by budding; sexual reproduction results in the development of a sac, or ascus, containing eight ascospores (sometimes four). Genera: *Peziza, Aspergillus, Penicillium, Sacchoromyces, Claviceps, Venturia,* etc.

Class Basidiomycetes

Club fungi. The septate filaments usually form a definite macroscopic reproductive body, the basidiocarp or sporophore. Following sexual reproduction, a club-shaped structure is formed, a basidium, bearing four basidiospores on small stalks. Genera: *Agaricus, Amanita, Puccinia, Fomes, Lycoperdon, Ustilago,* etc.

Class Deuteromycetes

Imperfect fungi. A large, miscellaneous, artificial group of fungi in which sexual reproduction does not occur or has not been found. Genera: *Candida, Alternaria, Colletotrichum, Fusarium, Botrytis, Cercospora,* etc.

Class Lichens

These plants are associations of an alga (Chlorophyta or Cyanophyceae) and a fungus (Ascomycetes or Basidiomycetes).

SUB-KINGDOM EMBRYOPHYTA

In these plants a multicellular embryo is retained in the female sex organ, the archegonium, for some time. The sex organs and sporangia are multicellular and have sterile wall cells. They are oögamous. Chlorophylls "a" and "b" and carotenoids are present in plastids, as in Chlorophyta. They are land plants; a cuticle is present. A definite alternation of phases occurs.

DIVISION BRYOPHYTA

Mosses and allies. These are small plants which lack true roots, stems, and leaves; they are parenchymatous; they lack vascular tissue. Water is necessary for the transfer of sperm prior to fertilization. The gametophyte is dominant and nutritionally independent, whereas the sporophyte is permanently attached to the gametophyte and dependent upon it.

Class Musci

Mosses. The gametophyte has an early transitory protonemal stage which gives rise to "leafy" shoots; the mature gametophyte is usually erect and radially arranged. The spores are released from the sporophyte by a transverse splitting of the sporangium or capsule; no elaters are present. Genera: *Mnium, Polytrichum, Sphagnum*, etc.

Class Hepaticae

Liverworts. The mature gametophyte is prostrate and dorsiventrally differentiated; there is no protonemal stage or only a brief, indistinct one. The spores are released by a longitudinal splitting of the capsule. Genera: *Marchantia, Pellia, Riccia, Porella*, etc.

DIVISION TRACHEOPHYTA

Vascular plants. These plants have a well-developed vascular tissue, xylem and phloem, in the sporophyte, which is independent at maturity.

SUB-DIVISION PSILOPSIDA. The sporophytes have no roots or true leaves; no leaf gaps are present in the vascular cylinder. They are dichotomously branched, with terminal sporangia containing only one type of spore (homosporous). Water is necessary for the transfer of sperm previous to fertilization. Both sporophyte and gametophyte are nutritionally independent. Genera: *Psilotum* and *Tmesipteris*.

SUB-DIVISION LYCOPSIDA. Club mosses. The sporophytes have roots, stems, and small leaves, but no leaf gaps. Single sporangia are borne on the upper surface of leaves (or sporophylls) which are usually arranged in the form of a cone or strobilus. The sporophyte is dominant, and the gametophyte is small; both are nutritionally independent. Water is necessary for sperm transfer. Genera: *Lycopodium, Selaginella*, etc.

SUB-DIVISION SPHENOPSIDA. Horsetails. The sporophytes have roots, stems, and small leaves, but no leaf gaps. The leaves and branches are whorled; the stem is hollow and jointed. Groups of sporangia are borne on stalked, umbrella-like structures which are grouped to form strobili. The sporophyte is dominant, the gametophyte is small, and both are nutritionally independent. Water is necessary for sperm transfer. Genus: *Equisetum*.

SUB-DIVISION PTEROPSIDA. Ferns and seed plants. The dominant sporophytes have roots, stems, and large leaves; leaf gaps are present. Sporangia are borne on the lower surface of leaves or on leaf-like structures.

Class Filicineae

Ferns. Leaves are typically compound and uncoil as they develop (circinnate vernation). Roots are usually adventitious from a horizontal rhizome. The leaf and sporangial-bearing organs are not differentiated; most are homosporous. Seeds are not produced. The gametophyte is nutritionally independent, as is the mature, much larger sporophyte. Water is necessary for the transport of sperm. Genera: *Polypodium, Pteris, Ophioglossum, Marattia,* etc.

Class Gymnospermae

Naked ovules, which develop into seeds, are produced on the upper sides of scales which are usually parts of cones. Leaves are usually evergreen needles or scales. These plants are heterosporous; the very small gametophyte is nutritionally dependent upon the sporophyte, with the female gametophyte developing inside of the sporangium. They are wind-pollinated; pollen tubes are formed. Genera: *Pinus,· Picea, Abies, Sequoia, Thuja, Ginkgo, Zamia,* etc.

Class Angiospermae

Flowering plants. Sporangia are borne on modified branch systems, the stamens and carpels, which are parts of the flower. Seeds develop from ovules, which are enclosed in the carpels. These plants are heterosporous; the gametophyte is very reduced and dependent upon the sporophyte, with the female gametophyte developing inside of the sporangium. They are wind- or insect-pollinated; pollen tubes are formed. "Double fertilization" occurs.

Sub-class Dicotyledonae. Dicots. These plants have two cotyledons in the embryo; the flower parts are mostly in multiples of fours and fives; the leaves are net-veined; a cambium is usually present. Genera: *Ranunculus, Magnolia, Ulmus, Brassica, Rosa, Pyrus, Phaseolus, Acer, Quercus, Aster, Zinnea,* etc.

Sub-class Monocotyledonae. Monocots. These plants have one cotyledon in the embryo; flower parts are mostly in threes; the leaves are usually narrow and elongated, with parallel veins; a cambium is usually lacking. Genera: *Typha, Lilium, Allium, Carex, Bromus, Triticum, Hordeum, Festuca, Oryza, Avena, Zea,* etc.

236   To repeat: the preceding classification of the plant kingdom is based upon apparent relationships of plants; gaps exist in our knowledge of

exact relationships between some of the groups; changes quite likely will have to be made in this system as further investigations add to our knowledge.

Summary

1. Taxonomists, in studying plant classification, attempt to arrange plants into categories or groups which reflect the relationships among the various plants. In some instances artificial categories must be used until relationships are clarified by further investigations. In order to prevent confusion, a plant should always be referred to by its scientific name; this consists of the genus and species categories.

2. A species is rather difficult to define, but it may be considered as a group containing all of the individuals of a particular kind of plant and excluding all those that are different. Usually species are not capable of interbreeding.

3. Plants may reproduce asexually or sexually. In the former type no fusion of gametes occurs, and such reproduction is usually accomplished by fission, budding, spore formation, the formation of tubers or corms, runners, and other methods. Sexual reproduction involves fusion of gametes, cell division and growth, and meiosis.

4. In plants the zygote, as a result of mitotic divisions, develops into a multicellular diploid phase (the sporophyte) which produces spores as a result of meiosis. These spores develop into a multicellular, haploid phase (the gametophyte) which produces gametes. This rotation of a diploid and a haploid structure is termed alternation of phases. In some plants the gametophyte is dominant, in some the sporophyte, and in others both phases are of equal importance.

5. The classification of the plant kingdom presented in this text is based upon apparent relationships of plants. Systems of classification are being revised continually as new information is obtained, and various changes probably will have to be made in the present system.

REVIEW TOPICS AND QUESTIONS

1. Discuss the difference between a natural and an artificial system of classification. Why are all systems at least partially artificial?
2. What is meant when one speaks of the "scientific name" of an organism? Why are such names necessary?
3. Why is a "species" difficult to define?
4. Explain in detail what you should do in order to identify a plant which you have found. If you found only the roots, stems, and leaves of the plant, why would this make your task of identification more difficult?
5. Explain what is meant by "alternation of phases." Why is this term preferable to "alternation of generations"?

SUGGESTED READINGS

Bold, H. C. *Morphology of Plants*. New York: Harper, 1957.
————. *The Plant Kingdom*. Englewood Cliffs, N. J.: Prentice-Hall, 1960.
Dodd, J. D. *Form and Function in Plants*. Ames, Iowa: Iowa State Univ. Press, 1962.
Lawrence, G. H. M. *An Introduction to Plant Taxonomy*. New York: Macmillan, 1955.
Pool, R. J. *Flowers and Flowering Plants*. New York: McGraw-Hill, 1941.
Porter, C. L. *Taxonomy of Flowering Plants*. San Francisco: Freeman, 1959.
Russell, N. H. *An Introduction to the Plant Kingdom*. St. Louis: Mosby, 1958.

Sub-kingdom Thallophyta: Algal Forms

19.1 Alga versus fungus

In many older systems of classification, Thallophyta were subdivided into Algae and Fungi. An **alga** is any member of the Thallophyta which contains chlorophyll, while a **fungus** is any member which does not contain chlorophyll. This separation is very artificial and no longer used in classifying plants. However, to speak of "algae" and "fungi" is sometimes convenient, so these words have been retained, although having no real taxonomic significance.[1] In any of the sciences, care must be taken that words are well defined and used accurately.

In classifying organisms a characteristic, such as the presence or absence of a single pigment, is not considered to be sufficiently important for use as a diagnostic feature for a major group. The sub-kingdom Thallophyta consists of several divisions of equal rank which probably developed independently in a parallel series from a common ancestral form.

In this chapter we will study representative individuals of the following thallophyte divisions: Chlorophyta, Chrysophyta, and Phaeophyta. The bacteria and blue-green algae (Schizophyta) will be discussed in the next chapter, followed by the true molds (Eumycophyta). Thus, except for the blue-greens, algae will be covered first.

[1] Another such term of convenience is "vegetable" as used by most laymen. The term fruit has a specific meaning for botanists, but vegetable has no such connotation and therefore is not used. Try defining the word vegetable.

19.2   General characteristics of the sub-kingdom Thallophyta

The general consensus is that this grouping is largely an artificial one, although highly convenient, which includes several distinct phyla which are not really closely related. However, these diverse phyla do have certain features in common. No embryos are formed; the zygote does not develop into a multicellular structure contained within the preceding gametophyte or sporophyte phase. Although some of the more complex plants in this sub-kingdom appear to have bodies which are differentiated, these are not considered to be true roots, stems, or leaves, because they lack the vascular tissue and other characteristics of such structures in higher plants. The sex organs and sporangia are usually one-celled, or, if multicellular, the gametes and spores are not enclosed within a wall formed by a layer of sterile (non-reproductive) cells.

The members of the Thallophyta range in size from microscopic bacteria to extremely large multicellular forms often more than two hundred feet in length (brown algae). They are the most primitive members of the plant kingdom. Those which contain chlorophyll are autotrophic, while the rest are mainly heterotrophic, although a few of the bacteria are chemosynthetic autotrophes. The methods of reproduction vary greatly and will be discussed individually for certain typical examples from the different divisions.

Some members of this sub-kingdom are extremely important to life in general as food organisms, as oxygen producers, or as decay organisms. Others are important in demonstrating evolutionary advances. Specific individuals will be examined in some detail to emphasize these points.

19.3   Characteristics of the division Chlorophyta

The green algae include organisms which vary greatly as to structure and methods of reproduction. They are unicellular, colonial, or multicellular, the cells containing organized nuclei and plastids.[2] A **colony** merely consists of unicellular individuals which cohere to form a clump or group of various sizes and shapes, whereas a **multicellular organism** implies a differentiation of cells or tissues. In the former the cells are all alike and are individual plants themselves; in the latter the entire mass of cells comprises one plant, some cells of which are specialized or modified structurally and thus are not all alike. The chloroplasts contain chlorophylls "a" and "b" and carotenoid pigments

[2] Unless otherwise stated, all the plants discussed have nuclei and plastids in the component cells.

in the same ratio as is found in the higher green plants; filamentous types of green algae may have been the ancestors of the land plants. Food reserves are mostly starch and some fats, which is also similar to the higher green plants.

Most of the species (about 90 per cent) are fresh-water forms or marine forms, but some can exist on various damp surfaces, such as soil, bark, shingles, and bricks. Some unicellular, non-motile green algae are found growing in an intimate relationship with certain fungi, forming a lichen (see Section 21.11), or sometimes enmeshed in the tissues of an animal, such as *Chlorohydra* (a coelenterate). These are probably associations of mutual benefit.

Asexual reproduction in the green algae may be by fission, fragmentation, or zoospores. Sexual reproduction involves isogamy, heterogamy, or oögamy. Thus, an alternation of haploid and diploid phases occurs in most species, but many form no multicellular sporophyte. In these, meiosis occurs when the zygote germinates, and the only diploid structure is the one-celled zygote. However, in *Ulva* (sea lettuce) a definite alternation of a multicellular gametophyte and a multicellular sporophyte occurs.

Figure 19-1. *Chlamydomonas*. **A:** A sectional view of the unicellular plant showing the central nucleus partially enclosed by the single, cup-shaped chloroplast. A pyrenoid is shown, at the right, on the surface of the chloroplast. The pigment spot is above the pyrenoid, and the two contractile vacuoles are just below the left flagellum. **B:** The life cycle, indicating both asexual and sexual reproduction. Compare with Figure 19-2.

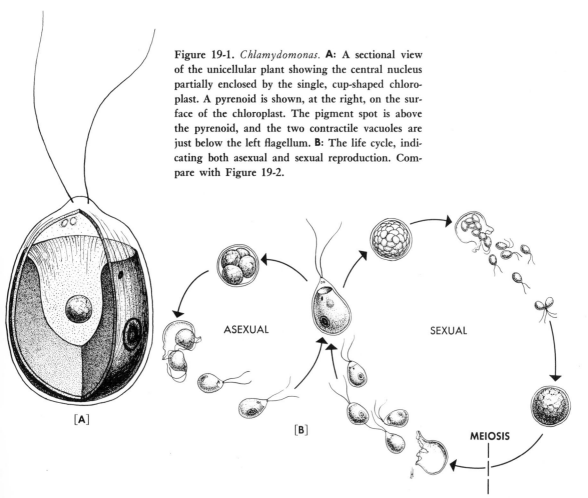

[A] ASEXUAL [B] SEXUAL MEIOSIS

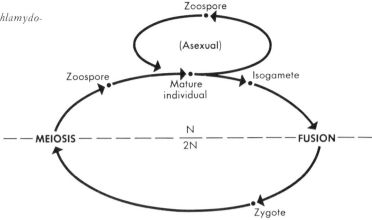

Figure 19-2. Life cycle of *Chlamydomonas* (word diagram).

19.4 Representative members of the Chlorophyta

The various kinds of green algae probably developed from a primitive motile unicellular type somewhat similar to, though more primitive than, *Chlamydomonas*. This organism will be discussed first, and then other individuals will be selected to indicate more advanced structures.

CHLAMYDOMONAS

The wall of this unicellular plant (see Figure 19-1A) is mainly composed of cellulose, and two equal **flagella** (hair-like appendages of cytoplasmic material), which project from the anterior end, pull the organism through the water. The nucleus is partially enclosed by a single, cup-shaped chloroplast, upon which is located a **pyrenoid.** This latter is a rounded proteinaceous body which seems to be the center of starch formation. Two small contractile vacuoles and a red pigment spot (frequently called an eyespot) are located near the anterior end of the cell. These vacuoles are possibly excretory in function, while the pigment spot is light-sensitive and results in the plant responding positively to a light stimulus.

Asexual reproduction is accomplished by the protoplasm forming into four to eight zoospores, similar in structure to the parent, which swim out and become new individuals when the parent cell wall ruptures. In sexual reproduction the protoplast produces sixteen to thirty-two isogametes, which are also like the parent but much smaller. These fuse in pairs, forming zygotes, which develop a thick wall and are resistant to adverse environmental conditions. The diploid zygote undergoes meiotic division, forming four haploid zoospores, which become mature plants when liberated. The life cycle of this plant is shown in Figures 19-1B and 19-2.

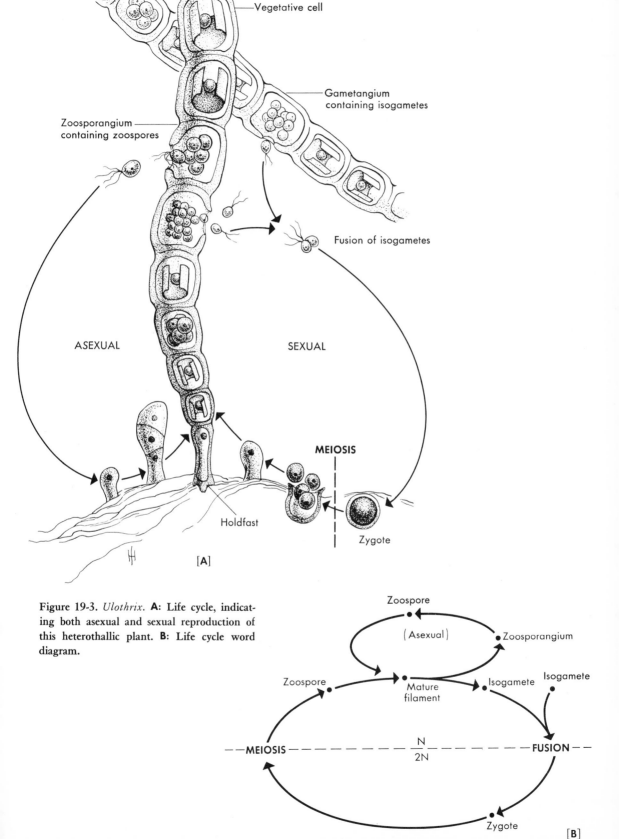

Vegetative cell

Gametangium
containing isogametes

Zoosporangium
containing zoospores

Fusion of isogametes

ASEXUAL

SEXUAL

MEIOSIS

Holdfast

Zygote

[A]

Figure 19-3. *Ulothrix*. **A:** Life cycle, indicating both asexual and sexual reproduction of this heterothallic plant. **B:** Life cycle word diagram.

Zoospore

(Asexual)

Zoosporangium

Zoospore

Mature
filament

Isogamete

Isogamete

MEIOSIS ———— $\dfrac{N}{2N}$ ———— FUSION

Zygote

[B]

[A]

[B]

[C]

Figure 19-4. *Ulva.* **A**: Habit sketch. **B**: Zoospores. **C**: Isogametes. **D**: Life cycle word diagram.

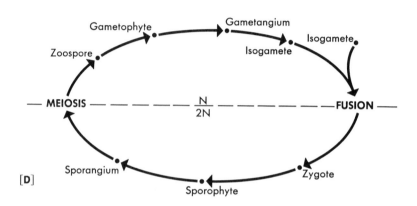

[D]

ULOTHRIX

This plant (Figure 19-3) is a truly multicellular organism; many cells form one individual having some differentiation of structure and function. This is a considerable advantage in efficiency over a structure such as the unicellular *Chlamydomonas* or various colonial forms. *Ulothrix* consists of a single unbranched filament in which the basal cell is a **holdfast** (finger-like projections anchor the filament to solid surfaces). Each cylindrical cell has a single collar-shaped chloroplast, with pyrenoids; the nucleus is usually partially enclosed by the chloroplast. The plant increases in length by mitotic divisions of the component cells.

Asexual reproduction is by fragmentation or by the production of zoospores. These latter are produced by certain cells, called **zoosporangia,** when the contents divide into several (4 to 16) protoplasts. Each

244

zoospore has four flagella, a chloroplast, a nucleus, and a pigment spot; it looks almost like a *Chlamydomonas* cell. After escaping when the wall of the zoosporangium ruptures, the zoospore swims about, attaches to a surface, and produces a new filament. In sexual reproduction some of the cells of a filament become **gametangia,** in which the contents divide to form 32 to 64 isogametes. These gametes are liberated into the water, but those from the same plant do not fuse. For isogamy to occur, isogametes from different filaments must be present, a condition termed **heterothallic.** These gametes are like small editions of zoospores but have only two flagella. The resistant, thick-walled diploid zygote eventually undergoes meiosis, producing four haploid spores, each of which is capable of developing into a new filament.

The general size and shape of the isogametes and zoospores of *Chlamydomonas* and *Ulothrix* have led to the suggestion that sexual reproduction probably first arose in a *Chlamydomonas*-type unicell: when small zoospores which did not contain sufficient stored foods to develop into mature new individuals were produced, the fusion of two such small structures would be a great advantage. The fact that isogametes of *Ulothrix* have two flagella while the zoospores have four is similarly suggestive, especially in view of the existence of a unicellular alga, *Carteria,* which differs from *Chlamydomonas* only in having four flagella instead of two and in being larger.

The advantage of even a very simple multicellular organism, such as *Ulothrix,* over a unicellular one arises from the increased number of zoospores and gametes which are produced by the former, as well as the differentiation which leads to greater efficiency. In the multicellular form vegetative cells are always carrying on photosynthesis at the same time that reproductive cells are being produced. This is, of course, not possible with unicells.

ULVA

This plant (Figure 19-4) is an edible marine alga commonly known as sea lettuce. The cells divide mainly in two planes, resulting in a flat, sheet-like plant body two cells in thickness. *Ulothrix,* of course, divides in one plane, resulting in its typical filament. The basal portion of *Ulva* forms a holdfast which consists of an entangled mass of finger-like outgrowths of many cells located in that region. This is quite different from the single-cell holdfast of *Ulothrix.* Each cell contains one nucleus and a cup-shaped chloroplast with a single pyrenoid.

Ulva undergoes a very definite alternation of multicellular phases, a condition not found in *Ulothrix,* where the diploid condition consists of the one-celled zygote. In *Ulva* biflagellate isogametes are formed by the dividing up of the protoplast of a cell, the gametangium. Gametes from different thalli [3] fuse to form a zygote which gives rise to a diploid thallus which produces only haploid zoospores. These zoospores (four flagella each) give rise to haploid thalli that produce only gametes. Although the chromosome numbers of the cells comprising the two kinds of thalli differ, the thalli look alike and can be distinguished only when reproductive cells are being formed. This alternation of phases is an important feature of plant life cycles; it is characteristic of most Phaeophyta, Rhodophyta, Bryophyta, and Tracheophyta.

PANDORINA

This plant is a spherical colonial form that is of interest because of the fusion of unequal gametes which takes place during sexual reproduction; though both are biflagellate, a small active gamete fuses with a large sluggish gamete. This is an example of **heterogamy** and is regarded as a very primitive stage in the differentiation of sex.

OEDOGONIUM

This plant (Figure 19-5) is an unbranched filament consisting of cylindrical cells each of which contains a nucleus and a single large chloroplast of irregular net-like shape with many pyrenoids. The basal cell is modified as a holdfast, and growth of the filament occurs as various cells divide mitotically.

Asexual reproduction is by fragmentation or by the production of a single large zoospore from the protoplast of a cell, which is then termed a zoosporangium. The anterior region of the zoospore is clear and is encircled by a crown of **cilia,** which are similar to flagella but much shorter. The zoospore is liberated by a rupture of the wall of the zoosporangium, swims about, attaches to a surface, and develops into a new filament. Sexual reproduction is of the oögamous type. Two sperm, which resemble zoospores but are much smaller, are produced in each of a number of small cells termed **antheridia** (singular **antheridium**). The sperm swims to an enlarged globose cell, the **oögonium** (plural, **oögonia**), enters through a pore in the wall of this cell, and fuses with the single egg contained therein. The diploid zygote develops a thick wall and is very resistant to adverse conditions. When the zygote germinates, it produces four haploid zoospores as a result of meiosis, each of which may develop into a new filament.

Oedogonium is considered to be a more advanced filamentous type

---

[3] Thalli: plural of thallus, a plant body which is not differentiated into tissues.

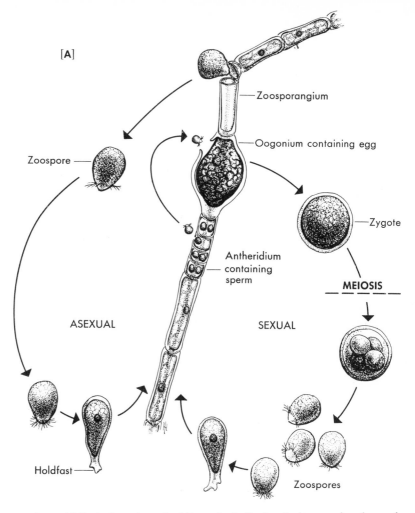

[A]

Zoosporangium

Oogonium containing egg

Zoospore

Zygote

Antheridium
containing
sperm

MEIOSIS

ASEXUAL

SEXUAL

Holdfast

Zoospores

Figure 19-5. *Oedogonium.* **A**: Life cycle, indicating both asexual and sexual reproduction of this oögamous plant. **B**: Life cycle word diagram.

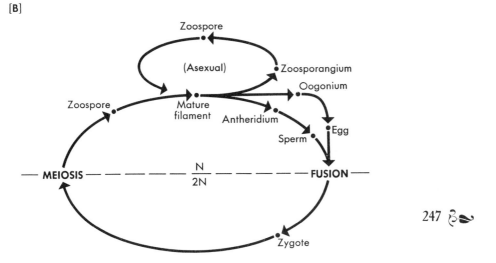

[B]

Zoospore

(Asexual)

Zoosporangium

Oogonium

Zoospore

Mature
filament

Antheridium

Egg

Sperm

MEIOSIS

$\dfrac{N}{2N}$

FUSION

Zygote

247

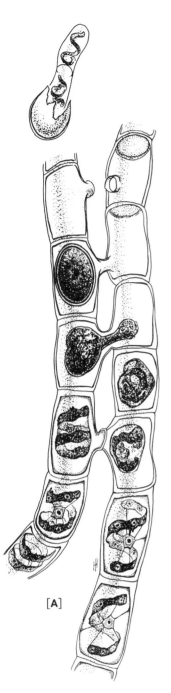

[A]

than *Ulothrix* because of the development of oögamy in the former. Such a differentiation of gametes has considerable survival value, due to the presence of a relatively large amount of food in the egg which is then available for the subsequent germination of the zygote and the growth of the resultant zoospores. Also, at least one of the gametes remains protected by the walls of the cell in which it is formed; the egg is not liberated into the surrounding water, as is the sperm. In the life history of any organism, the gametes are always the most delicate structures. They never have thick walls; any gametes which might by chance develop thick walls would find fusion with other gametes a rather difficult proposition. An organism which produced such peculiar gametes would have difficulty surviving. Therefore, any protection afforded to the gametes would be very advantageous to the plant. This should be borne in mind as various groups of the plant kingdom are studied.

SPIROGYRA

A *Spirogyra* plant (Figure 19-6) consists of an unbranched filament composed of cylindrical cells, each of which contains one or more ribbon-like chloroplasts in the form of a spiral band; pyrenoids are conspicuous on a chloroplast. Most of the interior of the cell is occupied by a large vacuole. Cytoplasm lines the cell wall and extends as strands toward the central region, where it surrounds the nucleus.

No zoospores are produced, and asexual reproduction is by fragmentation only. During sexual reproduction, when two filaments come in contact, projections grow singly from cells of each filament, and the

Figure 19-6. *Spirogyra*. **A: Two filaments to show sexual reproduction. The bottom two cells in each filament are in the vegetative condition. In the cells above conjugation tubes have formed; the protoplasm of one cell is shown moving through the tube and fusing with the protoplasm of the cell to the left. A thick-walled zygote is present in one of the cells at the upper left. A similar zygote is shown germinating at the top left of the diagram. B: Life cycle word diagram.**

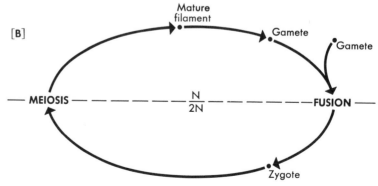

wall between the projections eventually dissolves. The protoplasm of one cell, acting as a gamete, moves through the connecting **conjugation tube** to the opposite cell and fuses with the protoplast of that cell. Usually all of the cells of a filament act alike so that, after fusion, one filament contains zygotes and the opposite filament consists of empty cells. The zygote develops a thick wall and is resistant to adverse conditions. On germination the diploid zygote nucleus undergoes meiosis, forming four haploid nuclei, three of which degenerate. The cell with the remaining nucleus grows into a new haploid filament by mitotic divisions and subsequent cell enlargements.

Spirogyra and similar Chlorophyta are side branches in the evolutionary scheme of things; they are a dead end and give rise to no other forms. This plant was discussed to indicate another type of sexual reproduction, a type which developed independently in the Eumycophyta, for example *Rhizopus* (Section 21.3).

19.5 Importance of the Chlorophyta

The green algae probably developed from motile unicells similar to *Chlamydomonas* and produced a variety of forms and types of reproduction only some of which have been discussed. This group presents a clear example of radiating evolutionary development. The development of sexuality has been emphasized because of the great importance of this type of reproduction in the development of variations, which are so significant in the survival of any group.

The green algae are also thought to have given rise to all of the higher green plants, the Embryophyta.

Many of the Chlorophyta in both fresh and salt water comprise food supplies for animals. Some, *Ulva* as an example, are utilized by man as food. In addition to supplying food, the photosynthetic process supplies the oxygen which is so necessary for life in the waters. Although the green algae themselves require oxygen for their respiratory processes and obtain their supply from photosynthesis, their rate of photosynthesis fortunately is much greater than the rate of respiration, and sufficient oxygen is left over to supply the needs of aquatic animals.

19.6 Characteristics of the division Chrysophyta

This division includes several groups (yellow-green algae, golden-brown algae, and the diatoms) but only the diatoms will be discussed (Figure 19-7). These plants are unicellular, sometimes forming colonies, each cell containing a nucleus and two or more chloroplasts in which are found chlorophylls "a" and "c" plus various yellow and

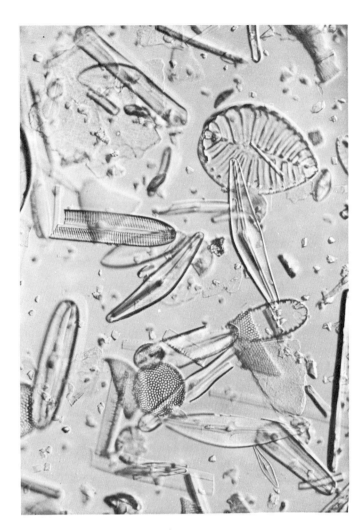

Figure 19-7. Photomicrograph of various diatoms. (Courtesy of General Biological Supply House, Chicago.)

brown pigments. The food reserves are in the form of volutin (a complex carbohydrate similar to starch), fats, and oils; no starch is formed. The wall of each cell consists of two overlapping halves composed of pectic substances impregnated with silica (one of the chief constituents of glass). The walls do not decay, at least not the silica portion. Exceedingly beautiful and delicate markings are found on the walls; microscopic examination reveals that these "lines" are actually rows of tiny dots or pits. (The effective resolution of a microscope is frequently tested by examining these markings.) Many diatoms move about slowly as a result of the streaming of cytoplasm which extrudes slightly through a long narrow opening or cleft which runs down the center of the top cell-half.

Asexual reproduction is by cell division (mitosis), during which the overlapping walls come apart, each partially enclosing one of the new protoplasts. A new half-wall is secreted inside of the old and is, of course, always smaller than the older half-wall (Figure 19-8); some of the diatoms have a tendency to become smaller and smaller. The original size is restored by the formation of **auxospores:** The walls may separate, the protoplasm enlarging to form an auxospore, which then produces two new half-walls. The auxospore may also result from sexual reproduction, the protoplast of two diatoms fusing to form an enlarged auxospore. Divisions of the auxospores then occur as described previously for other diatom cells. Whether meiosis occurs when gametes are formed or when the sexually derived auxospore (actually a zygote, of course) germinates is not known.

19.7 Importance of the Chrysophyta

The various groups of this division have many structural and reproductive features which are quite similar to groups in the Chlorophyta. The scope of this text does not allow us to discuss these similarities except to state that they can be accounted for by parallel development of the two distinct divisions. While the two may have been derived from different primitive flagellated unicells, these ancestors themselves were related.

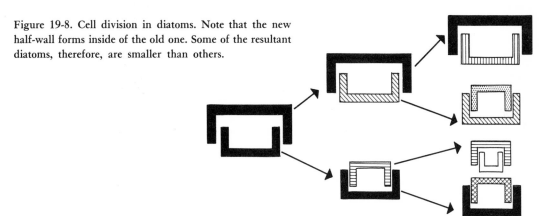

Figure 19-8. Cell division in diatoms. Note that the new half-wall forms inside of the old one. Some of the resultant diatoms, therefore, are smaller than others.

The diatoms, along with the Pyrrophyta,[4] are known as the "grass of the seas" and form the basis of most of the food chains in the seas. Small animals eat these plants and are in turn eaten by larger animals,

[4] The red tide that occasionally appears off the Atlantic or Pacific Coasts of North America consists of billions of tiny dinoflagellates (Pyrrophyta), usually *Gymnodinium* or *Gonyaulax;* up to ten million of these organisms may be in one cubic foot of water, which appears reddish because of pigments in the cells. These organisms are generally toxic to fishes, and red tides may be quite destructive.

and so on. The animals obtain their basic building materials for synthesizing cellular constituents from the sugars, fats, oils, and amino acids of these tiny plants. Even man, feeding upon fishes, is dependent upon these organisms which occur in such enormous numbers in the waters of the world.

Since the siliceous walls do not decay, great numbers of empty walls accumulate at the bottom of any water in which diatoms live. These rock-like deposits of **diatomaceous earth** are frequently very thick, and many are worked as open quarries. This material is used in filters, as insulation, in dynamite as an absorbent for liquid nitroglycerine, in cement to increase the workability and strength of concrete, and as a mild abrasive in metal polishes and toothpastes. One of the largest deposits of diatomaceous earth occurs at Lompoc, California, and is approximately one thousand feet deep and twelve miles square; since one cubic inch of diatomaceous earth contains about forty million diatom remains, this deposit originally contained somewhat more than 10^{24} diatoms.* Such deposits which occur above the water surface are the result of geological uplift; the area must have been under water at one time, because all diatoms are either marine or fresh water forms. Diatoms are also often found with oil deposits and are frequently of use to geologists as one of the diagnostic characteristics of oil-bearing soils. Diatoms quite possibly were involved in the production of the oil deposits in the first place, as is suggested by the typical oil food reserves in this group.

19.8   Characteristics of the division Phaeophyta

The brown algae vary in size from small filamentous types to the huge complex **kelps** usually found in cold waters; no unicellular or colonial forms have been found. The plastids contain chlorophylls "a" and "c," which are usually masked by an accompanying brown pigment, **fucoxanthin.** Some kelps have considerable parenchymatous tissue differentiation; in addition to the holdfast is a **stipe** (or stalk) which bears flattened **blades.** The stipe has a definite **epidermis,** a **medulla** in the central region consisting of elongated cells, and an intermediate **cortex** which consists of loosely arranged spherical cells. One type of cell in the medulla resembles the sieve tube elements in the phloem of higher plants; it is elongated, arranged end-to-end, and has perforated end walls similar to sieve plates. However, none of this group has any true vascular tissue and certainly no xylem, and the brown algae are not considered to have true roots, stems, or leaves.

* 10^{24} equals one followed by twenty-four zeroes.

Many of the larger forms bear **bladders,** gas-filled enlargements, which serve to buoy the upper portions near the surface. The food reserves are typically sugars and fats, and no insoluble carbohydrates are formed. The inner layer of the wall is composed of cellulose, but the outer layer consists of a slimy, gelatinous material called algin.

Brown algae may increase in size as a result of a growing apex or, as in kelps, by the activity of a meristematic region at the base of the stipe or at the juncture of stipe and blade. Asexual reproduction is occasionally by fragmentation, but usually by zoospores. Sexual reproduction is various; both isogamous and oögamous forms are found. An alternation of phases occurs, with a strong tendency toward a reduction of the gametophyte; the large kelps are sporophytes, and in *Fucus* the gametophyte phase is present only as gametes (no multicellular gametophyte). The motile cells, either zoospores or gametes, are pear-shaped with two unequal flagella attached at the side.

19.9 Representative members of the Phaeophyta

As was done with the Chlorophyta, a few individual brown algae will be discussed in order to emphasize evolutionary development.

Figure 19-9. *Ectocarpus.* **A:** Habit sketch. **B:** Life cycle word diagram.

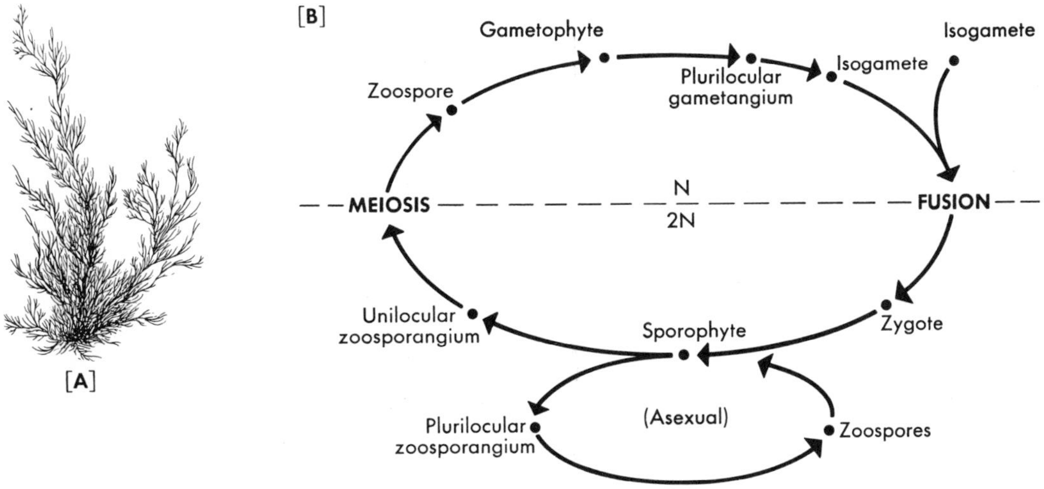

ECTOCARPUS

The genus *Ectocarpus* (Figure 19-9) consists of small, branched, filamentous forms in which the sporophyte and gametophyte phases are very similar and can be distinguished only by the type of repro-

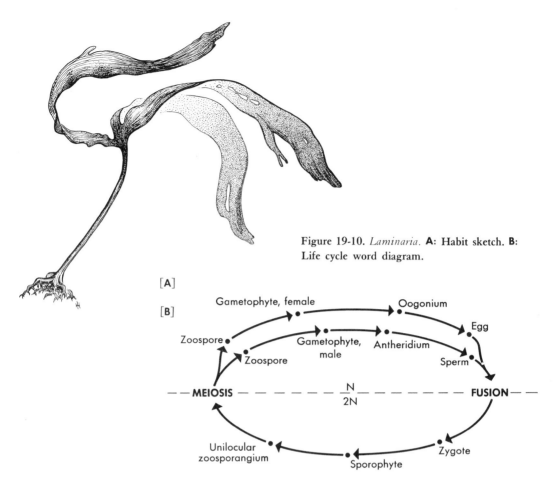

Figure 19-10. *Laminaria*. **A**: Habit sketch. **B**: Life cycle word diagram.

[A]

[B]

ductive cells which are produced. The sporophyte bears two kinds of sporangia: a **plurilocular** (multicellular) **zoosporangium** in which each cell produces a diploid zoospore which develops into a new sporophyte, and a **unilocular** (one-celled) **zoosporangium** in which meiosis occurs and the resultant numerous haploid zoospores develop into gametophytes. The gametophytes bear **plurilocular gametangia**,[5] which are very similar in appearance to the plurilocular zoosporangia, and the liberated isogametes from different plants fuse to produce the diploid zygote; germination of the zygote produces a sporophyte.

LAMINARIA

In this plant (Figure 19-10) the diploid sporophyte is very large, usually consisting of long expanded blades with a stout stipe held to the substratum by a holdfast, while the haploid gametophyte is ex-

[5] *All* of the cells are functional; there is no sterile layer, or jacket, of cells enclosing the reproductive cells. This is quite different from the situation found in the Embryophyta (see Section 22.1).

tremely tiny in size, consisting of but a few cells. Sexual reproduction is of the oögamous type; sperm are produced in antheridia by a male gametophyte, and eggs in oögonia by the female gametophyte. Fusion takes place with the egg partially extruded, and the zygote develops into a sporophyte. The nucleus of a unilocular zoosporangium of the sporophyte first divides meiotically, and then numerous mitotic divisions finally result in the production of many haploid zoospores, which are liberated and develop into gametophytes (half of which are male and half female). No asexual zoospores are produced.

FUCUS

This plant (Figure 19-11) consists of a flattened, dichotomously branched thallus with a stipe and a holdfast; air-filled bladders are frequently present and serve to buoy up the plant. The inflated tips **(receptacles)** of the thallus are covered with small wart-like swellings

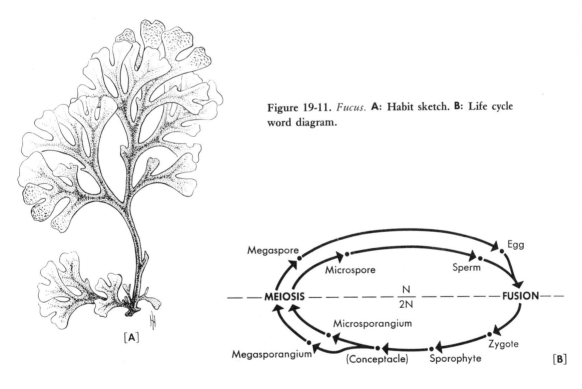

Figure 19-11. *Fucus.* **A**: Habit sketch. **B**: Life cycle word diagram.

which are actually the raised exits from embedded spherical chambers **(conceptacles).** Two kinds of sporangia are produced, either within the same conceptacle or in different conceptacles; in some species only one kind of sporangium is produced on any one plant. The **microsporangia** (male sporangia) are small oval structures borne on branched

255 ⟨⟩

filaments. As a result of meiosis, **microspores** (male spores) are produced, which undergo mitotic divisions to form numerous biflagellated sperm. The globose **megasporangium** (female sporangium) is produced at the end of a small stalk; meiosis results in the formation of four **megaspores,** which divide once more mitotically to produce eight eggs. The gametophyte as such is missing; gametes are formed directly from spores.[6] The gametes are released into the water, where fertilization occurs; the eggs float and become surrounded by a swarm of motile sperm. The zygotes sink to the bottom and develop into new sporophyte *Fucus* plants.

19.10 Importance of the Phaeophyta

Because of the lack of any simple brown algae, we cannot trace their ancestry, but they probably arose from flagellated brown unicells in a manner parallel to that of the Chlorophyta. The Phaeophyta have evolved further than the Chlorophyta; the former have considerable differentiation of tissues and some multicellular sex organs. An evolution of sexuality from the isogamous type (*Ectocarpus*) to the oögamous type (*Laminaria* and *Fucus*) has occurred; a general tendency for a reduction in the size of the gametophyte has also been noticed. In *Ectocarpus* the gametophyte and sporophyte are equal; in *Laminaria* the gametophyte is greatly reduced; in *Fucus* the gametophyte has disappeared completely.

Some of the kelps are used as food in China and Japan, and some are fed to cattle in the British Isles. The ash obtained by burning kelps is an excellent source of iodine and potassium. Kelps are harvested (Figure 19-12) off the Pacific coast of the United States especially for their algin content. This material is a colloid used in stabilizing many dairy products.

19.11 Biological significance of the algae

As has been mentioned previously, green plants form the basis of all food chains; they are the food-producing organisms.[7] Obviously, then, all organisms living in water are dependent upon algae for food. Man may, of course, turn to the algae themselves or to the fish feeding upon algae as a food source. The total food productivity of the seas

[6] In some texts the sporangia are considered to be gametangia which form the respective gametes, meiosis occurring during this formation.

[7] The chemosynthetic autotrophic bacteria, which will be discussed in Chapter 20, are unimportant as far as food supply is concerned.

Figure 19-12. Kelp harvester. (Courtesy of Kelco Company, San Diego, California.)

probably exceeds that of the land by at least ten-fold, and future human populations may well turn more and more to the sea for sustenance. Greater efforts will probably be made to "farm" algae, as do the Japanese now. In addition to their food content, algae also produce tremendous quantities of oxygen as a result of photosynthesis. Such oxygen is, of course, also necessary to animal life, as well as to the algae themselves.

Summary

1. The sub-kingdom Thallophyta consists of several quite diverse phyla and is a rather artificial grouping. However, these phyla all consist of plants which do not form embryos, which lack vascular tissue, and in which the sex organs and sporangia are either one-celled or at least have no sterile wall cells. Therefore, they are grouped together in one sub-kingdom.

2. The division Chlorophyta is characterized by the presence of chlorophylls "a" and "b" and carotenoids in chloroplasts and by the production of starch and fats as food reserves. Reproduction is of various types, and the plants range from unicellular organisms to multicellular plants of small size. Members of this division represent a clear example of radiating evolutionary development, beginning with simple unicellular forms and progressing to the complex multicellular forms with their specialization of functions. The development of sexuality is also apparent, beginning with the simple isogamous types and progressing through the heterogamous types to the more complex oögamous form of sexual reproduction. The higher green plants quite likely arose from the Chlorophyta.

3. The division Chrysophyta consists of those plants containing chlorophylls "a" and "c" or "e," accessory yellow or brown pigments, and food reserves in the form of volutin, fats, and oils; no starch is formed. The wall of each cell is composed of two overlapping halves which are impregnated with silica. These plants, especially the diatoms, are enormously important as the basis of food supplies in the seas. In addition to this, diatomaceous earth is used in filters, as insulation, and as a mild abrasive.

4. The division Phaeophyta consists of those members of the Thallophyta which have the greatest differentiation of tissues. Chlorophylls "a" and "c" are usually masked by the brown pigment, fucoxanthin, and the food reserves are sugars and fats. A well-developed alternation of phases occurs, and the motile cells are pear-shaped with two unequal flagella attached at the side.

5. The "algae" in general are important as food sources for the animals of the water.

REVIEW TOPICS AND QUESTIONS

1. Discuss the reasons why Thallophyta is considered to be an artificial grouping rather than a natural one.
2. Compare the life cycles of *Ulothrix* and *Oedogonium*, indicating for each structure whether the cycle is haploid or diploid. In what ways is *Oedogonium* considered to be more advanced than *Ulothrix*, and what advantages obtain to these characteristics?
3. Describe the life cycle of *Chlamydomonas*. Why is this plant considered to be more primitive than *Ulothrix*?
4. Discuss the differences among isogamy, heterogamy, and oögamy. List an example, from the Thallophyta, for each type of sexual reproduction.
5. What is meant when an organism is said to be "heterothallic"? What might be an advantage of such a situation?
6. Describe the life cycle of *Ulva*. How can the gametophyte phase be distinguished from the sporophyte phase?
7. How could you distinguish between a zoospore and an isogamete of *Ulothrix* if the flagella are not visible?
8. List at least five reasons why diatoms are important to man.
9. Describe the life cycle of *Ectocarpus*. How could you distinguish a plurilocular gametangium from a plurilocular zoosporangium?
10. A friend has collected specimens of an alga which he sends to you for identification. All of the structures are well-preserved, but the liquid preservative has bleached all the pigments. While you are waiting for a letter from your friend describing the color of a living specimen, what should you look for before placing this alga in the Chlorophyta, Chrysophyta, or Phaeophyta?
11. Describe the life cycle of *Laminaria*.
12. Distinguish between microsporangia and megasporangia.

SUGGESTED READINGS

Brown, W. H. *The Plant Kingdom*. Boston: Ginn, 1935.

Gibbs, R. D. *Botany, An Evolutionary Approach*. Philadelphia: Blakiston, 1950.

Fuller, H. J., and O. Tippo. *College Botany*. New York: Holt, 1954.

Robbins, W. W., et al. *Botany, An Introduction to Plant Science*. New York: Wiley, 1957.

Smith, G. M. *Cryptogamic Botany*. Vol. I: *Algae and Fungi*. New York: McGraw-Hill, 1955.

CHAPTER 20 ॐ

Division Schizophyta

20.1 General characteristics of the Division Schizophyta

The Division Schizophyta includes the blue-green algae (Class Cyanophyceae) and the bacteria (Class Schizomycetes), of which the latter are by far the more important. The plant body is unicellular or colonial, with the cells containing a poorly organized nucleus and no plastids. Even though the cells do not contain a definite nucleus with a membrane as do all other plants, they do have the genetic material, chromatin, and possibly chromosomes are also present in some. The outer wall layer is frequently mucilaginous, resulting in a slimy mass when large numbers of organisms are present. Reproduction is typically asexual by fission, although sexual reproduction has been demonstrated in one or two bacterial forms.

The demonstration of sexual reproduction in bacteria has been made by use of two strains which differ biochemically. To simplify, one strain can utilize compound *A* as a substrate but not compound *B*, while the second strain can use *B* but not *A*. When the two strains are grown together, the majority of the new cells are like the parents in that they can use either *A* or *B* but not both. However, a few of the progeny have characteristics of both parents and can utilize both *A* and *B*. The formation of these new cells can be explained only on the basis of an exchange of genetic material. Such sexual reproduction occurs but rarely and probably is not of any great significance in the usual development of bacterial populations. No type of sexual reproduction has been demonstrated in the blue-green algae.

20.2 Characteristics of the class Cyanophyceae

Included in the Cyanophyceae are the simplest green plants, consisting of but one cell; the pigments are in the peripheral region of the cell and not in plastids, and the chromatic nuclear material is in a central body, or incipient nucleus, which has no membrane. Chlorophyll "a" is usually masked somewhat by a blue pigment, **phycocyanin;** a red pigment, **phycoerythrin,** is present in the cells of some species. The stored food material is mainly **glycogen,** a type of starch similar to that found in many animals. Reproduction is by simple cell division, and the resultant cells frequently remain closely associated in the form of filamentous colonies. The cells and colonies are often enclosed in a slimy gelatinous sheath. A few species form resistant spores, called **akinetes,** but this is not a method of reproduction. A single cell enlarges and develops a thick wall. After a period of rest, during which the cell is very resistant to adverse environmental conditions, the wall ruptures, and the contents then function as a normal cell. No increase in numbers occurs as a result of such spore formation.

This group is of no real importance. It is a primitive group which never evolved further. Some blue-greens may be food for various organisms, and they contribute to the organic matter in soil. A few members of the Cyanophyceae are capable of utilizing nitrogen gas and may be beneficial by increasing the nitrogen supply in the soil (see Section 20.6). Members of this group are sometimes a nuisance in reservoirs and other bodies of water by imparting a fishy taste and odor, probably from waste products, the slimy sheath, or decay products. *Oscillatoria* is of some interest because of its motility. The filament glides back and forth while the tips swing from side to side. As in all members of this group, no organs of locomotion are present, and the mechanism of these movements is not known.

20.3   Characteristics of the class Schizomycetes

The bacteria are an extremely important, although structurally simple, group of plants. These unicellular plants lack chlorophyll and thus are largely heterotrophic; a few relatively unimportant species contain pigments similar to chlorophyll and are photosynthetic. Some of the bacteria are chemosynthetic autotrophes, and their importance will be emphasized in a later section (20.6). Bacterial metabolism is extremely variable and sometimes quite complicated, but it is useful in the classification of this group. Because of the bacteria's small size, averaging about 0.5 to 3 microns in diameter or length,[1] and lack of structural features, bacteriologists must rely upon various physiological characteristics, including staining, for identification.

---

[1] The high-power objective of the microscope must be used. In fact, most bacteria are viewed through an oil-immersion objective at a magnification of about 950. One micron = about $\frac{1}{25,000}$ of an inch.

Bacteria have three basic body forms (Figure 20-1) which are (1) **coccus,** or spheres, (2) **bacillus,** or rods, and (3) **spirillum,** or spirals (one or more curves in a rod). The bacilli and spirilli may be motile by means of flagella which extrude from all surfaces, in localized tufts at the ends, or singly at the ends. In many species the spheres or rods may cohere to form chains or colonies of cells. Some of the rod-forms produce resistant spores, but these are not reproductive structures; one cell produces one spore which germinates under favorable conditions to produce one cell.

Under favorable conditions, some bacteria may divide once every 20 or 30 minutes, which in 30 days would result in about 10^{20} cells, weighing about 1,500 tons, if they all survived. Obviously, this does not happen, and death is usually due to a lack of food or the accumulation of toxic waste products.

The substrates utilized by various bacteria include almost all forms of organic matter and even some inorganic materials, such as ammonia, nitrate salts, carbon monoxide, sulfur, hydrogen, and nitrogen. The products resulting from bacterial metabolism are just as varied in their way as the substrates used. Some bacteria require oxygen, some can grow either with or without oxygen, and some can exist only in the absence of oxygen or at extremely low concentrations of oxygen. Due to the enormously great variations in bacterial metabolism, these organisms are of almost universal occurrence. Many can withstand rather high temperatures, others are not adversely influenced by low temperatures, and still others can exist deep in the oceans under high pressures. Only a very few places exist where bacteria cannot be found. The many thousands of bacteria make impossible the discussion here of more than a few of these. We will discuss the general importance of bacteria to other plants and to humans and indicate the activities of some of the more important bacteria.

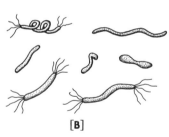

[A]

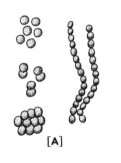

[B]

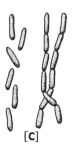

[C]

20.4   Importance of the Schizophyta

The bacteria and the blue-green algae are the oldest of living organisms. The oldest fossils are actually examples of Cyanophyceae. However, the immense iron deposits are believed to be products of iron-oxidizing bacteria and would indicate that bacteria were one of the first forms of life on earth. Botanists generally consider the Schizophyta as not having evolved much beyond the primitive organism. They are probably holdovers on a side branch of the evolutionary family tree and have not given rise to any of the more complex plants or animals.

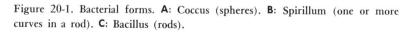

Figure 20-1. Bacterial forms. **A:** Coccus (spheres). **B:** Spirillum (one or more curves in a rod). **C:** Bacillus (rods).

20.5 Harmful aspects of the bacteria

Probably the first point to emphasize about harmful bacteria is that they are in the minority; not even one per cent of the known bacteria are harmful, and of these only a few are really of any great importance. However, most people immediately think of "harm" and "danger" when bacteria are mentioned, and these are the types most familiar to the average person. We will discuss the harmful aspects first, but the student should bear in mind that most bacteria are beneficial and that the great importance of the Schizomycetes relates mainly to their beneficial activities. This is not to imply that harmful bacteria are of no consequence. As will be discussed shortly, disease-producing bacteria have had, and still do have, a profound effect upon human populations. However, the beneficial aspects of the bacterial plants far overshadow the harmful aspects of a small minority of these organisms.

HUMAN DISEASES

In Table 20-1 are listed some of the bacterial diseases of man, the bacterium involved, and a brief comment about possible control. Of

Table 20-1. Some Bacterial Diseases of Man

Disease	Pathogen	Control
Plague	Pasteurella pestis	Rat extermination, sanitation; vaccine.
Asiatic cholera	Vibrio comma	Isolation, sanitation, disinfection; * vaccine.
Typhoid fever	Salmonella typhosa	Isolation, chloromycetin, sanitation, vaccine.
Pneumonia (lobar)	Diplococcus pneumoniae	Isolation; penicillin, sulfa drugs.
Boils, abscesses, pus-forming inflammations, etc.	Micrococcus pyogenes var. aureus	Disinfection,* cleanliness; penicillin.
Scarlet fever, sore throat, tonsilitis, etc.	Streptococcus pyogenes	Disinfection,* antitoxin for scarlet fever, sulfa drugs, penicillin.
Gonorrhea	Neisseria gonorrhoeae	Penicillin, sulfa drugs.
Epidemic meningitis	Neisseria intracellularia	Antiserum, sulfa drugs, penicillin.
Diphtheria	Corynebacterium diphtheriae	Antitoxin, erythromycin.
Tuberculosis	Mycobacterium tuberculosis var. hominis	Isolation, rest, disinfection; * streptomycin.
Tetanus (lockjaw)	Clostridium tetani	Antitoxin.
Botulism	Clostridium botulinum	Careful processing of canned foods; antitoxin.

* Disinfection of dressings, discharges, clothing, etc.

course, a variety of other human diseases are caused by bacteria, as well as diseases of other animals, such as livestock, cats, and dogs. A few of these diseases are somewhat more drastic in their influence on human populations; we will indicate the effect of some of them.

Plague. *Pasteurella pestis* causes bubonic and pneumonic plague in man, a disease which was known as the Black Death in the fourteenth century. Historians estimate that several cycles of bubonic plague during that century killed some 25 million people in Europe, about one-fourth of the total population at the time. The Great Plague of London in 1664–1665 killed about 68,000 people out of 460,000, almost 15 per cent of the population. Plague epidemics in other cities and countries have had similar results, and as late as 1905 over 900,000 persons died in India as a result of this disease. It is still responsible for thousands of deaths now, although in most areas it has almost been eliminated.

At the present time a plague vaccine is available which can be utilized to immunize people, but an easier control method is through the establishment of sanitary facilities, cleanliness, and rat extermination. This last point is of utmost importance. Plague is transmitted by the bite of infected fleas which obtain the bacterium mainly from the blood of rats. Infected rats act as a reservoir for the organism. This disease is almost never found in any locality in which modern sanitary facilities are available. It is a disease of crowded, poverty-ridden areas. In the United States only a few isolated cases occur, but the disease is still present in some Asiatic countries.

Asiatic cholera. *Vibrio comma* can exist in the human intestines and is spread by polluted water and food, found in areas where sanitary facilities break down or are non-existent. The intense diarrhea, prostration, and dehydration result in high rates of mortality. During the Crimean War in 1855–1856, at least half of the French troops were hospitalized by an outbreak of cholera. A similar outbreak in the ranks of the Chinese and North Korean armies during the Korean War in 1952 led to charges of bacteriological warfare.

Immunizing vaccines are available, but the establishment of sanitary facilities is a simpler and less expensive method of control. Asiatic cholera is an ever-present danger in the Orient and will remain so until the crowded conditions and poverty are alleviated.

Typhoid fever. *Salmonella typhosa* is also an intestinal pathogen, and the disease is spread by polluted water, by flies, and by food handled by individuals harboring the organism. Unfortunately, the bacterium may be present in some individuals without causing disease symptoms. Such persons, called **carriers,** are exceedingly dangerous to others if they are allowed to come in contact with food or the preparation of food.

Some historians believe that more battles have been lost because of typhoid fever epidemics and associated diseases, such as dysentery and cholera, than because of military opposition. Napoleon's campaign into Russia (1812) may be cited as an example. Although the extremely cold winter was one factor in the famous retreat, most of Napoleon's army was unfit for duty because of various epidemics, particularly typhoid fever and dysentery resulting from the crowded and unsanitary conditions which made possible the rapid spread of disease.

Immunizing vaccines and antibiotics are now available, but sanitation is once again of prime consideration. Occasional outbreaks of typhoid fever occur in almost all countries and cause the public health authorities to function as detectives. They must locate the source of infection, and this may involve considerable difficulty if a carrier is involved.

STERILIZATION AND PASTEURIZATION OF FOOD MATERIALS

Foods consumed by humans are also excellent media for the growth of various bacteria or are means whereby pathogens are transmitted from one person to another or from food animal to human. The decomposition of foods rich in carbohydrates generally results in various types of fermentation, which are usually harmless although somewhat unappetizing. Bacteria acting upon high-protein foods bring about putrefactions, which are objectionable and frequently dangerous. To prevent spoilage, food must be kept free of organisms, or these organisms must be prevented from multiplying, because such decomposition of food results from the activity of micro-organisms. The method usually used to achieve this end is heat treatment, a process basic to the canning and milk industries.

In **sterilizing** materials all organisms are destroyed by the high temperatures which are used. The amount of heat and the time of treatment varies with the kind and amount of food which is being processed; in general 60°C. for one hour in a liquid medium is sufficient to kill non-spore-forming organisms, but 120°C. for fifteen minutes is utilized to destroy all forms of life. This heating is usually done under pressure in an autoclave (or pressure cooker), because steam under pressure is hotter than free-flowing steam.[2] If the food is sealed in a container, re-inoculation of the contents by the universally present air-borne micro-organisms is not possible. Food carefully processed in this fashion may be preserved indefinitely.

265

[2] Free-flowing steam has a temperature of 100°C., compared to 121°C. for steam under fifteen lbs. pressure.

Pasteurization refers to the process of heating milk or milk products to 62°C. for thirty minutes or to 71°C. for fifteen seconds. This treatment is sufficient to destroy disease organisms without ruining the flavor of the milk. Pasteurization is not the same as sterilization. In the former treatment many non-pathogenic bacteria survive, and pasteurized milk is safe but not sterile.

Foods may also be preserved by drying, by adding salt, or by adding sugar. All of these treatments are designed to decrease the possibility of micro-organisms being able to multiply in the foods. Materials having a high osmotic concentration result in the plasmolysis of spores or cells which may have gained access to such foods (see Section 4.4). A deficiency of water would also prevent or greatly decrease bacterial multiplication.

PLANT DISEASES

Although everyone is aware that bacteria cause animal diseases, very few people realize that a great many diseases of plants also are caused by bacteria. A detailed discussion of such diseases would fill several volumes; the 1953 Yearbook of Agriculture, published by the United States Department of Agriculture, is devoted to plant diseases and includes some of the more important bacterial diseases. Table 20-2 lists some of the more important plant diseases and the pathogenic organism

Table 20-2. Some Bacterial Diseases of Plants

Disease	Pathogen	Susceptible Plants
Fire blight	Erwinia amylovora	Pear, apple.
Bacterial blight of stone fruits	Xanthomonas pruni	Plum, cherry, peach.
Common blight of bean	Xanthomonas phaseoli	Bean.
Halo blight of bean	Pseudomonas phaseolicola	Bean.
Soft rot	Erwinia carotovora	Storage disease of carrots, potatoes, onions, bulbs, etc.
Bacterial blight of cotton	Xanthomonas malvacearum	Cotton.
Bacterial wilt of corn	Bacterium stewarti	Corn, gama grass.
Alfalfa wilt	Corynebacterium insidiosa	Alfalfa and white sweet clover.
Bacterial wilt of cucurbits	Erwinia tracheiphila	Cucumber, cantaloupe, squash, watermelon, etc.
Crown gall	Agrobacterium tumefaciens	Apple, cherry, prune, grape, alfalfa, cotton, etc.
Brown rot of potato	Xanthomonas solanacearum	Potato, tomato, tobacco, etc.

involved. A bacterial disease of plants is rather difficult to control once it has become established, because the pathogen is usually in the vascular tissue or other tissues of the susceptible plant, and sprays or dusts do not penetrate readily to these areas. In general, the use of resistant plants, the use of disease-free seeds and stocks, and the surface disinfecting of seeds are utilized in attempts to control bacterial diseases of plants. In those diseases where the bacteria are carried from plant to plant by insects, the use of insecticides has greatly decreased the severity of the disease. However, the use of disease-free materials, resistant plants, and crop rotation are the only effective means of controlling bacterial infections, although soil sterilization by heat or chemicals can be utilized in greenhouses. Fortunately, plant pathogenic bacteria are poor competitors in the soil and are crowded out or destroyed by the true soil saprophytes. Thus, the pathogenic types do not remain alive for long periods in the soil.

In the United States and Canada, great losses from bacterial diseases occur in potatoes, fruit trees, beans, tomatoes, tobacco, and alfalfa. In California fire blight[3] has caused as much as a $2,000,000 loss in one year, including a loss of 100,000 trees, while the annual loss in the United States has gone as high as 5,000,000 bushels of apples and 500,000 bushels of pears. Bacterial wilt of alfalfa has become the most important disease of this crop and is a cause of much concern because of its widespread occurrence in most alfalfa-growing areas of the United States. In many fields of the southern United States, tobacco, tomatoes, and potatoes cannot be grown successfully because of a bacterial wilt disease known as brown rot. Bacterial blight annually may cause up to 50 per cent loss in beans in certain locations. In addition to these various diseases of plants in the field, serious losses of up to 100 per cent occur in stored crops, such as carrots, turnips, and potatoes, as a result of soft rot, which is of universal occurrence.

CAUSE OF SYMPTOMS

Diseases are generally recognized by characteristic symptoms which result from the activity of a pathogenic organism.[4] In some cases **toxins,** poisonous waste products of a protein nature, are excreted

[3] Fire blight, caused by *Erwinia amylovora,* is of particular interest because it was the first plant disease proven to be of bacterial origin. T. J. Burrill of the University of Illinois is considered the first to relate a bacterium to the cause of a plant disease; his reports were issued between 1878–1884.

[4] Some diseases, of course, are not caused by pathogenic organisms, but we are not concerned with these at this time. Vitamin deficiency diseases in animals and mineral deficiency diseases of plants are excellent examples of diseases which are not the result of a pathogen.

by the bacteria, and these poisons may be general or selective in their action on host tissues. In animals various cells of the body may produce substances, **antibodies,** which neutralize the toxins and render the animal **immune** to the disease. This **naturally acquired immunity,** a result of the animal actually having the disease and recovering from it, is quite different from **artificial immunity.** The latter type of immunity may be either active or passive. In **active artificial immunity** the patient's body is stimulated to produce antibodies by being injected with a **vaccine,** preparations of dead or weakened bacteria or non-poisonous products [5] of these bacteria. Vaccines are used against smallpox (a virus disease), typhoid fever, tetanus, cholera, and diphtheria; the period of immunity is from several years to a lifetime. **Passive artificial immunity** results from injecting the patient with antibody-containing serum; he is immune immediately, with no latent period during which the patient's body produces antibodies; he has them injected "ready-made." Such antibody-containing, or anti-toxin-containing, serum is usually obtained from horses which have had long series of injections of the proper vaccine; the horse has developed active artificial immunity. This type of serum is especially useful in treating tetanus and diphtheria. One should remember that such immunity is transitory and not lasting. Unfortunately, antibodies are not produced by plants.[6]

Symptoms may result from a removal of food from host tissues, which results in various abnormal growth responses and reduced yields of the latter, and also from mechanical plugging of xylem cells by large masses of the pathogen or by slimy and gummy secretions of the pathogen, which results in wilting of the susceptible plant. In some plant diseases, such as crown gall, the pathogen stimulates the host cells to excessive cellular divisions and growth; such abnormal enlargements are termed **hypertrophies.** In those diseases wherein the host cells are actually destroyed, the symptoms may be localized, e.g., leaf spots, or of a more general nature, in which individual branches or entire plants are severely injured or killed.

Many symptoms in plants, as in humans, are quite characteristic of specific diseases. However, proof that a disease is caused by a certain bacterium depends upon the application of Koch's [7] postulates. Basi-

[5] Toxins are rendered non-poisonous in a variety of ways and may then be used as vaccines.

[6] Some plants are thought to develop immunity to certain virus diseases, but antibody production has not been demonstrated.

[7] Robert Koch (1843–1910) was an eminent German bacteriologist who developed many techniques of staining and culturing bacteria.

cally, these postulates define the evidence which is necessary to prove an organism to be the cause of a disease:

1. The organism must be associated with all cases of a given disease.
2. The organism must be isolated from the diseased individual.
3. When this organism is subsequently inoculated into susceptible plants or animals, it must reproduce the disease.
4. The organism must be re-isolated from such experimental infections.

All of these postulates cannot be fulfilled in every case. Some diseases are caused by ultra-microscopic viruses; the pathogens for other diseases have never been grown in artificial media. Some diseases of man are not communicable to lower animals, and thus the third postulate might not be satisfied. However, in most such cases sufficient circumstantial evidence is available to indicate relationships between diseases and pathogen.

CONTROL OF PLANT DISEASES

Many techniques are utilized in the control of plant diseases, but they may be discussed as four general types. In all cases **control** refers to a reduction in the amount of injury caused by the disease-producing agent. This may mean only a slight diminution of injury or a complete eradication of the disease in question.

1. Exclusion. This term refers to any method which prevents the entrance and establishment of the pathogen into uninfested areas. Plant quarantine laws prevent the entrance of certain materials into the United States or, in some cases, from one state to another. Some materials can be disinfected and then brought into the area. Unfortunately, this cannot prevent the spread of pathogens over short distances by wind, insects, or water.

2. Eradication. The methods included under this category are those which seek the removal, elimination, or destruction of the pathogen from a given area. Various chemical sprays are useful to destroy the pathogen, or crop rotation may be used to decrease the amount of food which is available to the pathogen and thus eliminate it. It is also possible, of course, to remove and destroy (burn) the diseased plant along with the pathogen.

3. Protection. Protection refers to the interposition of an effective barrier between the susceptible plant and the pathogen. Many spray and dust applications, at least those applied early in the growth season, are protective, rather than eradicant, in nature. Once the pathogen becomes established, the same sprays and dusts are frequently used to destroy the organism (eradication).

4. Immunization. This term refers to methods utilized to render the plant immune, resistant, or tolerant to the pathogen. This is where plant breeding is important. Naturally-resistant varieties are sometimes available, but the production of resistant hybrids by breeding programs have made the most significant advances. In some diseases the use of resistant varieties is the only economically feasible means of control.

Three basic difficulties are involved in the breeding of plants for resistance to a specific disease: (a) more than one genetic factor is usually involved, (b) quality and quantity must not be sacrificed, and (c) the pathogen frequently produces new varieties which may attack previously resistant crop plants. This last point is especially true of plant diseases caused by members of the Division Eumycophyta (see the next chapter). However, if resistant plants are available or resistant hybrids can be produced, the use of such plants immediately results in monetary advantages to the farmer: one of the expenses involved in any type of farming is that incurred through spraying and dusting programs for disease control; resistant plants need little or no such treatment.

20.6 Beneficial aspects of the bacteria

As has been mentioned before, and should be emphasized again, most bacteria (at least 99 per cent) are not harmful, and almost all of these are beneficial. Any discussion of bacteria should really stress this point, especially since most humans are prone to regard and investigate harmful factors in attempts to negate such activity and then almost completely ignore the good derived from bacterial activity.

DECAY

Undoubtedly the most important activity of bacteria is the decay of complex compounds. **Decay** specifically refers to the decomposition or breakdown of compounds, eventually resulting in carbon dioxide, water, and minerals if decay is complete. As we have already seen, green plants use these simple materials in the presence of light and chlorophyll to produce the complex components of their cells; animals and non-green plants use the complex products of green plants to produce their own component parts. If this were the end of the matter, an enormous mass of complex organic compounds in the form of dead plants and animals would gradually accumulate upon the earth—life, of course, would then cease. Obviously this does not occur, and it does not occur because of the activity of untold millions of bacteria and fungi.[8] These are the organisms which make it possible for elements to be used over and over again. Complex materials are made by green plants and utilized by animals and non-green plants, they are converted to simple materials by micro-organisms, and then green plants make additional complex compounds from these simple products of decay.

In the book of Genesis of the Christian Bible may be found the statement ". . . for dust thou art and unto dust shalt thou return." In a way this is a fairly accurate, although over-simplified, statement. The addition of carbon dioxide and water to the "dust" is all that is needed. But after death, all bodies deteriorate and eventually disappear (dust?). Food comes from plants growing out of the earth (dust?) or from animals which eat plants. Thus, a cycle apparently exists, and we shall now examine this cycle in some detail.

Every bacterium does not decompose all organic material, and various bacteria specialize in the substrates which they utilize. However, no organic matter is produced by living organisms which is not decomposed by some bacteria or fungi. The decomposition of dead plant or animal material or their excretory products is not a simple process but represents the combined activities of many different kinds of bacteria. The final result, the production of carbon dioxide, water, and minerals, may take a long time, but it is always the same. Some organic materials merely decompose more slowly than others, and some may escape decomposition for a time because of certain environmental conditions, as in coal formation.

The decay of carbohydrates[9] and fats results in the production of carbon dioxide, water, and energy. The importance of such decompositions was discussed in Section 13.4, and we shall now deal more with nitrogen-containing organic compounds. Many of the minerals

[8] In this context "fungi" refers to the true fungi, members of the Division Eumycophyta. These will be discussed in the next chapter; therefore this chapter will be limited to a discussion of the bacteria, members of the Division Schizophyta.

[9] An interesting type of decay is the peculiar cellulose decomposition occurring in ruminants (cattle, sheep, goats, camel, deer, etc.). These animals, which feed mainly upon grass, have a preliminary digestive system of several compartments between the mouth and stomach. Food first enters this rumen and is thoroughly mixed with the semi-liquid mass contained therein, which includes large numbers of cellulose-fermenting bacteria. The food is regurgitated and thoroughly chewed, during which time bacterial fermentations decompose the cellulose to various materials readily absorbed by the animal. Ruminants are not capable of using cellulose and can exist on grass only because of the activity of the bacteria which they harbor in the rumen.

present in cells are there as salts or in loose combination with various organic materials. These minerals are readily released and restored to their mineral state upon the death of the cell and decomposition of the organic compounds. Three important elements, however, do form intimate parts of certain organic molecules of the living cell; they are phosphorus, sulfur, and nitrogen. Organic phosphorus, as in sugar phosphates and in adenosine triphosphates (ATP), is readily converted to inorganic phosphates by bacteria, and such phosphates are readily available to green plants. The situation with sulfur and nitrogen is more complex.

Sulfur conversions.[10] The element sulfur is found in the cell as sulfate salts, as part of various protein molecules, or as part of other complex organic molecules. The inorganic sulfates are released when the cell ruptures, and they are then available for use by plants. The sulfur in organic compounds, predominantly proteins, is converted to hydrogen sulfide gas as bacterial decomposition of these molecules takes place. This is one of the evil-smelling odors that result from putrefaction[11] and is poisonous. Fortunately, certain bacteria can oxidize hydrogen sulfide to elemental sulfur and then further oxidize the sulfur to sulfates, probably in the following manner:

$$2H_2S + O_2 \rightarrow 2S + 2H_2O$$
$$4S + 6O_2 + 4H_2O \rightarrow 4H_2SO_4$$

These oxidations supply energy which the bacteria use to produce organic compounds from carbon dioxide gas or dissolved carbonates; the bacteria are chemosynthetic autotrophes and can grow quite readily on inorganic media if hydrogen sulfide, or sulfur dioxide, and carbon dioxide gases are present. The bacteria, such as members of the genus *Thiobacillus*, actually produce sulfuric acid (H_2SO_4) as a waste product, and this reacts readily with soil particles to form sulfate salts. Such acid formation quite likely is of considerable importance in soil production as a factor in the chemical disintegration of parent rock material (see Section 16.2). Members of the genus *Beggiatoa* actually store sulfur granules as we might store fat from a diet of excessive carbohydrates. When the supply of hydrogen sulfide is exhausted, these bacteria oxidize the reserve sulfur granules to sulfates. Sulfate is the

[10] The decomposition, or breakdown, portions of these conversions are part of the general processes included in the term "decay"; they are considered separately because of the somewhat greater complexity involved.

[11] Putrefaction generally refers to anaerobic decomposition and is usually accompanied by the production of various obnoxiously-smelling materials. Complete, aerobic decomposition does not produce odors.

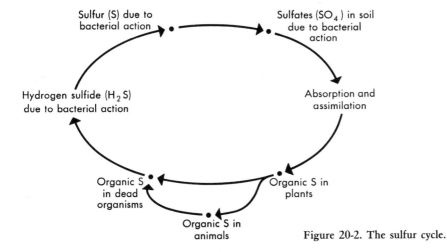

Figure 20-2. The sulfur cycle.

mineral form in which most plants, especially the green plants, obtain
their sulfur supply.

Figure 20-2 represents the various interconversions of sulfur and
sulfur-containing compounds as they tend to occur in nature. This is a
somewhat simplified version; not all of the various sulfur compounds
are indicated, nor are all types of sulfur bacteria included.

Nitrogen conversions.[10] All organisms require nitrogen. Green
plants obtain nitrogen in the form of nitrate (NO_3) salts or, less readily, as ammonium (NH_4) salts, whereas animals and non-green plants
are almost exclusively dependent upon green plants for their nitrogen
in the form of proteins or amino acids. The exceptions to the latter part
of the preceding statement are certain groups of bacteria, the chemosynthetic autotrophes, which can use inorganic nitrogen salts. Obviously, then, a supply of nitrogen salts in the soil is essential for all life.
However, such salts are not found as minerals in the soil, the way
potassium salts and phosphate salts are found. Nitrogen salts come
from the decomposition of dead plants and animals or their excretory
products, and this decomposition depends upon several groups of bacteria.

Many kinds of bacteria use as a substrate or food supply various organic nitrogen-containing compounds, which are mostly proteins, and
excrete ammonia as a waste product. This conversion of organic nitrogen compounds to ammonia is frequently termed **ammonification.**
The members of two genera of bacteria, *Nitrosomonas* and *Nitroso-
coccus,* oxidize ammonia to nitrite (NO_2). This is a respiratory process
which yields the energy for growth; carbon dioxide and water are used

in the production of organic compounds as in the green plants. The reactions [12] may be summarized:

(a) $$2NH_4^+ + 4O_2 \rightarrow 2NO_2^- + 4H_2O + \text{Energy}$$

(b) $$CO_2 + H_2O + \text{Energy} \rightarrow \text{Organic compounds}$$

Nitrite is toxic to most plants, but it does not accumulate in the soil because of the presence of another group of bacteria. Just as the preceding two groups oxidized ammonia, *Nitrobacter* species oxidize nitrites to nitrates (NO_3^-) and thereby obtain energy for growth and maintenance:

(a) $$2NO_2^- + O_2 \rightarrow 2NO_3^- + \text{Energy}$$

(b) $$CO_2 + H_2O + \text{Energy} \rightarrow \text{Organic compounds}$$

The conversion of ammonia to nitrite and then to nitrate is frequently termed **nitrification,** but one should be aware of the fact that two steps are involved, as well as three separate groups of bacteria.

The end result of this step-wise decomposition of organic nitrogen (proteins) to ammonia to nitrite to nitrate is the making available of nitrogen to green plants. Organic nitrogen compounds are not generally available for use by green plants. They require nitrogen in the form of salts which are absorbed by the roots from the soil. Without the bacterial decomposition taking place in the soil, nitrogen would soon be lost from use, and life would cease. So, once again, we are saved by the lowly microbe.

The atmosphere has a tremendous amount of nitrogen which is not available except to a few groups of bacteria. Nitrogen gas comprises a little over 79 per cent of the air we breathe, but this material cannot be used by any animals nor by most plants. A few blue-green algae (Class Cyanophyceae) have been shown to utilize gaseous nitrogen in the synthesis of amino acids and proteins, but these are relatively unimportant compared to three genera of bacteria: *Azotobacter, Clostridium,* and *Rhizobium.*

The **nitrogen-fixing** bacteria utilize organic compounds as their source of energy and can use some of this energy to convert nitrogen gas (N_2) to organic nitrogen compounds (mainly amino acids and then proteins):

[12] Ammonia (NH_3) dissolved in soil water will form ammonium (NH_4^+) ions or ammonium salts; the nitrites and nitrates will also be in the form of ions or salts (i.e., NH_4SO_4, KNO_3, $NaNO_3$, etc.).

(a)   Organic compounds → CO_2 + H_2O + Energy

$$\downarrow\text{---}$$

(b) N_2 + Energy → Organic nitrogen compounds [13]

These organic nitrogen compounds are basic constituents of the bacterial cell and are really not available to green plants. As the nitrogen-fixing bacteria die, however, ammonification and nitrification processes convert such nitrogen compounds to nitrogen salts which are then readily absorbed by plant roots. *Azotobacter* is a free-living organism which carries on aerobic metabolism, while *Clostridium* is also a free-living soil organism but functions anaerobically.[14]

Although *Rhizobium* is also a soil organism, it is not capable of fixing nitrogen unless it first invades the roots of various legume [15] plants. The bacteria penetrate through the root hairs and into the inner tissues where the cortical cells are stimulated to divide and grow. The clearly visible, localized swelling or enlargement of the root is termed a **nodule,** and the cells are filled with masses of bacteria; *Rhizobium* is frequently termed the **root nodule bacterium.** Once the relationship between the legume root cells and *Rhizobium* has been established, nitrogen fixation readily occurs. Neither the legume nor the bacterium alone is capable of fixing nitrogen, but when together nitrogen gas is converted to organic nitrogen. This is a relationship of mutual benefit. The green plant (legume) obtains nitrogen compounds from the bacteria which are within the root cells or from the dead bacteria; the bacteria (*Rhizobium*) obtain organic food materials from the root cells of the green plant. Actually, the legume probably supplies more than just food for the bacteria, since *Rhizobium* can live freely on soil organic matter but without fixing nitrogen. The exact relationship involved in nodule formation and nitrogen fixation is not known.

We should point out at this time that denitrification occurs occasionally in some soils under anaerobic conditions and in the presence of organic matter (substrate). Several species of *Pseudomonas* and *Bacillus* are capable of reducing nitrates to nitrogen gas. This is harmful to green plants, because it converts nitrogen from an available form

---

[13] Ammonia is probably formed first, but this is so rapidly converted to amino acids that no accumulation of ammonia occurs. The amino acids are in turn converted to proteins.

[14] All species of *Azotobacter* are nitrogen-fixers, but only a few species of *Clostridium* are capable of carrying out this process.

[15] The term "legume" refers to members of the bean family, *Leguminosae,* and includes: beans (*Phaseolus*), peas (*Pisum*), alfalfa (*Medicago*), clover (*Trifolium*), vetch (*Vicia*), sweet clover (*Melilotus*), etc.

($NO_3{}^-$) to a non-available form (N_2). Fortunately, the conditions required for denitrification to occur are not too common.

Figure 20-3 summarizes various important interconversions of nitrogen-containing compounds as discussed in the preceding paragraphs.

Figure 20-3. Nitrogen transformations.

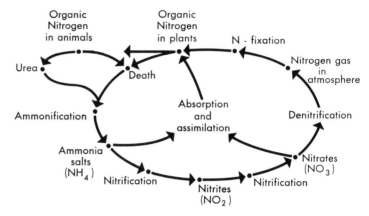

SEWAGE DISPOSAL

One of the difficult problems confronting city-dwellers is sewage disposal. The liquid which runs through sewer pipes contains human wastes, factory wastes, and water which is used in many daily operations of the home and at work (e.g., washing, bathing, and so on). The actual amount of material usually varies from 15 to 25 gallons per person. In small towns and isolated dwellings, this sewage can be disposed of in streams or applied to the land, where bacterial activity will convert the organic materials to carbon dioxide, water, and minerals—none of which are evil-smelling. In large cities such treatment would endanger the health of the population, as well as offend its aesthetic senses, because of the large amounts involved and the anaerobic conditions which soon develop as a result of rapid bacterial activity; the unwanted odors which accompany sewage are actually a result of fermentations or anaerobic bacterial activity. The problem thus revolves about producing an environment which is suitable for rapid, aerobic bacterial decay. This is the basis upon which all sewage disposal plants operate. One must remember that sewage can be disposed of only by bacterial activity. One may discard sewage by dumping it into a stream and thus eliminate a nuisance. The people downstream, however, would not maintain friendly relations with the people upstream under those conditions. Imagine for a moment the condition of the Mississippi River in the vicinity of New Orleans if all cities and towns on the river and its tributaries merely emptied sewer pipes into the streams and rivers. Not a very pleasant thought, I imagine, and much of this is still being done.

Many methods of sewage disposal are available, from small septic tanks to enormous plants capable of handling thousands of gallons of sewage daily. We shall discuss one method of complete sewage disposal. The material enters a large tank in which most of the solids settle to the bottom, and the turbid liquid passes over to a second settling tank and finally to filter beds. These latter usually consist of deep layers of porous rock, such as coke, upon which the liquid is sprayed and then allowed to percolate down. The use of porous rock, the sprinkling, and the percolation are all designed to increase the amount of air (actually, oxygen) to which the turbid liquid is exposed. Bacterial growth and development under these conditions are phenomenal, and the rock becomes covered with a slimy mass of bacteria. These micro-organisms rapidly decompose the suspended organic material, and the effluent is clear, pure water, which is usually chlorinated to insure the death of any harmful organisms. This liquid could be returned to the water supply of the city, but in most instances the purified water from a sewage disposal plant is foolishly discarded into the ocean or streams nearby.

The solid material, or sludge, is inoculated with sludge from a previous treatment. The latter contains enormous masses of bacteria and protozoa which insure rapid decomposition of the second batch of sludge, especially since this mass is aerated under pressure or stirred. Aerobic bacteria bring about decomposition of the organic matter and without obnoxious odors if aeration is adequate. The treated sludge contains masses of bacteria, soil and debris, and some non-decomposed material. It is dried and can be used as an organic fertilizer or as fill material; a portion of it is saved to inoculate the next batch of sludge.

Sewage disposal is really a matter of encouraging the proper bacteria to multiply rapidly and to metabolize actively. These are not special bacteria treated in a special way. The same results are obtained when small amounts of sewage are emptied into streams and rivers, or onto soil, or into septic tanks. A sewage disposal plant is necessary only in case of relatively large amounts of sewage. If this material were emptied indiscriminately into rivers, bacterial activity would rapidly deplete the waters of their oxygen supply, and at this point fermentations would give rise to their accompanying noxious odors. To prevent these odors and to dispose of sewage rapidly, the sewage disposal plants of the city have been developed. Since less than five per cent of the water used in a city is actually consumed, to purify sewage water and then discard it is very wasteful. In some cities the water from sewage disposal plants is at least used for irrigation. All cities should build

277

complete sewage disposal plants which can empty purified water into the reservoir systems of the cities. This would solve the water problem of many cities for a good number of years.

COMMERCIAL USES OF BACTERIA

The use of bacteria in sewage disposal plants is not considered to be a commercial venture, because such plants are almost always managed under the auspices of a municipal or county government. However, many commercial ventures do depend upon harnessing bacterial activity.

Cotton fibers occur separately and are readily used in manufacturing textiles. Other fibers, however, are embedded in stem or leaf tissues and must be freed before they can be used. **Retting** is the process whereby pectin-digesting bacteria bring about the separation of cells from one another. This is important in obtaining fibers from plants such as hemp (*Cannabis sativa*), jute (*Corchorus capsularis*), and flax (*Linum usitatissimum*). The plant material is placed in ponds or tanks where various anaerobic pectin-destroying bacteria, mainly species of *Clostridium,* rapidly separate fibers from other material. The plant material must be removed before too long, or cellulose-digesting bacteria will ruin the fibers. After washing in running water, the fibers are removed mechanically and used.

Initial steps in the tanning of leather make use of proteolytic [16] bacteria. Coffee "beans" and cocoa "beans" [17] are subjected to preliminary bacterial activity before further processing. Certain choice tastes and aromas of tobacco develop during the curing of green leaves and are probably due to bacterial fermentations. Vinegar and acetic acid are produced when *Acetobacter* oxidizes alcohol; acetic acid is the main component of vinegar and is obtained by distillation. Various other products are obtained as a result of bacterial activity: propionic acid, lactic acid, acetone, butanol (butyl alcohol), etc.

Various kinds of food materials are made available to us through the generous activity of various bacteria. Sauerkraut, pickles, butter, buttermilk, and certain cheeses obtain their flavors and aromas from bacterial metabolism. Soft cheeses, such as Limburger and Liederkranz, and hard cheeses, such as Swiss and Cheddar, are ripened by bacteria; the holes in Swiss cheeses result from gas production as the cheese solidifies. The different types of cheeses are produced by different treat-

[16] Proteolysis = decomposition of proteins.

[17] These are not "beans" in the strict sense. They are fruits of *Coffea arabica* and *Theobrama cacao* plants, although it is the seed which is eventually utilized.

ments which favor certain groups of bacteria over others. In most cases, pure cultures of bacteria are added to the milk, the type of culture depending upon the desired cheese.

After a bit of reflection, one should see clearly that bacteria are not only essential for our very existence but also supply us with a few added niceties which serve to make life somewhat more enjoyable.

Summary

1. The Division Schizophyta consists of unicellular or colonial forms which contain poorly organized nuclei and no plastids; reproduction is typically asexual by fission. In the Class Cyanophyceae (blue-green algae), chlorophyll is usually somewhat masked by other pigments, and the stored food material is mainly glycogen; this group is of minor importance.

2. The Class Schizomycetes (bacteria) consists of very small plants which are mainly heterotrophic. Metabolic activity of the bacteria is exceedingly diverse and is a useful tool for classifying organisms which have so few structural features.

3. Although bacteria cause a variety of plant and animal diseases, the great majority of these organisms are very beneficial to other living individuals. Microbial activity in bringing about the decay of complex organic compounds allows green plants to utilize the component parts of such complex molecules. These plants in turn provide other organisms with food and minerals.

4. Nitrogen salts are not found as minerals in the soil. The source of such salts is the nitrogen found in plants and animals and the nitrogen gas of the atmosphere. However, the bacteria are essential for the conversion of nitrogen gas to organic nitrogen and eventually to nitrogen salts, which may then be absorbed and utilized by green plants. Other organisms receive their essential nitrogen supplies from these plants or from animals which have eaten the plants. The processes of ammonification, nitrification, and nitrogen-fixation are basic to the continuation of life on earth.

5. Man has made use of many of the activities of various bacteria: retting; tanning; organic acid production; production of sauerkraut, pickles, cheese, vinegar; production of various organic solvents, etc.

6. Sewage disposal utilizes the general decay activities of microbes to destroy organic wastes rapidly. Sewage disposal plants are basically designed to produce an environment which is suitable for rapid aerobic bacterial activity. The obnoxious odors associated with sewage is a result of anaerobic decomposition.

REVIEW TOPICS AND QUESTIONS

1. What are the diagnostic characteristics of the Division Schizophyta?
2. Most systems of classification utilize morphological features. Since this is true, why are the Schizomycetes classified on the basis of physiological characteristics?
3. List at least three different ways in which bacteria are harmful.
4. Compare sterilization and pasteurization. Why are both methods used for preserving foods? Wouldn't either one alone be enough?
5. Define the following: toxin, antibody, acquired immunity, passive immunity, and vaccine.
6. Discuss the techniques utilized in the control of plant diseases. Explain which of these techniques are useful in controlling human diseases.
7. What is meant by "decay," and why is it important?
8. List at least ten ways in which bacteria are used by man.
9. A labeled nitrogen atom in a nitrogen gas molecule over a bean field collides with a labeled carbon atom in a carbon dioxide molecule. The nitrogen atom is next discovered as part of a nitrate salt in the soil, while the carbon atom exists as part of a starch molecule in a bean stem. Later, these two atoms are found in the same protein molecule in a bean seed.

   Explain in detail and in logical sequence the processes involved and where they take place, the cells and tissues and structures concerned, and the forces and essential factors necessary to bring about such transformations and movements of the two atoms. Where more than one pathway is available, discuss all possibilities.

10. A labeled sulfur atom is found in a protein molecule of a dead earthworm in the soil under a pea plant. Later this atom is absorbed by the pea plant and eventually is found in a protein molecule in a pea seed.

    Explain in detail and in logical sequence all of the processes and transformations involved in the movement of the sulfur atom, including means of transport, chemical changes, energy changes, essential factors, and the cells and tissues in which each occurs.

SUGGESTED READINGS

Clayton, R. K., and M. Delbruck. "Purple Bacteria," *Scientific American,* 185 (November 1951), 68–72.

Clifton, C. E. *Introduction to the Bacteria.* New York: McGraw-Hill, 1958.

Gibbs, R. D. *Botany, An Evolutionary Approach.* Philadelphia: Blakiston, 1950.

Pelczar, M. J., and R. D. Reid. *Microbiology.* New York: McGraw-Hill, 1958.

Stanier, R. Y., et al. *The Microbial World.* Englewood Cliffs, N. J.: Prentice-Hall, 1957.

Thimann, K. V. *The Life of Bacteria.* New York: Macmillan, 1955.

Wollman, E. L., and F. Jacob. "Sexuality in Bacteria," *Scientific American,* 195 (July 1956), 109–118.

CHAPTER 21

Division Eumycophyta

21.1 Characteristics of the Division Eumycophyta

The true fungi constitute a large and diverse group of non-chloro-phyll-containing thallophytes; they are usually filamentous, although some unicellular forms are present. Various types of spores are formed which produce elongated, cylindrical threads upon germination. A single thread (filament), or a branch, is termed a **hypha,** and the en-tangled mass of **hyphae** which constitutes the thallus or vegetative plant body is termed a **mycelium;** unicellular forms obviously lack a my-celium. All of these plants are heterotrophic, mostly saprophytic and aerobic, and are usually colorless, although a few do produce non-photosynthetic pigments. In most of these latter, the asexual spore con-tains the pigment. Starch is not found in the Eumycophyta, the soluble food being transformed into **glycogen,** a type of starch.

The majority of fungi form two or more kinds of spores in the life cycle. The asexual spores are sometimes produced in a sporangium and sometimes individually or in chains at the end of specialized hyphae, the **conidiophores.** Spores of the latter type are termed **conidia** (sing., **conidium**). Sexual reproduction is varied, as in the algae. The sexual spores are produced only after sexual reproduction and form imme-diately following meiosis. The separation of the true fungi into four classes is based upon differences in the sexual stage, with the Class Deuteromycetes being reserved for those having asexual stages which have not been identified with any sexual stage. This latter group is an arbitrary one, one of convenience, and the organisms placed therein properly belong in one of the other classes, probably the Class Asco-mycetes for the most part. When one of the Deuteromycetes is proved to be an asexual stage of a known member of one of the other classes, it passes automatically to that group; many such transfers are made. In a number of cases, fungi with only asexual stages are placed within the natural groupings, and not in the Deuteromycetes, because of other characteristics which clearly indicate the proper relationships.

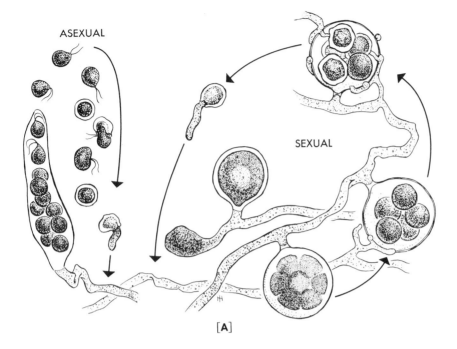

ASEXUAL

SEXUAL

[A]

Figure 21-1. *Saprolegnia.* **A**: Life cycle. At the left, primary zoospores are liberated from the zoosporangium. Later this zoospore
develops into a secondary zoospore which then forms a new
mycelium. At the right, fertilization tubes from the antheridia
penetrate to the eggs in the oögonium and zygotes are formed.
After meiosis, these zygotes develop into new haploid mycelia.
B: Life cycle word diagram.

[B]

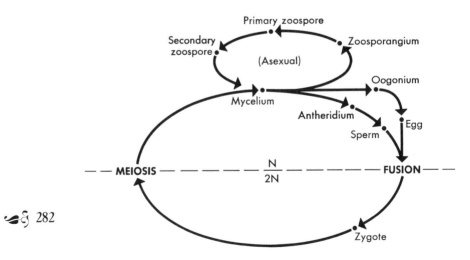

Division
Eumycophyta

21.2 Characteristics of the Class Phycomycetes

The plants of this group are frequently referred to as the algal fungi, and the methods of sexual reproduction are quite similar to the algae, in that isogamy, heterogamy, and oögamy are all represented. The non-septate **(coenocytic)**, branching filaments do not form a compressed body but remain a cottony mass; a few of the simpler forms are uni-cellular. Cross-walls, or septations, form only when reproductive structures are produced. Asexual reproduction is typically by means of spores **(sporangiospores)** borne in a sporangium, and they may be motile or non-motile; the hypha on which a sporangium is borne is termed a **sporangiophore.** Some Phycomycetes are parasitic on other plants or on animals (usually fish or insects).

21.3 Representative members of the Phycomycetes

The Phycomycetes are subdivided into eight orders and their component families and genera, but only two representative genera will be discussed in any detail.

SAPROLEGNIA

The members of this genus (Figure 21-1) are mainly saprophytic water molds, but some species are serious parasites of fish. The body consists of slender, branched, loosely tangled, coenocytic hyphae anchored to the substratum by profusely-branched hyphae termed **rhizoids.** Asexual reproduction is by means of biciliated zoospores produced in a zoosporangium which develops as a swollen hyphal tip delimited from the rest of the hypha by a cross-wall. These **primary zoospores** are liberated through a pore at the end of the zoosporangium, swim about, become quiescent, and develop a resistant wall. Later this wall ruptures, liberating a biciliated **secondary zoospore,** which develops into a new mycelium. Sexual reproduction is oögamous, with an oögonium containing several eggs developing next to an antheridium containing many nuclei. **Fertilization tubes** from the antheridium penetrate the oögonium and reach the eggs; eventually an antheridial nucleus fuses with each egg to produce several zygotes in the

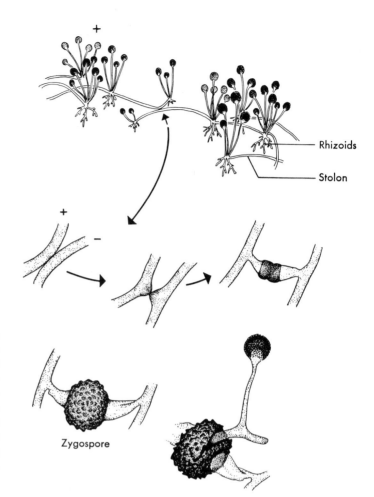

Figure 21-2. *Rhizopus* life cycle. The sporangia formed during asexual reproduction are shown in the uppermost figure. The arrows indicate sexual reproduction which culminates in the formation of a thick-walled zygote shown at the lower left. Meiosis occurs when the zygote germinates, lower right, and the resultant sporangium contains haploid spores.

Rhizoids

Stolon

Zygospore

oögonium. These zygotes each develop into new plants, meiosis occurring at this time.

RHIZOPUS

The members of this genus (Figure 21-2) are commonly found growing on damp organic material, such as bread and ripe fruit. The mycelium is usually a dense mat of intertwined hyphae, the main branches of which grow horizontally over the surface of the substratum. Such hyphae are termed **stolons,** and, where they touch the surface, slender much-branched filaments called rhizoids grow downward, penetrating into the substratum. The rhizoids serve in a manner analogous to roots; they anchor the plant and absorb nutrients. The fungi are heterotrophic, and the material absorbed is mainly water and dissolved organic matter. Enzymes secreted by the hyphae bring about this digestion and dissolution. Usually at the point of contact, upright hyphae are produced which bear single sporangia at the tip. A sporangium is formed by the enlargement of the tip of a sporangiophore, and the outer portion of the protoplasm in this enlargement is subdivided into large numbers of asexual spores. The rest of the protoplasm in the tip is delimited by the formation of a wall, projects into the sporangium as a sterile portion known as the **columella,** and is continuous with the rest of the sporangiophore (see Figure 21-3). When the sporangial wall ruptures, the spores are blown about by the wind and develop into new mycelia if they happen to land in a suitable environment. *Rhizopus* is heterothallic, and zygotes develop only when hyphae from different plants come into contact. At the point of contact, small side branches with enlarged tips are produced, and each tip is cut off from the rest of the hypha by a cross-wall. These two terminal cells are touching, the wall between them disintegrates, and the cells fuse, forming a single-celled zygote.[1] The zygote enlarges, develops a thick wall, and becomes a resistant **zygospore.** On germination, the thick wall ruptures, and a sporangiophore emerges. Meiosis occurs at this time, and the spores which are produced are haploid. Germination of these spores results in the formation of two kinds of mycelia, only one mycelium per spore, of course. Because the two kinds of mycelia look alike, they are referred to as + and − strains; no visible sexual dif-

Figure 21-3. *Rhizopus,* **development of sporangium and spores.**

ference allows the use of the terms male and female. Certainly a difference does exist, even though it is not obvious, and zygotes are produced only when + and − strains touch, never between + and + or − and −.

[1] The cells which fuse to form the zygote each have many nuclei. They should probably be thought of as gametangia which function as gametes. The zygote is multinucleate, but nuclei from the different hyphae pair off and fuse, giving diploid nuclei.

21.4 Importance of the Phycomycetes

The origin of the Phycomycetes is debatable; two main points of view are current. The first suggestion is that these fungi arose from various members of the Chlorophyta. This is based upon the similarity in reproduction between certain Phycomycetes and certain green algae, such as conjugation in *Rhizopus* and *Spirogyra*. The different types of reproduction in the Phycomycetes result from the origin of these fungi from Chlorophyta with similar variations in their type of sexual reproduction. The other viewpoint holds that the Phycomycetes and the Chlorophyta were derived from some common ancestor and that the similarities in reproductive structures is an example of **parallel evolution,** in which genetically different plants followed similar pathways. In the Phycomycetes the trend is for sporangia to be transformed into **sporangioles** (small sporangia with few spores) and these into conidia; a small sporangium containing a single spore is quite similar to a conidium. We shall not consider this trend in detail except to indicate the possibility that such a tendency could lead toward the Ascomycetes and Basidiomycetes, where conidia are quite typical.

The Phycomycetes are very important in bringing about the decay of dead plants and animals and their wastes, especially cellulose materials. A few members of this class of fungi are useful commercially in the production of fumaric acid, oxalic acid, and various enzymes. Some of these fungi are also important in the spoilage of stored fruits and vegetables, and others are parasitic on various crop plants (Table 21-1). The late blight of potato, caused by *Phytophthora infestans,* is

Table 21-1. Some Plant Diseases Caused by Phycomycetes

Disease	Pathogen	Control
Late blight of potato	Phytophthora infestans	Bordeaux mixture * as a spray.
White rust of crucifers (cabbage, cauliflower, radish, turnip, etc.)	Albugo candida	Crop rotation, destruction of infected crops.
Downy mildew of grape	Plasmopara viticola	Bordeaux mixture.*
Damping-off of seedlings	Pythium debaryanum	Seed treatment with Ceresan † or Semesan,† soil disinfestation.
Club root of crucifers	Plasmodiophora brassicae	Crop rotation, soil disinfestation.

* Bordeaux mixture: 4 lbs. copper sulfate, 4 lbs. lime, and 50 gal. water.
† Ceresan and Semesan are organic mercury compounds.

one of the most famous of plant diseases and was the basic cause of the migration of 1,500,000 Irish people to the United States in the late

1840's. The staple crop of Ireland was the potato, and the economy of that land was built upon that crop; no other crops were of any significance. The late blight disease struck with disastrous suddenness in the 1840's and resulted in the tremendous famine of 1845, when the potato crop was almost completely destroyed. Almost 1 million people starved to death. The total reduction of population, death plus migrations, due to this one plant disease was somewhat more than two-and-one-half million people, or almost one-third of the total population. Although the discovery of Bordeaux mixture as a control spray has greatly decreased the severity of this disease, losses in the United States still range from 1 million to 50 million bushels per year. The higher figures result from failure to spray crops, usually as a result of some "good years" with little loss causing growers to become indifferent. The United States lost over 54 million bushels, nearly one-eighth of its potato crop, in 1938; up to 45 per cent of the crop was lost in some areas.

21.5 Characteristics of the Class Ascomycetes

A few of the Ascomycetes are unicellular, but in most the hyphae are septate, and in the majority a fruiting body, or **ascocarp**, develops

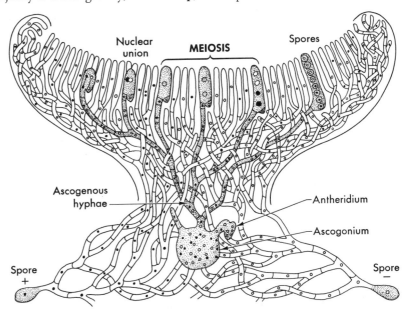

Figure 21-4. Diagram of the sexual life cycle of a heterothallic ascomycete. The early stages are in the lower portion of the diagram and later stages in the upper portion. Long before the apothecium and the spores are mature, the sex organs have disappeared. (Redrawn from L. C. Sharp, *Fundamentals of Cytology.* Copyright 1935 by McGraw-Hill and used with permission.)

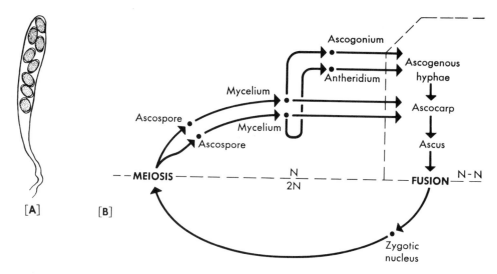

Figure 21-5. Ascomycete. **A:** Ascus with ascospores; from *Morchella*. **B:** Life cycle word diagram.

as a result of sexual reproduction. This group is primarily characterized by the production of **asci** (singular, **ascus**), each containing typically eight **ascospores,** within the ascocarp. These fungi are usually heterothallic, and the mycelium is really a mixture of male and female strains. The female sex organ is termed an **ascogonium** and consists of a swollen, multinucleate, basal cell and an elongated cell, or **trichogyne.** The male sex organ, or **antheridium,** is long and slender and usually curves around the ascogonium, eventually fusing with the trichogyne. The nuclei of the trichogyne and the wall at its base disintegrate as the nuclei of the antheridium move to and pair with the nuclei of the ascogonium. These nuclei do not fuse; they divide as a unit. **Ascogenous hyphae** grow out from the ascogonium and intertwine with vegetative hyphae to form the ascocarp. The cells of the ascogenous hyphae differ from the vegetative hyphae in that the former have

Figure 21-6. An ascocarp (apothecium) showing the location of the hymenium. The enlargement at the left shows several asci with ascospores and numerous sterile hyphal tips.

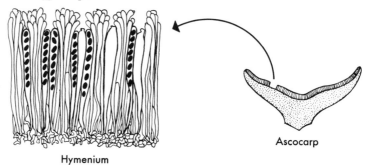

Hymenium

Ascocarp

paired nuclei, a **dicaryon** (N-N) [2] condition. In the ascocarp, the end cells of various hyphae become somewhat swollen and enlarged, or sac-shaped. The paired nuclei in these cells fuse, the condition now being diploid (2N), and then undergo three divisions (including meiosis), resulting in eight haploid (N) nuclei. Walls form around the eight nuclei and a small amount of cytoplasm for each, and the resultant structures are ascospores contained within an ascus (see Figures 21-4 and 21-5).

Ascocarps are of three general types, depending upon the particular fungus involved. In all of these the asci are produced in a layer interspersed with sterile hyphal tips; such a layer is termed the **hymenium** (Figure 21-6). The rest of the ascocarp (or fruiting body) is composed of densely interwoven hyphae, the cells of which may be so swollen as to give a parenchymatous aspect. An **apothecium,** as in *Peziza,* is an open cup-shaped structure with the hymenium lining the concave surface of the cup. A **cleistothecium,** as in *Erysiphe,* is a spherical structure in which the asci are completely enclosed; the cleistothecium splits and the asci protrude when they are mature. A **perithecium,** as in *Claviceps purpurea,* is similar to a cleistothecium except that the former has a pore through which the hyphae may protrude.

Asexual reproduction in the Ascomycetes is typically by the formation of conidia, although budding occurs in the yeasts. The shape and branching of the conidiophores and the color of the conidia are useful as diagnostic characteristics in classifying these organisms.

21.6 Representative members of the Ascomycetes

The classification of this group is in a state of flux and is variously subdivided into numerous orders, families, and genera, but only a few of the more common forms will be discussed.

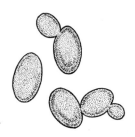

Figure 21-7. Yeast (*Saccharomyces cerevisiae*). **The uppermost plant on the right has one bud, whereas the one beneath has a second bud projecting from the first bud.**

SACCHAROMYCES

The yeasts (Figure 21-7) are one of the few members of the Ascomycetes which are unicellular. Reproduction in these plants is almost always asexually by **budding,** in which a small protuberance develops

[2] Haploid is designated as N, diploid as 2N.

from the parent cell, the nucleus divides, and one part migrates into the bud, after which a wall forms delimiting the bud from the original cell. Several buds may be produced before they actually separate from the parent plant. In a few species ascospores are produces after two yeast cells fuse, the entire cell functioning as a single ascus.

Yeasts, particularly *S. cerevisiae,* are extremely important commercially in the production of alcoholic beverages and industrial alcohol. Sugars contained in grapes and other fruits are metabolized anaerobically (fermentation), producing alcohol, carbon dioxide, and various by-products which serve to flavor the resultant liquid or wine. In the production of beer, germinated barley grains are ground and mixed with water plus various adjuncts, such as carbohydrates from corn or rice. Enzymes from the barley, especially diastase, digest these carbohydrates, and the soluble materials are used as food by the yeasts (which are added later). The germinated barley grains mainly digest starch to sugar, a necessary preliminary step due to the inability of yeast cells to utilize starch. The grains are finally removed, hops [3] are added for flavoring, and then special strains of yeast are added. Fermentation by these yeast plants results in the production of beer. The actual flavor of the beer depends upon all of the various factors: barley, kind of adjuncts, strain of yeast, hops, length of fermentation, temperature, and water. Industrial alcohol is made by adding yeast to any inexpensive supply of sugar, such as molasses. The production of carbon dioxide gas by yeast plants as they respire causes dough to "raise" when making bread. The heat of the oven eventually kills the yeast, evaporates any alcohol which may have been produced, and causes the dough to harden in the raised condition. The production of alcohol (over 350 million gallons per year in the United States alone) and the making of bread products constitute the most important uses of yeast.[4] However, yeast plants contain a high percentage of proteins, some fats, and certain vitamins (thiamin, riboflavin, biotin, pyridoxine, pantothenic acid, and calciferol), and their utilization as food or a food supplement may become exceedingly important in the future. A few yeasts are pathogenic to man, causing skin infections or infections of the lung and central nervous system, but these are not really of any great importance.

---

[3] Hops: the ripe, dried female flower of a twining vine, *Humulus lupulus.*

[4] An interesting note is that these two important aspects of yeast culture utilize two quite different physiological processes of the yeast plant. In the production of alcohol, fermentations are utilized; to produce the large quantities of yeast used in the bread industry, the yeast cultures are aerated to insure respiratory activity rather than fermentation. Why?

Figure 21-8. *Peziza,* **habit sketch of the apothecium.**

PEZIZA

The members of this genus (Figure 21-8) are saprophytes usually found growing on fallen trees or in soil which contains much organic matter. The apothecium is the conspicuous portion of the plant, but an extensive vegetative mycelium penetrates the substratum (e.g., decaying wood) and obtains food materials. Asci are produced along the inner surface of the cup-shaped fruiting body, and the spores are discharged when a lid at the tip of each ascus opens. Ascospores are disseminated by the wind and give rise to vegetative mycelia when they germinate. Apothecia, asci, and ascospores are produced only as a result of sexual reproduction.

Figure 21-9. *Morchella,* **habit sketch of the ascocarp.**

MORCHELLA

In spite of its somewhat different appearance, *Morchella* (Figure 21-9) is quite similar to *Peziza* in basic structure. The former, sometimes called a morel or sponge fungus, has a stalked sponge-like ascocarp in which each depression is comparable to the cup-shaped ascocarp of *Peziza*. The morel is one of the most delicious of the edible fungi.

ASPERGILLUS

The members of this genus (Figure 21-10) are usually encountered as conidial fungi growing on all sorts of organic material in damp places. The plant body is a loosely interwoven mass of hyphae of no definite form, and the sexual stage is found in only a few species. However, the asexual structures (conidia and conidiophores) are so characteristic that even those reproducing only asexually are placed in this class rather than among the Deuteromycetes (Fungi Imperfecti). *Aspergillus* species cause the decay of many stored fruits and vegetables, bread, leather goods, and other fabrics; some cause ear and lung infections in domesticated mammals and in man. *Aspergillus niger* is used in the production of citric and oxalic acids.

Figure 21-10. *Aspergillus niger,* **conidia borne on a conidiophore.**

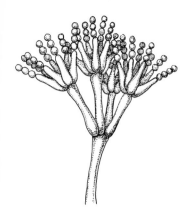

Figure 21-11. *Penicillium notatum,* **conidia** borne on a branched conidiophore.

PENICILLIUM

The blue-green molds are also found mainly as conidial stages, the color being due to masses of pigmented conidia that are produced. As in *Aspergillus,* some species of *Penicillium* (Figure 21-11) reproduce sexually, forming a cleistothecium containing asci. Various species are responsible for the spoilage of fruits (especially citrus), paper, books, leather, lumber, and bread. *Penicillium camemberti* produces the flavoring in Camembert cheese by means of the products of casein hydrolysis; similar hydrolysis of butter fats by *P. roqueforti* imparts flavors to Roquefort cheese. The conidia, which are produced in enormous numbers, are visible as bluish-green streaks in these cheeses. One of the most important members of this genus is *Penicillium notatum,* which is famous as the producer of the antibiotic penicillin. Antibiotics [5] are substances which are produced by one organism and inhibit or destroy other organisms. Penicillin has proved effective against many bacterial diseases of man: gonorrhea, syphilis, pneumonia, streptococcus infections, staphylococcus infections, etc.

21.7 Importance of the Ascomycetes

The origin of the Ascomycetes is as debatable as that of the Phycomycetes, and again two main viewpoints are held. According to one view, the similarity of sexual reproduction in the Ascomycetes and in the Rhodophyta indicates a relationship, and the suggestion is that these fungi are degenerate descendants of the red algae. The viewpoint held by most mycologists, however, is that the Ascomycetes are probably descended from Phycomycetes. In addition to the sporangium-conidium relationship already discussed (Section 21.4), the similarity between the ascogonium and the oögonium (as in *Saprolegnia*) is presented as evidence in favor of this second view. Further discussion of such relationships is beyond the scope of this text.

The Ascomycetes are important decay organisms, bring about spoil-

---

[5] Many antibiotics have been isolated from various molds, bacteria, and actinomycetes. The actinomycetes are members of the Class Schizomycetes, as are the bacteria, and one species produces streptomycin, an antibiotic second only to penicillin in usefulness. Unfortunately, most antibiotics are too toxic to man to be used, but at least a dozen or so can be utilized to control various diseases. Other antibiotics very likely will be isolated in the future.

age of various materials, and some are parasitic on various crop plants (Table 21-2). A number of commercial applications of various mem-

Table 21-2.   Some Plant Diseases Caused by Ascomycetes

Disease	Pathogen	Control
Scab of cereals	Gibberella zeae	Sanitation * and crop rotation, seed treatment with Semesan.†
Apple scab	Venturia inaequalis	Bordeaux mixture ‡ and lime sulfur.
Chestnut blight	Endothia parasitica	None.
Ergot of grains and grasses	Claviceps purpurea	Crop rotation, use of disease-free seed, sanitation.*
Powdery mildew of cereals	Erysiphe graminis	Resistant varieties.
Peach leaf curl	Taphrina deformans	Bordeaux mixture. ‡

* Sanitation refers to the destruction of crop residues.
† Semesan is an organic mercury compound.
‡ Bordeaux mixture: 4 lbs. copper sulfate, 4 lbs. lime, and 50 gal. water.

bers of the Class Ascomycetes have already been mentioned. We might emphasize once more that the beneficial aspects of these fungi as decay organisms greatly outweigh any possible harm they may cause as parasitic agents. This is not to imply that plant diseases caused by Ascomycetes are unimportant; some of the diseases result in enormous losses. Remember, however, that "harmful" and "beneficial" are relative terms, and an over-all view always indicates that the beneficial aspects predominate.

The ergot disease of grains, especially of rye, is interesting in that this disease not only decreases the yield of crop plants but also results in the poisoning of animals which feed upon diseased grains. The "Holy Fire" of the Middle Ages was actually ergotism, resulting from the use of diseased rye grains in baking bread. This fungus, *Claviceps purpurea,* transforms rye grains into enlarged purplish bodies filled with hyphae. Ergot poisoning is caused by an alkaloid, ergotinin, which is contained within these purplish structures. In humans blindness, convulsions, hallucinations, and paralysis may occur. Since the discovery of the cause of ergotism around 1845, this disease has been relatively rare in humans, although grazing animals are frequently affected. However, as recently as 1951, ergotism flared up in France as a result of using infected rye grain, and over 200 people required medical attention. Surprisingly, a drug is prepared from ergot which is useful as a constrictor of smooth muscle in cases of excessive bleeding (hemorrhage) and as an aid in childbirth.

21.8 Characteristics of the Class Basidiomycetes

In most of the members of this class, the septate hyphae form a fruiting body, the **basidiocarp** or **sporophore,** after sexual reproduction has occurred. The primary characteristic of the Basidiomycetes is the production of **basidia** (sing., **basidium**), each bearing four **basidiospores** externally on small stalks (**sterigmata;** sing., **sterigma**). The plant may be homothallic or heterothallic, and no sexual organs are formed; sexual reproduction results from the fusion of hyphae.[6] Nuclear fusion is delayed, as in the Ascomycetes, and the dicaryon hyphae $(N + N)$ form the basidiocarp wherein is located the hymenium. The end cells of various hyphae in the basidiocarp become swollen and club-shaped, the paired nuclei fuse (2N), and then they undergo meiosis, forming four haploid (N) nuclei. The club-shaped basidium produces small protuberances into which the nuclei migrate and are cut off by the formation of walls at the base of each projection. Enlargement of the structures in which the nuclei are now located completes the formation of basidiospores, borne externally on the basidium [7] (Figure 21-12). The fruiting body is of various sizes and

Figure 21-12. Development of a basidium and basidiospores. Second from the left: meiosis occurs immediately after fusion, and the four resultant nuclei are haploid. Far right: four mature basidiospores borne externally on a basidium.

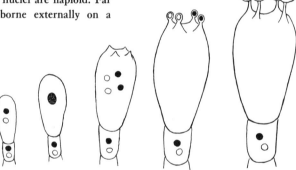

shapes, some of which are shown in Figure 21-13. Asexual reproduction is typically by the formation of conidia, but such spores are not nearly as prevalent in the Basidiomycetes as they are in the Ascomycetes; some of the former have never been found in the conidial stage. A few of the parasitic Basidiomycetes produce more than two kinds of spores and may have two hosts in their life cycle, but all of them produce basidia and basidiospores at some time.

[6] In some Basidiomycetes such fusion occurs between hyphae and individual small cells.

[7] In some Basidiomycetes the basidium is septate.

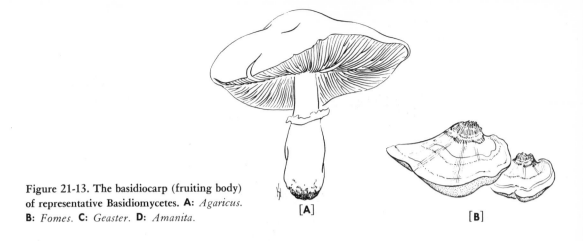

Figure 21-13. The basidiocarp (fruiting body) of representative Basidiomycetes. **A:** *Agaricus*. **B:** *Fomes*. **C:** *Geaster*. **D:** *Amanita*.

[A]

[B]

21.9 Representative members of the Basidiomycetes

The classification of this group of fungi has engendered considerable controversy, but we will limit our discussion to a few of the more common or interesting genera.

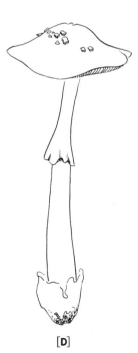

[C]

AGARICUS

Agaricus (Figure 21-13A) is the common edible mushroom [8] which may be purchased in any grocery store, either fresh or in cans. It is a saprophytic plant deriving its food supply from various organic materials in the soil, the vegetative mycelium penetrating extensively through the substratum. The basidiocarp grows upwardly above ground and consists of a densely woven mass of hyphae that form a fleshy structure; the **stipe** (stalk) is capped by an umbrella-shaped **pileus.** On the underside of the pileus are thin, sheet-like **gills** [9] extending from the stipe to the edge of the cap; basidia cover the surfaces of the gills (Figure 21-14). The basidiospores are blown about by the wind and germinate to form new mycelia.

AMANITA

Amanita (Figure 12-13B) is very similar in appearance to *Agaricus,* but the former is quite poisonous. (The student should not collect and

[8] The terms mushroom and toadstool have no botanical significance except as convenient descriptions. The latter term probably means a "poisonous mushroom" and will not be used at all.

[9] Basidiomycetes possessing these structures are frequently referred to as the "gill fungi."

[D]

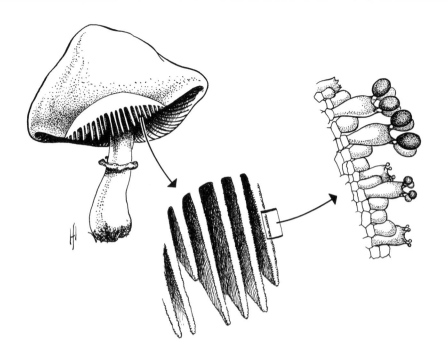

Figure 21-14. *Agaricus.* Left: the basidiocarp with a small portion cut off so that the gills are visible. Center: gills enlarged. Right: a portion of a gill enlarged showing basidia and basidiospores with some of the latter not yet mature.

eat wild species. The cultivated mushroom purchased in a store is much safer.)

FOMES

The genus *Fomes* (Figure 21-13D) includes perennial woody bracket or pore fungi, which are most commonly found as shelf-like growths on the sides of trees or logs. The under surface of the basidiocarp has many pores which are actually the openings of long tubes; the hymenium lines these tubes, and the basidiospores are blown about by the wind after they fall to the outside. The vegetative mycelium develops rather extensively through the tree trunk before the fruiting body develops. *Polyporus* is similar to *Fomes* but produces only one layer of pores, whereas the latter may produce a new layer each year.

LYCOPERDON

The puffballs have a spherical fruiting body which is homogeneous at first but later separates into a thin outer layer and a central region. Cavities lined with hymenia develop in the central region. At maturity, most of the inner hyphae disintegrate, and the puffball consists of an outer layer with an apical pore enclosing a powdery mass of basidiospores. Mechanical disturbances result in a puff of "powder," and the spores are then distributed by the wind. Puffballs are exceedingly tasty before they are mature. Once the spores have formed, eating a puffball would be like eating talcum powder. Some puffballs are extremely large, the fruiting body approaching 100 cm. in diameter.

21.10 Importance of the Basidiomycetes

The Basidiomycetes are generally regarded as being descended from the Ascomycetes. The dicaryon condition of certain hyphae and the formation of conidia in both groups are characteristics which indicate such a relationship. The general development of the basidium is essentially like that of the ascus; fusion of male and female nuclei, followed by meiosis, occurs immediately preceding the formation of both basidiospores and ascospores.

The Basidiomycetes are especially active in bringing about the decay of woody materials but, as with most fungi, also attack a great variety of organic matter. A few members of this group are edible, especially *Agaricus campestris,* but others are distinctly poisonous if eaten, such as *Amanita* species. Although most of these fungi are saprophytic, some are parasitic and cause enormous economic losses. Table 21-3

Table 21-3. Some Plant Diseases Caused by Basidiomycetes

Disease	Pathogen	Control
Stem rust of grains and grasses	Puccinia graminis	Resistant varieties; sulfur dusting; eliminate barberry.
Cedar apple rust	Gymnosporangium juniperivirginianae	Eliminate one host; sulfur dusting.
Blister rust of pine	Cronartium ribicola	Eliminate *Ribes* host.
Bunt of wheat	Tilletia tritici and T. laevis	Seed treatment with Ceresan,* etc.; resistant varieties.
Loose smut of wheat	Ustilago tritici	Resistant varieties, hot water treatment of seeds.†
Common smut of corn	Ustilago zeae	Crop rotation, sanitation.‡
Rhizoctonia disease (black scurf) of potatoes	Corticium vagum	Crop rotation, use of clean "seed pieces."

* Ceresan is an organic mercury compound.
† Enough heat is involved to kill the fungus mycelium but not the plant embryo (in the seed)
‡ Sanitation refers to destruction of crop residues.

lists a few of the more common plant diseases caused by Basidiomycetes.

The stem rust disease of grains and grasses, caused by *Puccinia graminis,* deserves attention because of the severity of losses, the great variety of host plants involved, and the excellent example this disease provides of competition between artificial evolution (plant breeding programs) and natural evolution. As is true of most plant diseases, stem rust is very dependent upon weather conditions, and crops will suffer negligible losses some years, while other years may result in a loss of 60 per cent of the wheat crop in some areas. Severe rust years

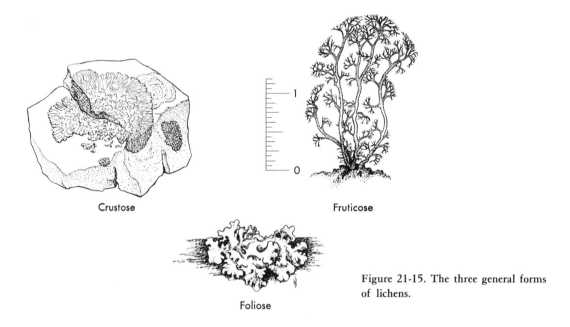

Crustose

Fruticose

Foliose

Figure 21-15. The three general forms of lichens.

result in millions of bushels of wheat lost—160 million bushels in 1935—at a total cost of millions of dollars. Although stem rust of wheat is the most economically important rust disease, *Puccinia graminis* is subdivided into a number of varieties: *P. graminis tritici* on wheat, *P. graminis avenae* on oats, *P. graminis secalis* on rye, and others, mainly on grasses. Each variety in turn is subdivided into various numbered physiologic races. Each of these races is able to attack certain varieties of wheat, for example, and unable to attack other wheat varieties. Well over 150 physiological forms of *P. graminis tritici* are known.

The wheat rust fungus produces five types of spores and utilizes two hosts to complete its life cycle. Control of this disease by eradicating barberry (*Berberis vulgaris,* one of the hosts) is important in isolated areas having cold winters and in any area to prevent sexual reproduction of the fungus, since the sexual stage develops on barberry. Eliminating barberry cannot prevent stem rust in areas with mild winters, because some of the spores which re-infect wheat without barberry as an intermediate may survive. The southerly winds in the Plains Area of the United States serve to blow these spores from the warmer Southern states, where they over-winter, to the Northern states where they cannot survive. Eradicating barberry does not prevent infection. It does, however, prevent sexual reproduction of the fungus. Control of stem rust is accomplished mainly by the use of resistant wheat varieties; sulfur dusting is effective but expensive. Such wheat varieties do not retain their resistance; they become attacked more and more severely and are soon listed as susceptible varieties. This loss of resistance is not due to any change in the wheat but to the appearance of new physiological races of the stem rust fungus. New races are a normal result of variations due to new genetic combinations which occur during sexual reproduction. The plant breeder is in a continual struggle to produce resistant varieties more rapidly than the fungus develops new strains of rust. This is what was meant by the comment concerning the competition between artificial and natural evolution.

21.11   Characteristics of the Class Lichens

The members of this group are actually composed of close associations between a fungus, usually Ascomycete, and an alga, either Chlorophyta or Cyanophyceae. Their exact position in the plant kingdom is not clear, but they are usually placed with the fungi because the greater proportion of the plant body consists of the fungal component. There are three general types of lichens (Figure 21-15) which are (1) **crustose,** or crust-like, (2) **fruticose,** or shrub-like, and (3) **foliose,** or leaf-like. Closely interwoven hyphae form the structure, including rhizoids, and enclose algal cells near the upper surface; in some cases **haustoria** (short hyphal branches) penetrate the algal cells. Reproduction is by means of **soredia,** small masses of hyphae enclosing a few algal cells, which form as powdery masses on the surface of the lichen. The soredia blow about and are capable of developing into a lichen in a suitable environment. In many of these plants, apothecia are formed, and the ascospores may germinate upon liberation. If the proper species of alga is encountered, the hyphae will continue to form a lichen; the fungus alone cannot survive.

The relationship between the fungus and the alga in a lichen is rather peculiar. The latter obtains water and minerals from the former, while the fungus obtains food from the photosynthetic process of the alga. The penetrating rhizoids and the organic acids produced during the metabolic activity of the fungus undoubtedly aid in dissolving and obtaining essential minerals from the substratum. The lichen, thus, can exist where neither component alone could survive. However, the alga can "go it alone" in a suitable environment, but the fungus cannot. Some botanists maintain that a lichen is a good example of symbiosis, the living together of two organisms in an association which is mutually beneficial. Other botanists claim that the fungus is parasitic on the alga, because the former cannot live alone. The true relationship is probably somewhere between these two points of view; the fungus is surely parasitic, but the alga derives considerable benefit from the association.

The lichens are exceedingly important as pioneers in plant succession, especially upon bare rock where other organisms cannot survive. The surface of the rock is gradually broken as a result of mechanical forces and chemical disintegration, thus setting the stage for gradual soil formation. Debris blown by the wind accumulates in the rough surfaces of the lichen structure, and this, plus the plants themselves when they die, adds to soil development. Eventually, when enough soil is accumulated, other plants become established. In this fashion more and more debris, including organic matter from dead plant structures, accumulates and converts a barren area into one which can support vegetation.

Some lichens are sources of food for grazing animals in the arctic regions. Other lichens are used in the perfume industry, in dyeing processes, and as a source of litmus. The latter is used in chemistry laboratories as an indicator for acids and alkalies.[10]

Summary

1. The division Eumycophyta consists of non-chlorophyllous thallophytes which are usually filamentous. A single filament is termed a hypha, and the entangled mass of hyphae is termed a mycelium. Two kinds of spores are produced; one of these types develops only after sexual reproduction. If a sexual stage is not found and if relationships are not obvious, the fungus is placed in the class Deuteromycetes. The other classes in this division are: Phycomycetes, Ascomycetes, and Basidiomycetes.

2. Members of the Class Phycomycetes are readily distinguishable because of their coenocytic filaments. Septations form only when reproductive structures are produced. The Phycomycetes and the Chlorophyta probably are descended from some common ancestor.

3. Phycomycetes are important decay organisms. Some of them are utilized commercially in the production of various organic acids and

[10] The natural purple color of litmus is changed to red by acids and to blue by alkalies.

enzymes. A number of serious plant diseases are caused by members of this group.

4. The Ascomycetes produce an ascocarp, containing asci and ascospores, as a result of sexual reproduction. This fruiting body may be variously shaped. This group is probably descended from the Phycomycetes.

5. Many of the Ascomycetes are of great economic importance. They are used in the production of alcohol, bread, cheese, antibiotics, and a variety of other products. They are also useful decay organisms. Some members of this group cause plant diseases.

6. The Basidiomycetes produce a basidiocarp, containing basidia and basidiospores, as a result of sexual reproduction. This fruiting body may be of various shapes. This group is probably descended from the Ascomycetes.

7. The Basidiomycetes are active decay organisms. Some of them are edible, but others are distinctly poisonous. A number of plant diseases are caused by members of this class.

8. The Lichens are actually close associations between a fungus and an alga; the greater portion of the plant body consists of fungal hyphae. This association enables the lichen to grow in areas which would not support the growth of either component alone. Actually, the fungus has never been grown separately. These plants are important in soil development and plant succession.

REVIEW TOPICS AND QUESTIONS

1. Define the following: conidium, conidiophore, ascus, ascospore, basidium, basidiospore, ascocarp, apothecium, basidiocarp, hypha, and mycelium.
2. If you had collected a fungus specimen, describe in detail what you would have to do to determine the identity of the plant (differentiate as to which class of the Eumycophyta).
3. If a fungus specimen had no sexual stages, what other characteristics could be used for identification purposes? On what bases could you restrict this specimen to one or more of the classes of Eumycophyta?
4. A piece of moist bread left on a table gradually becomes covered with a cottony mold growth which eventually contains many black specks and a fewer number of small, dark, globose structures. Examination with the microscope enables you to identify *Rhizopus nigricans*. Describe in detail the development of this organism, including the reproductive structures, the food source, and the kinds of hyphae produced.
5. In what ways are the Phycomycetes important to humans?
6. Wine production by individuals usually consists of merely crushing grapes and allowing them to ferment. What is the source of the yeast plants? Describe the growth of the yeast plant. Discuss the activities of the yeast plants which result in the formation of wine.

301

7. List at least ten ways in which the Ascomycetes are important to humans.
8. Describe the life cycle of *Agaricus*.
9. Explain why it is unlikely that a resistant wheat variety will remain resistant to stem rust (caused by *Puccinia graminis*).
10. Discuss how lichens aid in the establishment of plants on rock surfaces.
11. Decay by fungi frequently creates serious problems in the tropics. Explain.

SUGGESTED READINGS

Alexopoulos, C. J. *Introductory Mycology*. New York: Wiley, 1952.

Bessey, E. A. *Morphology and Taxonomy of Fungi*. Philadelphia: Blakiston, 1950.

Bonner, J. T. "The Growth of Mushrooms," *Scientific American*, 194 (May 1956), 97–106.

Christensen, C. M. *The Molds and Man*. Minneapolis: University of Minnesota, 1951.

Emerson, R. "Molds and Man," *Scientific American*, 186 (January 1952), 28–32.

Fitzpatrick, H. M. *The Lower Fungi, Phycomycetes*. New York: McGraw-Hill, 1930.

Foster, J. W. *Chemical Activities of Fungi*. New York: Academic Press, 1949.

Gray, W. D. *The Relation of Fungi to Human Affairs*. New York: Holt, 1959.

Lamb, I. M. "Lichens," *Scientific American*, 201 (October 1959), 144–156.

Niederhauser, J. S., and W. C. Cobb. "The Late Blight," *Scientific American*, 200 (May 1959), 100–102.

Wolf, F. A., and F. T. Wolf. *The Fungi*. Vol. I and II. New York: Wiley, 1947.

CHAPTER 22

Sub-kingdom Embryophyta:

Division Bryophyta

IN SOME systems of classification, "sub-kingdoms" are not used because of their rather artificial nature. Previous chapters have pointed out that the Sub-kingdom Thallophyta is comprised of many forms which may be related only distantly. A similar situation exists in the Embryophyta, but the existence of some similarities in basic structure makes the concept useful even if some groupings are not natural. In those systems where sub-kingdoms are not utilized, the divisions stand alone and are of equal rank.

22.1 General characteristics of the Sub-kingdom Embryophyta

The members of the Embryophyta are subdivided into the Divisions Bryophyta and Tracheophyta and comprise those plants which are most familiar to us—mosses, ferns, cone-bearing plants, and flowering plants. The plants in this grouping provide us with food, shelter, miscellaneous materials, and beauty. Some of the products which they supply to humans and some of the human endeavors which depend upon them will be mentioned when the pertinent sub-groups are discussed in more detail. But first we must mention the characteristics which these seemingly diverse plants have in common.

As the name indicates, all members of the Embryophyta produce a multicellular embryo which is retained within the female sex organ, the archegonium, or within the tissues of the gametophyte; the former situation obtains in the lower groups. The zygote is not released from the parent until it has divided to form a mass of cells, whereas in the Thallophyta the zygote is released soon after formation or is never within the parent plant at all. The **embryo** may be considered to be an immature new plant which receives essential nutrients from the parent tissues.

The retention of an embryo within parental tissues is an evolutionary change of major importance in the transition of plants from a water habitat to land. The chances of survival are greater in such a situation than in one in which the zygote is exposed to the possibility of desiccation by its early release. In some groups, the seed plants especially, the embryo becomes **dormant** or quiescent before developing into a new mature individual and is rather resistant to adverse environmental conditions while in this condition.

The Embryophyta are all oögamous, and the sex organs are multicellular, the outer layer of cells forming a sterile jacket enclosing the gametes. This affords additional protection to the delicate gametes, protecting them from drying out. The male sex organ, **antheridium** (Figure 22-1), is usually spherical to oval in shape and may project from the surface on a stalk or may be partially embedded in the gametophyte tissue. The antheridium first consists of densely packed cells, but, as it matures, the cells in the central region become sperm, which are enclosed in a cavity which develops as the entire structure enlarges. These sperm are liberated when the wall cells rip apart or disintegrate. The female sex organ, **archegonium** (Figure 22-1), is generally flask-shaped; the enlarged base, or **venter**, containing the single egg, may be embedded or exposed on a small stalk. The canal cells of the neck disintegrate, leaving a channel through which the sperm may reach the egg. The antheridium and archegonium likely evolved from plurilocular gametangia (see Section 19.9). If only the outer cells of a plurilocular gametangium became sterile and did not produce gametes, the structure would essentially be an antheridium. As will be discussed later, some of the advanced members of the Embryophyta have greatly reduced gametophytes and gametangia.

The sporophytes produce multicellular sporangia of various sizes and shapes, but all have an outer sterile layer enclosing sporogenous tissue in which the cells undergo meiosis as they develop into haploid spores. In the more advanced groups, these spores are differentiated as male spores, **microspores,** giving rise to male gametophytes, and female spores, **megaspores,** developing into female gametophytes.

The Embryophyta are basically land plants and have a cuticle. The more advanced forms are not dependent upon water for fertilization, although most of the lower groups have motile sperm and are dependent upon a film of water to insure fertilization. A few of the higher plants have become adapted to a water habitat (e.g., *Lemna*, or duckweed), but they are known to be essentially land plants, be-

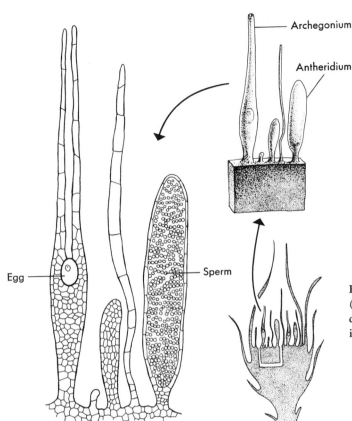

Egg — Sperm —

Archegonium

Antheridium

Figure 22-1. The tip of a moss (*Mnium*) gametophyte. The sperms are contained in an antheridium; the egg is in an archegonium.

cause the nearest relatives are well-established land plants. A definite alternation of a multicellular sporophyte with a multicellular gametophyte occurs, a feature which is lacking in many Thallophyta, where the only diploid structure is the one-celled zygote. Either or both of the phases may be photosynthetic; chlorophyll "a" and "b" and the carotenoid pigments are found in plastids in the same ratio as in the Chlorophyta.

The land plant is thought to have been derived from a group of algae which possessed a definite alternation of phases, as does *Ulva,* and in which vascular tissue, cuticle, and various other structures eventually evolved. This concept of the evolution of land plants will be considered in more detail when the Tracheophyta are discussed.

22.2 Characteristics of the Division Bryophyta

The Division Bryophyta consists of the mosses and their allies, subdivided into three classes, of which only one will be discussed. These are all small plants (usually less than six inches in height) which are parenchymatous and lack vascular tissues; thus, they have no true roots, stems, or leaves. The absence of vascular tissue with the attendant lack of efficient water conduction is undoubtedly the cause of the small size and the general restriction of the bryophytes to moist habitats. The plant body is essentially a thallus with hairlike rhizoids which penetrate the substratum and absorb water and minerals.

The gametophyte phase is nutritionally independent and structurally more complex than the sporophyte. In some species the sporophyte may contain chloroplasts, as the gametophyte always does, but the former is permanently attached to the latter and derives water and minerals from the tissues of the gametophyte. The gametophyte may bear both antheridia and archegonia—a **monoecious** type; if male and female gametophytes are separate, the plant is **dioecious.** In either case the sperm are motile and swim to the egg through a film of water.

Quite likely the Bryophyta arose from the Chlorophyta but independently of the vascular plants. The similarities in chlorophyll pigments and storage of starch indicate such a relationship. However, the presence of antheridia and archegonia suggests the possibility that the Bryophyta may be a degenerate line from some of the simpler vascular plants. Most botanists favor the suggestion of algal ancestry. All agree that the Bryophyta are a dead-end side branch and have given rise to no other group.

In some instances mosses are influential in soil development by their participation in plant succession. They may become established on rock surfaces after lichens have paved the way, or they may be pioneers themselves. The mosses assist in preventing erosion, in collecting debris, and in adding organic matter to the developing soil when they die.

22.3 Characteristics of the Class Musci

The mosses are common plants of the woodlands and various moist areas. The green mat consists of many rather erect and "leafy" gametophytes. These appendages, arranged spirally around the axis, look and function like leaves, but they do not contain vascular tissue and thus are not considered to be true leaves. At the base of this "leafy" structure are rhizoids, small filaments which function as do the roots of higher plants, and at the apex are found the sex organs. In *Mnium* (Figure 22-1) both antheridia and archegonia are found on the same gametophyte, whereas in *Polytrichum* male gametophytes produce only antheridia and female gametophytes produce only archegonia. The sperm are flagellated and swim to the archegonium, actually being stimulated to move in that direction by secretions from the archegonium or egg.

The zygote develops into an embryo which is retained for a short

Figure 22-2. Habit sketch of a moss plant with the sporophyte projecting from the top of the "leafy" gametophyte. The calyptra is still in place on the former.

time within the venter of the archegonium. Further cellular divisions and differentiations produce the recognizable young sporophyte, the lower end of which (the foot) is buried in the tissues of the gametophyte. The archegonium enlarges considerably, but the elongation of the sporophyte ruptures the archegonium and carries the upper part along as a cap, the **calyptra,** covering the tip of the sporophyte. The upper part of the sporophyte develops into an enlarged **capsule,** or sporangium, separated from the foot by a relatively long stalk. At this time, the calyptra usually shrivels and is easily blown away by the wind. Figure 22-2 represents a moss plant with a young sporophyte projecting from the top of the gametophyte; the foot of the sporophyte is not shown, but the calyptra is still in place. As the sporophyte matures, the capsule enlarges, and sporogenous tissue develops in a cylindrical fashion around a central sterile mass of cells called the **columella.** Figure 22-3 is a longitudinal section through such a young capsule, showing also the **operculum,** or lid, and the **peristome,** the ring of tooth-like structures just beneath the lid. The sporogenous tissue actually consists of diploid **spore mother cells** which, after meiosis, give

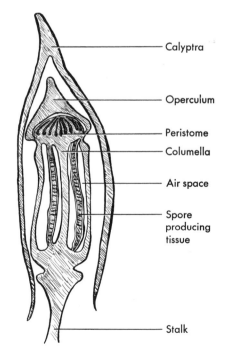

— Calyptra

— Operculum

— Peristome
— Columella

— Air space

— Spore
producing
tissue

— Stalk

Figure 22-3. Moss capsule with the calyptra still in place, longitudinal section.

rise to haploid spores. The sterile cells break down, the spores occur as a powdery mass, and the lid is shed. Dissemination of spores is facilitated by the teeth, which bend in when moist and then bend outward when the air is dry; this results in the scooping-out of spores or at least the escape of spores, after which they will be blown about more readily by wind currents.

When a moss spore is in a suitable environment, it germinates to produce a **protonema,** which is a long, filamentous, multicellular, branching structure growing along the soil surface. The cells contain chloroplasts; thus the protonema produces its own food supply. At intervals, rhizoids growing from the protonema penetrate the soil; no chloroplasts are present in the cells of the rhizoids. Numerous small projections, or "buds," appear on the protonema and develop into the "leafy" erect structures which will eventually bear the gametangia. Additional rhizoids develop at the base of such erect structures, which become independent individuals upon the death and disappearance of the protonema. Figure 22-4 represents this development of protonema, rhizoids, buds, and **gametophores**[1] (the generally erect structures which will bear antheridia and archegonia). The over-all life cycle of the moss plant is represented in Figure 22-5.

Although the *Musci* are a comparatively large group of plants, little is known of their evolutionary history, and they are also of little

Figure 22-4. Development of a moss gametophyte. The spore has germinated and produced a horizontal protonema. From the latter, rhizoids project down into the soil and erect gametophores are produced at intervals.

significance economically. The only genus of any economic importance is *Sphagnum,* the bog or peat moss. Peat actually consists of a mixture of plants, but by far the greatest amount of the material is compressed *Sphagnum.* The waters in which these plants grow is very acid. This plus the antiseptic properties of *Sphagnum* result in exceedingly slow decay, and the plant parts gradually accumulate as peat. This material may be dried and used as fuel. It is also useful in horticulture because

[1] Strictly speaking, all of the structures which develop from the spore are parts of the gametophyte phase. Because the "leafy" structure is really only a part of the gametophyte, it is termed the gametophore.

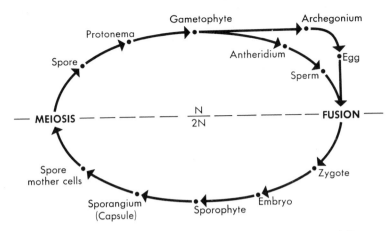

Figure 22-5. Moss life cycle (word diagram).

of its water-holding capacity and is frequently mixed with sandy or humus-poor soils for this reason. As *Sphagnum* develops, large empty cells become dispersed among the smaller living ones; the former absorb and hold water much as does a sponge. *Sphagnum* has even been sterilized and then used as wound dressings because of this water-holding characteristic.

Summary

1. The main diagnostic characteristic of the sub-kingdom Embryophyta is the formation of an embryo. These plants also have a well-developed alternation of phases and are basically land plants. In the more advanced groups microspores and megaspores are produced.

2. Members of the division Bryophyta are small plants which lack vascular tissues. The gametophyte phase is nutritionally independent and structurally more complex than the sporophyte. The latter is attached to, and dependent upon, the gametophyte.

3. In the mosses (Class Musci) the antheridia and archegonia may be found on the same, or on different, gametophytes. The sperm are flagellated and swim to the archegonium, where fertilization occurs. The zygote develops into an embryo which is retained within the archegonium for a short time. When the mature sporophyte develops, the basal portion remains embedded in the tissues of the gametophyte. Haploid spores are produced in a capsule (sporangium) as a result of meiotic divisions. After the spores are liberated, they develop into a filamentous protonema and eventually the mature gametophyte.

4. The Bryophyta probably arose from the Chlorophyta but have themselves not given rise to any other groups.

309

REVIEW TOPICS AND QUESTIONS

1. Compare the Embryophyta with the Thallophyta.
2. Describe the life cycle of a dioecious moss, indicating which structures are haploid and which are diploid.
3. Diagram an immature archegonium (before the neck canal cells have disintegrated). Label fully.
4. Diagram a mature capsule in transverse (cross) section. Label fully.
5. Present reasons why the Bryophyta are limited to moist areas.
6. Define the following: protonema, rhizoid, embryo, venter, microspore, megaspore, monoecious, columella, operculum, and calyptra.
7. A moss gametophyte which had toothed leaves with midribs was crossed with a moss gametophyte which had non-toothed leaves and no midribs. Assume that these characteristics are determined by the following genes: T = toothed leaves, T_1 = non-toothed leaves, M = midribs, M_1 = no midribs. T and T_1 are alleles; M and M_1 are alleles.

    The spores produced subsequent to this cross developed into the following: (a) 150 plants with toothed leaves and midribs, (b) 160 plants with non-toothed leaves and no midribs, (c) 7 plants with toothed leaves and no midribs, and (d) 5 plants with non-toothed leaves and midribs.

    Diagram the cross described, and give the genotypes of all the plants mentioned (both parents and progeny). Explain the proportions of the various groups in the progeny.

SUGGESTED READINGS

Bold, H. C. *The Plant Kingdom*. Englewood Cliffs, N. J.: Prentice-Hall, 1960.

Fuller, H. J., and O. Tippo. *College Botany*. New York: Holt, 1954.

Gibbs, R. D. *Botany, An Evolutionary Approach*. Philadelphia: Blakiston, 1950.

Russell, N. H. *An Introduction to the Plant Kingdom*. St. Louis: Mosby, 1958.

Division Tracheophyta: Subdivisions Psilopsida, Lycopsida, and Sphenopsida

23.1 General characteristics of the Division Tracheophyta

Although the Division Tracheophyta is not recognized by some morphologists, in which case the subdivisions are raised to the rank of division, it is a useful grouping to emphasize the importance of the development of vascular tissue. All of the plants considered to this point have no distinct vascular tissue, although very primitive conducting phloem strands have been demonstrated in some members of the Phaeophyta (see Section 19.8) and tracheid-like cells in some members of the Bryophyta. The most obvious characteristic, then, of the Tracheophyta is the presence of tracheids or their derivatives which comprise the main portion of the xylem. This division includes all of the vascular plants—plants which have a well-developed xylem and phloem. These plants, of course, also possess the general characteristics of the Embryophyta which were discussed in Section 22.1.

The plants of this group have a relatively large, elaborate sporophyte phase which is dominant and nutritionally independent at maturity, only the embryo or very young sporophyte depending upon the gametophyte. In the primitive forms the gametophyte is nutritionally independent, while in the more advanced forms the gametophyte is dependent upon the sporophyte. All representatives of this division are essentially land plants, and in the higher forms the sperm do not require free water for transport to the egg.

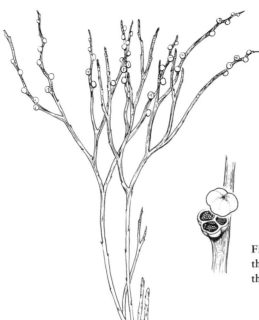

Figure 23-1. *Psilotum.* **The enlargement at the right shows the sporangium dissected so that the spores are visible.**

23.2 Characteristics of the Subdivision Psilopsida

Most of the members of this group are known from fossil remains, and only two genera contain living examples. Their importance stems from the fact that they are the most primitive vascular plants, having a central cylindrical core of xylem surrounded by a cylinder of phloem. No pith or cambium is present, and the phloem is practically nothing but elongated parenchyma cells. The plant body itself, utilizing *Psilotum* as the example (Figure 23-1), is a very simple structure consisting of a dichotomously [1] branching axis without roots or leaves, or with exceedingly small scale-like leaves which are mere flaps of tissue. The underground stem, or rhizome, may bear rhizoids. This is the sporophyte, and sporangia are borne terminally on very short branches; only one kind of spore is produced, the plants being termed **homosporous.**

The spore is haploid and develops into a small, bulky, cylindrical, branching gametophyte which lacks chlorophyll and exists saprophytically underground (Figure 23-2). The archegonia, antheridia, and method of fertilization are similar to the mosses, although the game-

[1] Dichotomous branching: dividing into two equal branches, each of which grows for a while and then also forks or divides into two equal branches.

tophyte dies shortly after the sporophyte forms. In some species of *Psilotum*, vascular tissue has been shown to be present in the gametophyte. This is the only instance in which vascular tissue has been found in a gametophyte and is of great importance with regard to the origin of land plants, as will be discussed in the next section.

Figure 23-2. *Tmesipteris tannensis* **gametophyte, sectioned to show archegonia and antheridia. It is very similar to** *Psilotum*, **which is described in the text.**

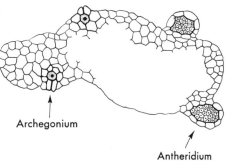

Archegonium

Antheridium

23.3 The origin of land flora

According to the **homologous [2] theory,** with which botanists are in general agreement, land plants arose from a group of algae which had a life-cycle similar to that of *Ulva* (see Section 19.4). In such a life-cycle, two phases which are essentially alike in structure, size, shape, and even somewhat in reproductive structures alternate regularly with each other. The gametophyte phase is haploid and bears gametangia; the sporophyte is diploid and bears sporangia which are similar to the gametangia but in which meiosis occurs. The transmigrant, that hypothetical plant which bridged the gap between aquatic and terrestrial existence, thus had similar gametophyte and sporophyte phases *both* of which migrated on to the land; both phases are considered to have possessed in a primitive state such necessary land plant characters as vascular tissue and cuticle.

ORIGIN OF THE BRYOPHYTA

As was mentioned in the previous chapter, the Bryophyta probably arose from the Chlorophyta through a transmigrant-type but have not themselves given rise to any more advanced group. The earliest known land plants with vascular tissue occurred in the Silurian and Devonian Periods about 350 to 380 million years ago, whereas Bryophyta remains are not found earlier than 300 million years ago (in the Carboniferous Period). The tendency in the bryophytes has been toward a reduction of the sporophyte and an elaboration of the gametophyte, but not much evolutionary change as a whole has occurred.

[2] Homologous refers to a similarity in structure and origin.

ORIGIN OF THE TRACHEOPHYTA

The Tracheophyta are also considered to have arisen from some algal group, most likely the Chlorophyta. Actually, no one algal group has all the characters necessary for land plants, but most such characters do appear in an incipient form somewhere in some algal group. The earliest known land plants, members of the Psilopsida, are not much more than a dichotomizing algal plant with vascular tissue.

The type of life cycle found in *Ulva*, a member of the Chlorophyta, and the proportion of specific photosynthetic pigments found in these algae and the vascular plants is evidence of a direct relationship to the Tracheophyta. The close similarity of the sporophyte and gametophyte in some of the Psilopsida, as well as the occurrence of tracheids in the gametophyte, is considered strong evidence that the phases of the life cycle were at one time independent and equal.

CHIEF PROBLEMS OF LAND PLANTS

The transition from an aquatic to a terrestrial environment placed the plant in a precarious position with regard to dessication, transport of materials, and support, problems which do not obtain when the plant is immersed in water. The theory for the migration of plants to the land assumes that the transmigrant just happened to combine enough of the land characters to enable it to live successfully on dry land.

Characters or adaptations inherited from the algae. In the algae, especially the Chlorophyta, are found individuals which have the type of life cycle suggested for the transmigrant, the proportion of chlorophylls "a" and "b" found in land plants, and also the multicellular, branching, parenchymatous plant body which is so similar to the primitive land plants. In addition to this, one finds some internal differentiation of tissues, including vascular tissues, and a type of multicellular sex organ in the Phaeophyta which suggests the possibility of such structures in unknown members of the Chlorophyta or the possibility of their development in the transmigrant. Oögamous reproduction, so characteristic of land plants, is also found in many groups of algae (e.g., *Oedogonium*). Certain of these characteristics are of benefit with regard to water retention and protection of gametes, while others of these structures are of importance in transporting materials or in support.

Characters or adaptations not found in the algae. The development of a cuticle on the aerial parts of plants and on spores was an extremely important factor in making a land existence possible. The chance occurrence of such a structure resulted in a tremendous decrease in the amount of water lost from such parts and greatly decreased the water requirement of that plant. This is a considerable boon to any existence out of water. The production of an outer layer of sterile cells, forming a protective jacket, as part of a multicellular sex organ enabled gametes to survive more readily in a non-aquatic, as well as an aquatic, environment; a similar change occurred with regard to the sporangium. The retention of the young embryo in the archegonium during its early development also resulted in further protection of the more sensitive portions of the plant.

As a result of these adaptive characteristics, plants could exist on land. Additional development of vascular tissue, as shown in the more advanced members of the Tracheophyta, increased the possibility of large plants maintaining themselves on land by enabling them to transport water and minerals from the soil and food from the leaves to all parts of the body. This tissue also provided the support which is essential in exposing leaves to light and a supply of carbon dioxide.

Let us emphasize at this point that *none* of these adaptive characteristics developed *in order to* enable a plant to exist on land, free of its watery environment. Such a *purpose* in developmental changes is an impossibility. As a *result* of such adaptations arising *by chance,* plants have been enabled to exist on land. Also, these structural adaptations must be inherited for them to be of any significance. (Why?) Further discussion of this idea of chance versus purpose will be found in Section 27.10.

23.4 Characteristics of the Subdivision Lycopsida (club mosses)

The dichotomously branching sporophytes have roots, stems, and leaves, and the vascular tissue in most consists of a solid core of xylem surrounded by a cylindrical sheath of phloem. The spirally arranged leaves are very small, **microphyllous** leaves, and may merely be an

Figure 23-3. Vascular supply to microphyllous leaf; no leaf gap.

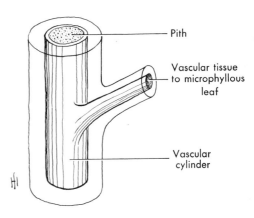

Pith

Vascular tissue to microphyllous leaf

Vascular cylinder

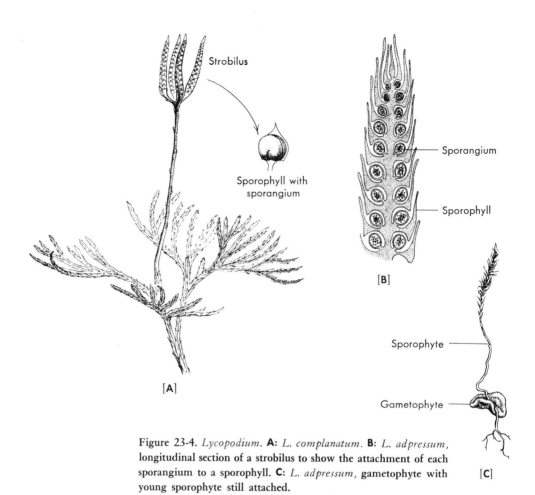

Figure 23-4. *Lycopodium.* **A:** *L. complanatum.* **B:** *L. adpressum,* longitudinal section of a strobilus to show the attachment of each sporangium to a sporophyll. **C:** *L. adpressum,* gametophyte with young sporophyte still attached.

extension of the outer tissues of the stem. The small vascular bundle projecting into the leaf has no effect on the shape of the vascular tissue, and no leaf gaps are present (Figure 23-3). Sporangia are borne singly on the upper surfaces of leaves, the **sporophylls,** which are usually arranged in the form of a cone, or **strobilus,** and the plant is either homosporous or **heterosporous** (two kinds of spores are produced in the latter). The sporophyte is large and dominant, as compared to the gametophyte, and it is also nutritionally independent except as an embryo.

The haploid spore develops into a small independent gametophyte which may be either saprophytic or autotrophic, depending upon the species concerned.'In some genera the gametophyte remains enclosed within the spore wall, a very important situation which will be discussed more fully later. Water is necessary for the transfer of sperm from the antheridium to the archegonium.

23.5 Representative members of the Lycopsida

Division
Tracheophyta:
Subdivisions
Psilopsida,
Lycopsida, and
Sphenopsida

Several hundred species are organized into numerous genera and several orders, but our discussion will be limited to two genera.

In the genus *Lycopodium* (Figure 23-4) the sporophyte is relatively small and has an underground stem from which the roots extend. In some species the sporophylls are organized in strobili, and all are homosporous. Meiosis occurs in the sporangium, and the spores germinate to produce a gametophyte which bears both antheridia and archegonia. The sperm swims to the egg, which is retained in the archegonium, apparently as a result of chemicals secreted by the egg. The sporophyte remains attached to the gametophyte for only a short period, and then the latter dies.

In *Selaginella* (Figure 23-5) the well-organized strobili bear two kinds of sporangia and spores; the plant is heterosporous. The larger sporangia, containing four large spores, are borne lower down in the strobilus; **megaspores** are produced in a **megasporangium** borne on a **megasporophyll.** The smaller sporangia, containing many small spores, are borne in the upper portion of the strobilus; **microspores** are produced in a **microsporangium** borne on a **microsporophyll.** In prostrate forms, the microsporangia are borne in upper ranks and the megasporangia in lower ranks. The size of the spores and sporangia is not important except as a means of description and identification. The important factor is the structure which develops when the haploid spore germinates.

Figure 23-5. *Selaginella.* **A:** Habit sketch. **B:** Longitudinal section of a strobilus, the microsporophylls form the upper portion and the megasporophylls form the lower portion of the strobilus. **C:** A megasporangium with three of the four megaspores. **D:** A microsporangium with many microspores.

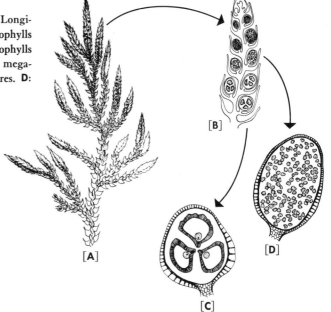

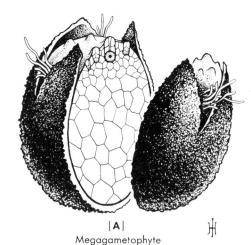

[A]
Megagametophyte

Figure 23-6. *Selaginella*. **Both gametophytes are still retained within their respective spores at this stage of development. A: Megagametophyte with one mature and three developing archegonia in the upper area.** (Redrawn from Bruckmann, *Flora,* **104** [1911–1912], 180–224.) **B: Microgametophyte with the enclosed sperms.** (Redrawn from R. A. Slagg, *American Journal of Botany,* **19** [1932], 106–127.)

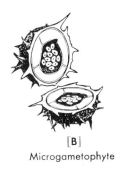

[B]
Microgametophyte

The megaspore germinates to form a gametophyte which remains almost completely embedded in the spore. This gametophyte, although multicellular and having rhizoids, is very reduced in size and produces small archegonia and no antheridia; it is a female gametophyte, or **megagametophyte** (Figure 23-6A). The microspore germinates to form a male gametophyte which is completely retained within the spore (Figure 23-6B). This gametophyte is greatly reduced in size, consisting only of a single sterile somatic (body) cell and one antheridium with its enclosed sperm. Both types of spores begin germinating while still in their respective sporangia. Fertilization occurs after the spores have fallen to the moist soil, or in some species the megaspore is not shed until after fertilization (a situation somewhat akin to that in seed plants). In the latter case microspores, and their enclosed **microgametophytes,** sift down to the lower portions of the strobilus.

The life cycles of *Lycopodium* and *Selaginella* are presented for comparison in Figures 23-7 and 23-8.

23.6 Importance of the Subdivision Lycopsida

The members of this group are of no real economic significance, but they do indicate certain evolutionary advances over the Psilopsida from which they have probably evolved. The presence of true leaves and roots, the greater development of vascular tissue, and the general arrangement of sporophylls in strobili are all considered to be characteristics of a more advanced nature than those found in the Psilopsida. Even though the Lycopsida do not appear to have given rise to more advanced groups of plants, heterospory, the retention of gametophytes in the spores, and the retention of the megaspore in the megasporangium (as in some species of *Selaginella*) are important steps toward a seed habit as found in the more advanced groups. This again is an indication that evolutionary trends may be followed in various groups.

Division
Tracheophyta:
Subdivisions
Psilopsida,
Lycopsida, and
Sphenopsida

23.7 Characteristics of the Subdivision Sphenopsida (horsetails)

The only living representatives of this group are in the genus *Equisetum* (Figure 23-9) and are generally herbaceous plants which usually do not exceed three feet in height. The microphyllous leaves occur in whorls at the nodes of hollow stems, which have vertical ridges. The tissues are impregnated with silica, giving such an abrasive consistency to the structures that these plants have been used for scouring

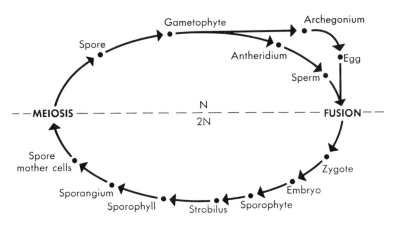

Figure 23-7. Life cycle of *Lycopodium* (word diagram).

Figure 23-8. Life cycle of *Selaginella* (word diagram).

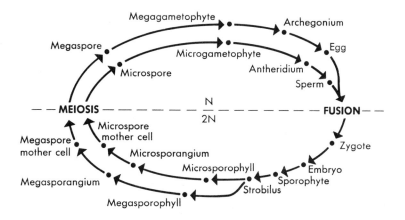

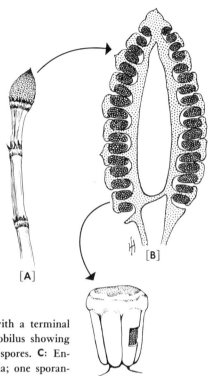

Figure 23-9. *Equisetum.* **A:** Reproductive stem with a terminal strobilus. **B:** Longitudinal section of a mature strobilus showing the location of the sporangia and their enclosed spores. **C:** Enlarged view of a sporangiophore with its sporangia; one sporangium is cut open to show the spores.

kitchen utensils and floors. The members of this group are homosporous, although one extinct genus was heterosporous, and the sporangia are borne on specialized structures called **sporangiophores,** which are arranged in strobili. The sporangiophores have a horizontal stalk and a flattened table-top-shaped upper portion[3] from which the sporangia hang parallel to the stalk. In *Equisetum* most of the species produce two kinds of stems; vegetative stems are green and branched, while reproductive stems are usually not green, are not branched, and bear strobili at the tips.

Meiosis occurs in the sporangia, and the mature haploid spores are liberated by a longitudinal splitting of the sporangial wall. The wall of the spore is laminated, and four ribbon-like bands, or elaters, separate from the rest of the wall except for a common point of attachment. The elaters are hygroscopic, uncoiling as they dry out and recoiling with the addition of moisture (Figure 23-10). These movements probably aid in the discharge and dispersal of spores. Tiny, green, ribbon-like gametophytes, usually containing both antheridia and archegonia, develop from the spores. After fertilization, the embryo sporophyte is

[3] The sporangiophore is peltate.

briefly dependent upon the gametophyte but rapidly develops leaves and an independent existence as the gametophyte degenerates.

These plants are of no economic importance except, as is also true of the Lycopsida, as participants in coal formation during the Carboniferous Period, when they were a significant part of the flora. The Sphenopsida probably arose from the Psilopsida, but they themselves never gave rise to any higher groups.

Division Tracheophyta: Subdivisions Psilopsida, Lycopsida, and Sphenopsida

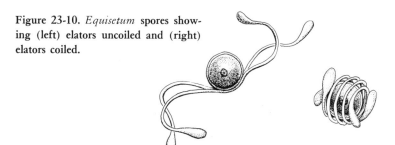

Figure 23-10. *Equisetum* spores showing (left) elators uncoiled and (right) elators coiled.

Summary

1. The Tracheophyta is a somewhat artificial category which includes all plants which have tracheids. In general the sporophyte is large, dominant, and nutritionally independent at maturity.

2. The Psilopsida are the most primitive of the vascular plants, consisting basically of a branching axis without roots and with small scale-like leaves (or none). Sporangia are borne terminally, and the plants are homosporous.

3. The gametophyte of the Psilopsida exists saprophytically underground and dies shortly after the sporophyte develops.

4. Land plants probably developed from a group of algae which had a life cycle similar to that of *Ulva* (a member of the Chlorophyta), a life-cycle in which the two phases are essentially alike. The tendency in the Bryophyta has been toward a reduction of the sporophyte and an elaboration of the gametophyte; this is just the opposite of the tendency in the more successful land plants. Some of the primitive Tracheophyta are not much more than a dichotomizing algal plant with vascular tissue.

5. The main problems of land plants are desiccation, transport, and support. Some of the structures found in the more advanced algae tend toward at least the protection of gametes and toward support and transport. The Tracheophyta, however, have developed many features

which tend to make possible a plant's existence on land: cuticle, extensive vascular tissue, protected gametes, protected embryo, and a relatively large sporophyte phase.

6. The Lycopsida have roots, stems, and small leaves, but no leaf gaps. Sporangia are borne on the upper surfaces of sporophylls which are usually arranged as a strobilus; the plants are homosporous or heterosporous. The gametophytes may be saprophytic or autotrophic.

7. The Lycopsida probably arose from the Psilopsida but apparently did not themselves give rise to more advanced groups. The retention of gametophytes in spores and the retention of the megaspore in the megasporangium (as in some species of *Selaginella*) are tendencies toward the seed habit found in advanced groups, an indication of similar evolutionary trends in various groups.

8. In the Sphenopsida the leaves are borne in whorls, and the sporangia are borne on sporangiophores arranged as strobili. The gametophytes are tiny and autotrophic. This group probably arose from the Psilopsida.

REVIEW TOPICS AND QUESTIONS

1. Compare the Tracheophyta with the Bryophyta. Why were the former more successful in surviving in various terrestrial environments than the latter?
2. Describe the life cycle of *Psilotum*.
3. Discuss the ways in which the Lycopsida may be considered as more advanced than the Psilopsida.
4. Describe the life cycle of *Selaginella*.
5. Discuss the theory which attempts to explain the origin of land plants.
6. Present reasonable explanations as to why the Bryophyta were not as successful on land as the Tracheophyta. If vascular tissue had developed in the gametophyte phase, would the Bryophyta have been as successful as the Tracheophyta?
7. Diagram a sporangiophore and its sporangia in longitudinal section.
8. Define the following: microphyllous, homospory, heterospory, sporophyll, megasporophyll, megaspore, microsporophyll, microspore, megagametophyte, microgametophyte, strobilus, and sporangiophore.

SUGGESTED READINGS

Eames, A. J. *Morphology of Vascular Plants, Lower Groups*. New York: McGraw-Hill, 1936.

Foster, A. S., and E. M. Gifford, Jr. *Comparative Morphology of Vascular Plants*. San Francisco: Freeman, 1959.

Fuller, H. J., and O. Tippo. *College Botany*. New York: Holt, 1954.

Gibbs, R. D. *Botany, An Evolutionary Approach*. Philadelphia: Blakiston, 1950.

Subdivision Pteropsida:

Class Filicineae

24.1   General characteristics of the Subdivision Pteropsida

In addition to the characteristics which are common to all members of the Division Tracheophyta, members of the Pteropsida, which includes the ferns and the seed plants, are those plants which have a dominant sporophyte with roots, stems, and large leaves. Such **megaphyllous** leaves are believed to have originated from the modification of a branch system; they are not merely extensions of the outer tissues, as appears to be the case with microphyllous leaves. The vascular supply to megaphyllous leaves is quite extensive and is associated with a parenchymatous area, known as a **leaf gap** (Figure 24-1), in the vascular tissue of the stem. In this region of interrupted vascular tissue, the parenchyma cells of the pith are continuous with the parenchyma cells of the cortex. Such leaf gaps are not found in the lower vascular plants, which were discussed in the previous chapter, and this is considered to be one of the basic distinctions between the Pteropsida and the other subdivisions of the Tracheophyta.

The sporangia in the plants of this subdivision are usually borne on the lower surfaces, or on the margins, of sporophylls, but the situation in the seed plants is quite complex and must await future clarification. Sporangial position can be considered as a general distinguishing characteristic, although one which possibly cannot be used as a constant criterion in the classification of major groups. The situation with respect to the ferns is clearer than that with respect to the gymnosperms (cone-bearing plants and their allies) and the flowering plants. This matter will be discussed more thoroughly as each group is examined in detail.

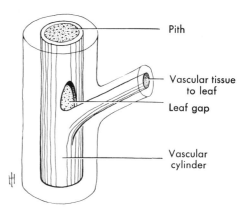

Figure 24-1. Vascular supply to mega-phyllous leaf; leaf gap present.

Pith

Vascular tissue
to leaf

Leaf gap

Vascular
cylinder

The Pteropsida are further subdivided into three great classes: Class Filicineae, Class Gymnospermae, and Class Angiospermae. In this chapter the discussion will be limited to the Filicineae.

24.2 Characteristics of the Class Filicineae (ferns)

Fern leaves (**fronds**) are typically compound and uncoil as they develop, a condition referred to as **circinnate vernation.**[1] Roots usually arise adventitiously from horizontal rhizomes, although the tree ferns of tropical areas have upright stems appearing much like a tree trunk. In general the leaf and sporangial-bearing organs are not differentiated, most ferns are homosporous, and seeds are not produced. The haploid spores develop into small, nutritionally independent gametophytes, and the sperm which are produced require a film of water in their movement toward the egg. The ferns are further subdivided into four orders, of which only the Filicales, or true ferns, will be discussed.

The fern plant (Figure 24-2), common to many gardens, consists of large conspicuous leaves and the underground stem with its tiny adventitious roots. The vascular tissue is quite prominent as the veins of the leaf, and a cross-section of the rhizome demonstrates that both xylem and phloem, but no cambium, are present. On the lower surfaces or at the margins of the leaves are the **sori,** or clusters of sporangia. In some ferns each **sorus** is covered by a small flap of tissue, the **indusium,** or by the rolled-in margin of the leaf. Each sporangium in a sorus consists of a stalk and a capsule in which spore mother cells undergo meiosis in the production of haploid spores. Dissemination of the spores is facilitated by the structural development of the capsule. A ring of cells, the annulus, extends from the stalk over and around about three-fifths of the circumference of the capsule; all except the

[1] Nearly everyone has seen young fern fronds in the coiled state; frequently they are termed "fiddle heads," "croziers," or "monkey-tails."

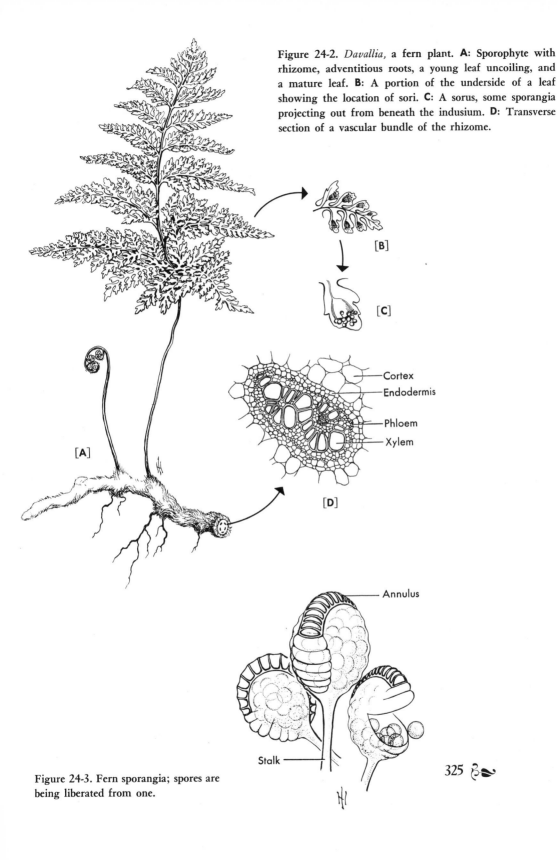

Figure 24-2. *Davallia,* a fern plant. **A:** Sporophyte with rhizome, adventitious roots, a young leaf uncoiling, and a mature leaf. **B:** A portion of the underside of a leaf showing the location of sori. **C:** A sorus, some sporangia projecting out from beneath the indusium. **D:** Transverse section of a vascular bundle of the rhizome.

[B]

[C]

Cortex
Endodermis
Phloem
Xylem

[A]

[D]

Annulus

Stalk

Figure 24-3. Fern sporangia; spores are being liberated from one.

outer walls of these ring cells are much thicker than the walls of the cells comprising the rest of the capsule (Figure 24-3). As the cells of the sporangium dry, the thick walls of the annulus cells tend to pull together. This places tension on the thin-walled cells of the sporangium, and they rupture. The spores are thus flung out of the capsule and distributed by wind currents.

If a spore lands in a suitable environment (shady, moist, cool soil), it germinates to form a filamentous structure which rapidly develops into a green, heart-shaped gametophyte which is seldom more than 1.5 cm. in diameter. Rhizoids project from the lower surface of this **prothallus** and absorb water and minerals from the soil. Also on the lower surface, near the notch of the heart-shaped structure, are found archegonia, and antheridia are located near the basal end among the numerous rhizoids (Figure 24-4). As the antheridium matures, the central cells develop into sperm, the outer cells remaining as a sterile jacket or layer. If mature gametophytes are moistened, the antheridium ruptures and the sperm are liberated. As the archegonium matures, the canal cells disintegrate, and the cells at the lip of the neck spread apart. Sperm are attracted to the archegonium, possibly by the disintegration products of the canal cells or by secretions from the remaining

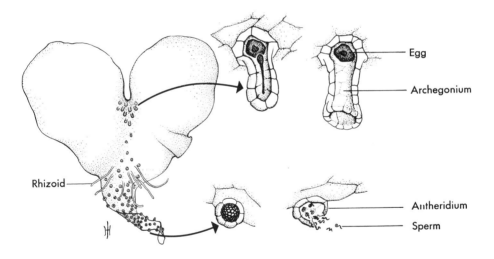

Figure 24-4. Fern gametophyte with archegonia and antheridia.

archegonial cells, and swim down to the egg in the embedded venter, where fertilization takes place.

The fertilized egg (zygote) begins mitotic divisions while in the archegonium, developing into the embryo, which obtains nutrients from the gametophyte through a specialized group of cells called the

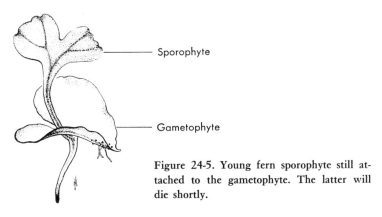

Figure 24-5. Young fern sporophyte still attached to the gametophyte. The latter will die shortly.

foot. Quite rapidly various groups of cells of the embryo produce a root, stem, and leaf (Figure 24-5); the embryo enlarges, and the young sporophyte is soon independent of the gametophyte, which dies. Further growth and development produce the mature fern plant with its sporangia and spores.

The many species of ferns have a life cycle similar to that described (Figure 24-6), although they may differ from one another with regard to homospory, heterospory, position of sori, indusium, leaf size and shape, and the presence of specialized reproductive leaves. Most ferns may be propagated vegetatively by cutting the rhizome, each portion of which may then continue growing with its complement of leaves and roots as an individual plant.

24.3 Importance of the Class Filicineae

Except for their contribution to coal formation during the Carboniferous Period, ferns are economically important primarily from an

Figure 24-6. Life cycle of a fern (word diagram).

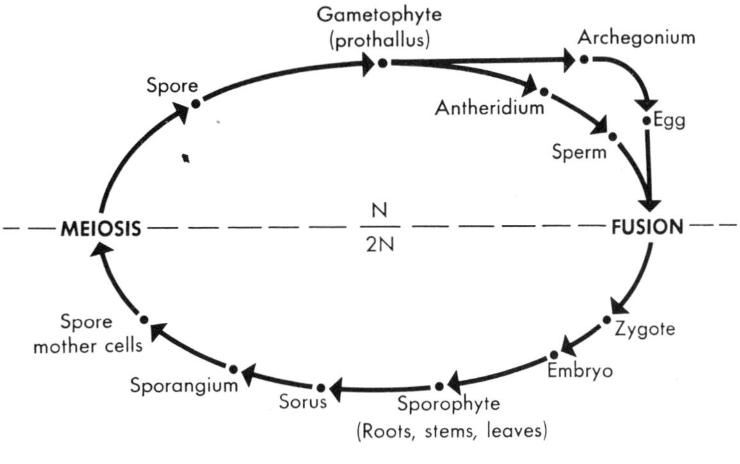

aesthetic viewpoint. They are grown almost universally in gardens, homes, or hot houses (greenhouses), and are often used in bouquets and floral arrangements. However, one medicinal use of ferns might be mentioned. A drug from *Dryopteris filix-mas,* the male fern, has been utilized since the days of Nero in curing tapeworm.

As with all plants with a reduced gametophyte, this situation may be considered to present a distinct advantage in that the motile sperm have a relatively short distance to cover in reaching the egg. Also, both male and female reproductive structures are located on the lower surface of the gametophyte, where the most moisture is likely to be present. The large sporophyte, in addition, insures the widespread dissemination of great numbers of spores. Such spores may spread to suitable environments which are at considerable distances from the parent plant.

With the evidence at hand, botanists believe that the Filicineae probably evolved from the psilopsids. Some extinct ferns resemble Psilopsida rather closely. Many botanists also hold the opinion that certain of the extinct ferns were the ancestors of gymnosperms and angiosperms, the two groups which comprise the seed plants.

Summary

1. The Pteropsida have a dominant sporophyte with roots, stems, and large leaves. The vascular supply to such megaphyllous leaves is quite extensive and results in the formation of a leaf gap, a parenchymatous area in the vascular tissue of the stem. This group is subdivided into three classes: Filicineae, Gymnospermae, and Angiospermae.

2. In general the Filicineae have leaves which uncoil as they develop and an underground stem (rhizoid) with adventitious roots; they are usually homosporous. The haploid spores develop into small, nutritionally independent gametophytes. The sperm swim to the egg, and fertilization takes place in the archegonium.

3. The zygote develops into an embryo and then into a sporophyte, which is dependent upon the gametophyte for a short period. Sporangia develop in clusters, sori, on the undersides of the leaves. Within these sporangia spore mother cells undergo meiosis, and the resultant haploid spores germinate to form gametophytes.

4. The Filicineae probably developed from the Psilopsida, and some extinct forms may have been the ancestors of the seed plants. The ferns are considered to be more advanced than groups previously discussed because of the reduced gametophyte and the large sporophyte with their attendant advantages.

REVIEW TOPICS AND QUESTIONS

1. What are the diagnostic characteristics of the Pteropsida?
2. Explain in detail what is meant by a "leaf gap." What fills the gap, since it is not actually a hole?
3. What is meant by "circinnate vernation"?
4. Describe the life cycle of a fern, indicating which structures are haploid and which are diploid.
5. Define the following: sorus, indusium, annulus, prothallus, rhizome, and spore mother cells.
6. Diagram the cross-section of a fern rhizome, and label fully. Show only tissues; do not show individual cells.
7. In what ways are the ferns more suited to a terrestrial existence than are the Sphenopsida, Lycopsida, and Psilopsida?
8. Why are most ferns limited to fairly moist areas?
9. Why are gametes more sensitive to environmental conditions than are spores? Which factor of the environment is most important as far as the gametes are concerned?

SUGGESTED READINGS

Bold, H. C. *The Plant Kingdom*. Englewood Cliffs, N. J.: Prentice-Hall, 1960.

Eames, A. J. *Morphology of Vascular Plants, Lower Groups*. New York: McGraw-Hill, 1936.

Foster, A. S., and E. M. Gifford, Jr. *Comparative Morphology of Vascular Plants*. San Francisco: Freeman, 1959.

Fuller, H. J., and O. Tippo. *College Botany*. New York: Holt, 1954.

Gibbs, R. D. *Botany, An Evolutionary Approach*. Philadelphia: Blakiston, 1950.

Russell, N. H. *An Introduction to the Plant Kingdom*. St. Louis: Mosby, 1958.

CHAPTER 25

Class Gymnospermae

25.1 Characteristics of the Class Gymnospermae

In addition to the general characteristics of the Pteropsida, the plants which comprise the Class Gymnospermae produce unenclosed (naked) seeds which are located on the upper surfaces of bracts which are usually parts of **cones.** Of the plant groups which have been discussed, this is the first in which the seed habit is found, although a tendency toward seed production is found in *Selaginella,* one of the Lycopsida (see Sections 23.5 and 23.6). The gymnosperms are woody plants, chiefly trees, and sometimes of considerable size with much secondary growth; the leaves are usually evergreen needles or scales. The sporophyte is heterosporous, and the tiny gametophytes are nutritionally dependent upon the sporophyte, the female gametophyte actually developing inside of the megasporangium and never having a free existence. Water is not necessary for fertilization; the young male gametophyte, or **pollen grain,** is carried by wind currents to the megasporangium, where the growth of pollen tubes through this tissue brings the sperm to the egg.

Gymnospermae are further subdivided into two classes of several orders each, but only the genus *Pinus* of the Coniferales will be discussed in detail as a representative of this large group. Any discussion of the various other members of the Gymnospermae is beyond the scope of this text.

25.2 Life cycle of pine

The pine tree usually grows for many years, and much secondary tissue is produced. The general anatomy of pine stems and roots is similar to that of the woody dicotyledonous plant already discussed (Chapters 6 and 8), except that no vessels are found in pine wood, only tracheids. However, large resin ducts are present in pines, and care should be taken not to confuse these with vessels (Figure 25-1).

The photosynthetic needle leaves of this tree occur in clusters on short lateral branches, a situation unique to this member of the conifers, and the number of leaves in a fascicle depends upon the species involved. The leaf (Figure 25-2) has a thick cuticle, thick-walled epidermal cells, and a layer of sclerenchymatous cells beneath the epidermis. These features, plus the sunken stomata are considered to be characteristics of xerophytic plants. This type of leaf may be of considerable benefit to such an evergreen plant during winters, when water absorption is difficult. Since the leaves are retained (pines do not lose all of their leaves each year, as do **deciduous** plants), transpiration

**Class
Gymnospermae**

Figure 25-1. Photomicrograph of pine stem, transverse section. The resin ducts are visible as rather large openings, especially in the xylem. Growth rings are also visible. (Courtesy of General Biological Supply House, Chicago.)

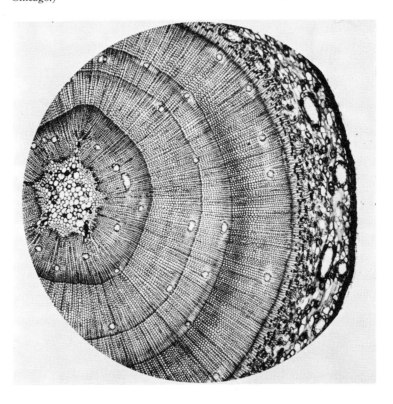

during winter months would be quite detrimental. Pines are also frequently found in drier areas than are neighboring deciduous trees.

Two distinct types of cones are produced in pines; both the **microsporangiate cones** and the **megasporangiate cones** are borne on the same tree. The former are frequently referred to as male or pollen cones, while the latter may be called female or seed cones.

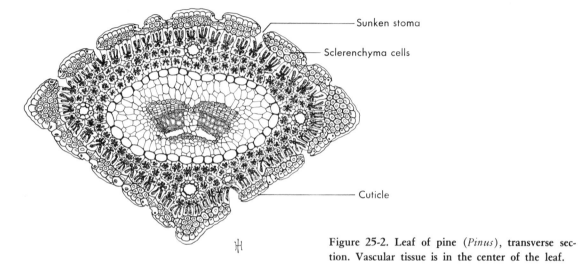

Figure 25-2. Leaf of pine (*Pinus*), **transverse section. Vascular tissue is in the center of the leaf.**

DEVELOPMENT OF MEGASPORES AND MEGAGAMETOPHYTES

The female cone is initiated during the late spring or summer, but differentiation is interrupted by the onset of winter, and development continues during the succeeding year. This cone is compound in structure, consisting of a central axis bearing a series of **bracts** (reduced, scale-like leaves), each of which is more or less fused with an ovuliferous scale in the axil of the bract. Two ovules are borne on the upper surface of the scale, which is generally considered to be a fused reduced branching system and not merely a modified leaf. This is of considerable evolutionary significance as evidence relating present-day pines to fossil gymnospermae.

The **ovule** (Figure 25-3) consists of a megasporangium surrounded by and fused with an additional tissue, the **integument**, and contains a single megaspore mother cell (**megasporocyte**), which is readily distinguishable by its large size. After meiosis, the resultant four haploid

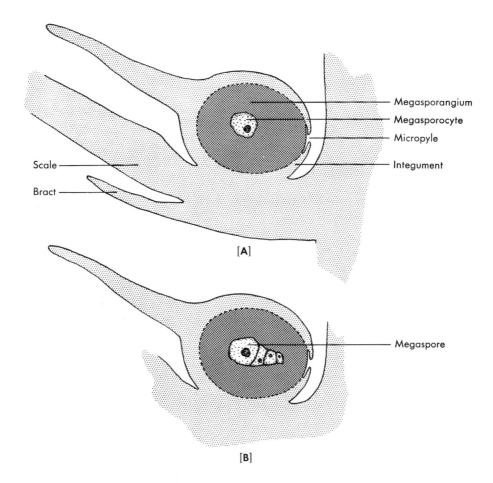

Figure 25-3. Ovule of pine (*Pinus*), longitudinal section. **A**: Young ovule with a megasporocyte (megaspore mother cell). **B**: After meiosis, the ovule with four haploid megaspores; three are disintegrating.

megaspores are arranged in a row; three of them disintegrate, while the one farthest from the **micropyle** (a small tubular opening in the integument) remains functional. This megaspore germinates within the megasporangium; enlargement and free nuclear divisions are followed by the formation of cell walls around each nucleus. The result is a multicellular megagametophyte with two to five archegonia differentiated at the micropylar end. The mature archegonium of pine is greatly reduced, consisting of a few neck cells with the large egg cell beneath (Figure 25-4). The various structures which develop when the megaspore germinates are composed of haploid cells, since the megaspore is haploid, and subsequent nuclear divisions are mitotic.

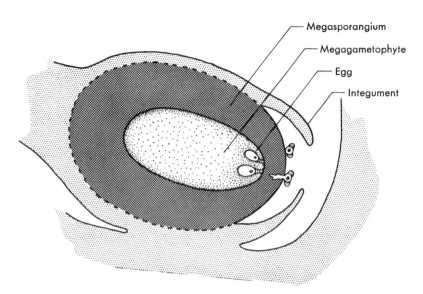

Megasporangium

Megagametophyte

Egg

Integument

Figure 25-4. Ovule of pine (*Pinus*), mature, longitudinal section. Only two archegonia, each with an egg, are shown. Two pollen grains have arrived at the megasporangium; one is growing toward an archegonium.

DEVELOPMENT OF MICROSPORES AND MICROGAMETOPHYTES

The male cone develops early in the spring and consists of a central axis bearing numerous spirally-arranged **microsporophylls** (Figure 25-5). On the lower surface of these modified leaves are borne two microsporangia in which numerous microspore mother cells (**microsporocytes**) undergo meiosis, each producing four haploid microspores. Each microspore undergoes mitotic divisions during which two small **prothallial cells**, a **generative cell**, and a large **tube cell** are formed. The first two cells begin to disintegrate rapidly, and the young male gametophyte is set free as a **pollen grain** by the rupturing of the microsporangium (see Figure 25-6). Large numbers of pollen grains are blown about by the wind, and some sift down through the young megasporangiate cone, coming to rest in a drop of exudation at the micropyle of the ovule. This transfer of pollen is termed **pollination.** As the drop of liquid dries, the pollen grains are drawn through the micropyle to the megasporangium, where a **pollen tube** develops from the tube cell, and the generative cell divides to form a **stalk cell** and a **body cell.**

A considerable period of time lapses between pollination and fertilization. After the male gametophyte has reached the stage of development indicated in the preceding paragraph, further growth during the winter is very slow. During the following spring, development

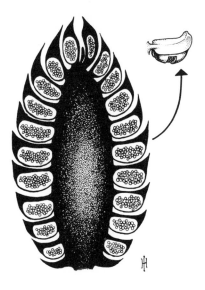

Figure 25-5. Microsporangiate (male) cone of pine (*Pinus*), longitudinal section. Upper right figure shows a microsporophyll bearing two microsporangia, one of which is cut open to show the microspores.

becomes more rapid, and the body cell divides to form two sperm nuclei, which are carried through the megasporangium to the archegonium by the actively growing pollen tube. Rupture of the tube discharges the sperm nuclei, one of which fuses with the egg nucleus. Eventually the other cells and nuclei of the male gametophyte disintegrate.

DEVELOPMENT OF THE SEED

Although the megagametophyte produces more than one archegonium, only one zygote usually develops into an embryo. During this development, tiers of cells are produced. The embryo tier is at the apex away from the micropyle and is forced into the gametophyte tissue by great elongation of the **suspensor cells,** which comprise the next tier. Several embryos may begin to develop from the apical tier, but only one survives and is pushed farther and farther into the tissues of the female gametophyte. The cells of this latter structure are digested and utilized in the growth of the embryo. The fully developed embryo of *Pinus* consists of a whorl of approximately eight **cotyledons** (seed leaves) surrounding the **epicotyl** (shoot apex) and a bulky **hypocotyl,** that part of the embryo axis below the point at which the cotyledons are attached. The basal tip of this axis is the **radicle,** or root apex. Growth eventually ceases, and the embryo remains dormant for a varying period of time until conditions are suitable for germination.

Figure 25-6. Development of the microgametophyte of pine (*Pinus*). The young male gametophyte is set free as a pollen grain while cellular divisions are continuing. The body cell eventually divides to form two sperms. (From C. J. Chamberlain, *Gymnosperms, Structure and Evolution,* by permission of the University of Chicago Press. Copyright 1935.)

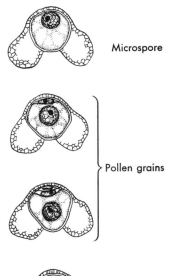

Microspore

Pollen grains

Generative cell
Tube cell

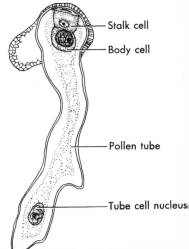

Stalk cell

Body cell

Pollen tube

Tube cell nucleus

The various tissues which comprise the ovule enlarge and differentiate further as the embryo develops. The megagametophyte becomes the food storage tissue (**"endosperm"** [1]) within which the multicellular, diploid embryo is embedded. The integument enlarges and becomes quite tough and hard, forming the **seed coat.** The remains of the megasporangium can usually be detected as a very thin layer of cells just inside of the seed coat. At this point, the seed (Figure 25-7) is mature and consists of the new immature sporophyte embedded within the tissues of the female gametophyte, which in turn is surrounded by modified tissues of the old sporophyte. The seed is really a ripened ovule containing an embryo. In many pines a portion of the scale remains attached to the seed as a wing which aids in dispersal of the seed by winds. The seeds are eventually liberated when the female cone opens.

Under suitable environmental conditions, the seed absorbs and imbibes water, swelling in the process. Since proteins and carbohydrates swell to a greater extent than cellulose, the seed coat is ruptured in the early stages of germination; the seed coat is largely cellulose and does not swell proportionately with the embryo. The entire embryo grows rather rapidly, the cotyledons functioning as leaves for a brief period while the epicotyl is developing into the shoot structure. The hypocotyl elongates somewhat, and the radicle develops into the root sys-

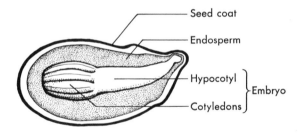

Figure 25-7. Mature seed of pine (*Pinus*).

tem with great rapidity and much branching. As indicated in previous chapters, the stem tips and root tips remain meristematic throughout the lifetime of the pine tree, with secondary tissues eventually developing from a vascular cambium. As the tree matures, several years of vegetative growth precede any development of cones, but then cones are normally produced each year throughout the lifetime of the pine.

The generalized life cycle of pine is indicated in Figure 25-8.

[1] The term "endosperm" as used in discussing the pine life cycle should not be confused with the endosperm of angiosperm seeds (Section 26.5).

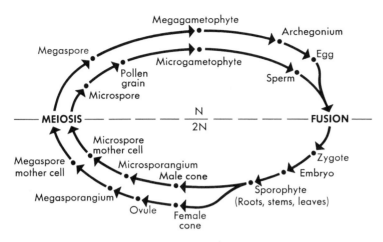

Figure 25-8. Life cycle of *Pinus* (word diagram).

25.3 Importance of the Class Gymnospermae

The group of plants of which pine was selected as an example constitute an important part of the world's flora, forming great forests in the mountains and in the north. Although they were more abundant in past geological ages, having given way in many areas to the flowering plants (Angiospermae), they are still our most important source of timber and timber products. Many of the less expensive grades of paper are made from wood pulp of various conifers, particularly spruce (*Picea* spp.), although southern yellow pine (*Pinus palustris*) is also much used.

Some of the largest and oldest of living organisms are found among the Gymnospermae. The redwood (*Sequoia sempervirens*) frequently grows to a height of 200 feet and a diameter of 20 feet and is hundreds of years old. The wood is reddish in color, presenting an attractive appearance when used for shingles, siding, and cabinet work; the burls [2] are deeper red, presenting a beautiful color when carved and burnished. The Big Tree (*Sequoiadendron gigantea*), restricted mainly to California, as is the redwood, is probably the oldest living thing; one of these is at least 3,500 years old and has a diameter of approximately 40 feet. Some of the bristlecone pines (*Pinus aristata*) have been estimated to be 4,000 years old, but these trees are rather twisted and gnarled, which makes such estimates less exact than those of the Big Tree.

[2] A burl is a dome-shaped growth on the root or trunk of a tree. The grain presents a beautiful design because of the tangled growth of xylem and rays.

Numerous materials of economic value are obtained from the conifers and their close relatives. Tannins, complex organic compounds which are used in the tanning [3] industry, are obtained mainly from hemlock (*Tsuga canadensis*) bark; this material is also used in the preparation of some kinds of inks. Resins are extracted from various conifers, especially *Pinus palustris,* and are used in the manufacture of varnishes, perfumes, linoleum, and various other products. Distillation processes are utilized in obtaining turpentine, certain oils, and methyl alcohol from the wood of various conifers. In addition to these and other products, some pine seeds are edible by man or other animals, especially those seeds from *Pinus edulis, Pinus torreyana,* and *Pinus pinea.*

25.4 Evolutionary advances featured in the Gymnospermae

The stroboli, in which are borne the microgametophytes and megagametophytes, are more complex and well-developed than in the lower vascular plant group, especially the megasporangiate cone. The gametophytes are retained within the protective tissues of the cones during a portion of their development or are permanently retained. Even the male gametophyte, as it is transported to the female gametophyte during pollination, is still somewhat protected by the relatively thick wall of the microspore within which it has developed. The gametes are never really exposed; the sperm develop within the pollen tube and are liberated at the archegonium, while the egg is continuously surrounded by gametophyte tissue. The covering (integument) about each megasporangium insures further protection, not only to the eggs but also to the developing embryos. The great simplification of both gametophytes and their parasitic existence upon the sporophyte are distinctly advantageous for gamete survival. The seed [4] habit, including dormancy, is considered to be one of the major evolutionary advances within the plant kingdom. In the Gymnospermae one finds the first example of protective and nourishing tissues surrounding a zygote and subsequently the developing sporophyte (embryo). The development of such tissues provides the new sporophyte with an advantage not afforded the sporophytes of lower groups. Many seeds, in the dry condition, are resistant to adverse environmental conditions and remain viable for years. This enables the sporophyte (embryo) to con-

---

[3] Tanning results from the reaction between the proteins of animal skins and tannins; the soft, pliable, and resistant material which results is leather.

[4] Gymnosperm means "naked seed" and refers to the fact that these seeds are freely exposed and not covered by additional tissues. The latter condition obtains in the Angiospermae and will be discussed in the next chapter.

tinue further development (germination) when conditions are more favorable. One should remember, however, that seeds will not remain viable indefinitely. In general, the percentage of germination within a group of seeds will decrease during storage; the amount of decrease varies with the kind of seed as well as with the storage conditions.

Many botanists believe that the gymnosperms probably evolved from ancient psilopsids or from ancient ferns. As additional evidence is gathered, this situation may be clarified.

Summary

1. The Gymnospermae produce naked seeds on the upper surfaces of bracts which are usually parts of cones. They are woody plants, usually with evergreen needles or scales. The sporophyte is heterosporous; the tiny gametophytes are nutritionally dependent upon the sporophyte. Water is not necessary for fertilization; the pollen grain and the pollen tube are structures which transport the sperm to the egg.

2. *Pinus* species produce microsporangiate (male) and megasporangiate (female) cones. The ovules, which develop in the latter, each consist of a megasporangium surrounded by and fused with the integument. An opening, the micropyle, in the integument enables pollen grains to be deposited on the megasporangium. A single megaspore gives rise to a megagametophyte in each ovule. Several archegonia, each with an egg, are produced by each female gametophyte.

3. The many microsporocytes in a microsporangium undergo meiosis, producing four microspores each. Several mitotic divisions result in the development of a microgametophyte. The young male gametophyte, or pollen grain, is blown to the female cone, where maturation is completed. As the pollen tube grows toward the archegonium, it carries the two sperm cells to the vicinity of the egg.

4. Although more than one egg may be fertilized and more than one embryo start to develop, only one embryo actually survives. The integument develops into the seed coat, the megagametophyte develops into a food storage tissue, and both surround the embryo; this structure is the seed. On germination of the seed, the basal portion of the embryo, the radicle (which is really the lowest portion of the hypocotyl), forms the root system, and the epicotyl of the embryo produces the shoots.

5. The Gymnospermae are important sources of timber and timber products, tannins, resins, turpentine, methanol, and many other materials. Some pine seeds are edible.

6. Various features of the Gymnospermae are distinctly advantageous to a terrestrial existence. The seed habit, including dormancy, is

339 𝔅

considered to be a major evolutionary advance. Such a structure protects the megagametophyte, the female gametes, the male gametes
(after pollination), the zygote, and the embryo. The large sporophyte
with its well-developed vascular tissue enables large numbers of spores
and seeds to be produced and disseminated.

REVIEW TOPICS AND QUESTIONS

1. Discuss those characteristics of the pine which endow it with a greater
   chance of surviving in a variety of terrestrial environments than is possible in the case of ferns.
2. Describe a pine seed. Of what advantage is the presence of a seed coat?
3. Would the rate of photosynthesis tend to be more rapid in the cells of a
   pine leaf than in the cells of a broad-leaved plant, such as a bean? Why?
4. Would the rate of transpiration tend to be more rapid from the leaves
   of a pine than from an equal surface area of a broad-leaved plant, such
   as a bean? Why?
5. What structural feature results in a pine leaf being rigid or stiff?
6. Diagram the root tip of a pine tree as seen in longitudinal section.
   Show regions and tissues but not the individual cells.
7. List the tissues and regions from outermost to the center of a twenty-
   year-old pine trunk.
8. Describe a tracheid and a sieve-tube element of a pine.
9. Describe the development of a microgametophyte of pine, starting with
   a microspore mother cell. Indicate where the development takes place
   and whether each structure is haploid or diploid.
10. Repeat Problem 9 for a female gametophyte, starting with the mega-
    sporocyte.
11. Define the following: pollination, endosperm, deciduous, integument,
    micropyle, epicotyl, cotyledons, and radicle.

SUGGESTED READINGS

Foster, A. S., and E. M. Gifford, Jr. *Comparative Morphology of Vascular
Plants*. San Francisco: Freeman, 1959.

Fuller, H., and O. Tippo. *College Botany*. New York: Holt, 1954.

Gibbs, R. D. *Botany, An Evolutionary Approach*. Philadelphia: Blakiston,
1950.

Hill, A. F. *Economic Botany*. New York: McGraw-Hill 1937.

CHAPTER 26

Class Angiospermae

26.1 Characteristics of the Class Angiospermae (flowering plants)

In addition to the general characteristics of the Pteropsida, members of the Class Angiospermae produce enclosed seeds in specialized structures which are collectively termed the flower. Pollen grains are formed, much as in the gymnosperms, but the gametophytes are even more reduced than those of the cone-bearing plants. The flowering plants are the dominant members of the world's flora, consisting of at least 250,000 species which vary from minute non-woody types to enormous woody trees. They are of fairly recent origin, fossil remains probably not being older than 125 million years (from the Cretaceous period), and are considered to be the most advanced of all plant life.

The general structure and function of the roots, stems, and leaves have been discussed in previous chapters. Most of our knowledge concerning the angiosperms is based upon an intensive study of north temperate floras, modern botany having its origins in Europe. Our knowledge of tropical and arctic floras is quite meager as compared with that of North America and Europe, but future investigations will undoubtedly add to our present concepts and may even cause us to modify some of our suggestions concerning relationships of organisms.

26.2 The flower

Angiosperms are commonly referred to as flowering plants, and this distinctive structure will be discussed in some detail. Figure 26-1 is a diagrammatic representation of a mature, complete flower which has developed from a bud. As pointed out in Section 6.1, such buds may be mixed; that is, they develop into both flowers and leaves. The enlarged portion of the flower stalk, to which the various flower parts are attached, is called the **receptacle.** As the flower bud enlarges and

Figure 26-1. Mature, complete flower. Top figure shows one of the anthers enlarged and sectioned to show the pollen grains.

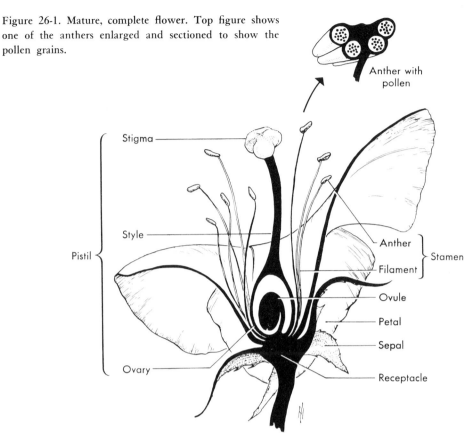

unfolds, the outermost whorl or parts, the **sepals,** open out to expose the more showy, colored parts, the **petals.** The size, shape, and number of such parts varies with the particular plant involved, and some may even be lacking in certain plants. The sepals are usually green and leaf-like and serve to protect the more delicate tissues which are developing within the bud; the sepals collectively are termed the **calyx.** As one would suspect from their appearance, the petals serve to attract insects, which then become the unsuspecting agents of pollination in their travels from flower to flower. Such attraction is increased in many plants by the presence of glandular nectaries at the base of the petal. The sweet liquid secreted by these nectaries is utilized by many insects. Essential oils and floral fragrances also insure the presence of insects at the flowers of different kinds of plants. The petals collectively are termed the **corolla,** while the term **perianth** refers to both sepals and petals. Through anatomical investigations, these structures have been considered to be modified leaves.

The next innermost whorl of parts comprise the **stamens,** each consisting of a slender **filament** (or stalk) and an enlarged portion called the **anther.** Within the anther the pollen grains are formed; the swollen, sac-like portions are actually microsporangia. The size, shape, and number of stamens vary considerably from one kind of plant to another but is constant within any one type.

In the central portion of the flower is the **pistil,** consisting of the **stigma** at the tip, an elongated **style,** and the bulbous **ovary** at the base. Pollen lands on the stigma, the pollen tube growing through the intervening tissues into the ovary, which contains the ovule. The seed (i.e., an ovule containing an embryo) is thus enclosed within the ovary, and the latter structure develops into the **fruit** of the flowering plant. The pistil is composed of one or more units called **carpels.** These latter structures are considered to be reduced branching systems which have fused. A simple pistil is composed of one carpel, as in the garden pea (*Pisum* spp.), whereas a **compound pistil** consists of two or more fused carpels, as in the lily (*Lilium* spp.); both conditions are represented in Figure 26-2. As with perianths and stamens, the size, shape, number, and kind of pistils varies, depending upon the flower under discussion.

Figure 26-1 has been referred to as representing a complete flower, which certainly implies the existence of incomplete flowers. The sepals and petals are not directly concerned with reproduction and are accessory parts of the flower, while the **essential** parts are the stamens and pistils. An **incomplete** flower lacks one or more of the floral organs, as in the grasses (Family Gramineae) which contain no petals.

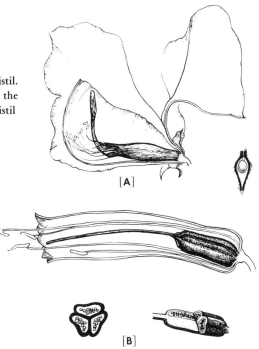

Figure 26-2. **A**: Garden pea flower with a simple pistil. The pistil is also shown in section to expose one of the seeds. **B**: Lily (*Lilium*) flower with a compound pistil Lower sectional views of the ovary with seeds.

integument = seed coat

[A]

[B]

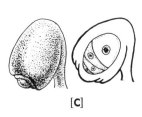

[C]

[D]

[E]

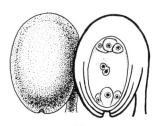

[F]

Figure 26-3. Development of the megagametophyte of angiosperms. **A, B, C:** The megasporocyte is undergoing meiosis as the integuments develop around the megasporangium; only one megaspore remains functional. **D, E:** The nucleus of the functional megaspore is undergoing mitotic divisions. **F:** The mature megagametophyte has developed within the ovule. (From W. H. Brown, *The Plant Kingdom.* Copyright 1935 by Ginn and Co., Boston.)

An **imperfect** flower lacks one of the essential organs. Flowers may be **staminate,** as the tassel flowers of corn (*Zea mays*), or **pistillate,** as the flowers of corn which form the ears lower down on the stem. *Zea mays* produces both kinds of flowers on the same plant, a **monoecious** condition. A plant such as willow (*Salix*) is **dioecious,** because staminate and pistillate flowers are produced on separate plants of that species. Additional variations in flower patterns will be discussed later in Section 26.10.

26.3 Development of megaspores and megagametophytes

One to many ovules are produced in an ovary, and the former structures are quite similar to the ovules of pine (see Figure 26-3). The integuments (**inner** and **outer**) develop along with the megasporangium and eventually surround it completely except for the tubular micropyle. The single, large, diploid megasporocyte (megaspore mother cell) undergoes meiosis which results in the formation of four haploid megaspores. Three of these megaspores degenerate, while the nucleus of the remaining one undergoes mitotic divisions which result in eight haploid nuclei being located within the enlarged megaspore.[1] Three of these nuclei migrate toward the micropylar region, three migrate to the opposite end, and two remain near the central region of the megaspore. Membranes eventually form around each of the nuclei at the extremes but not around the central nuclei. As a result, the mature megagametophyte (female gametophyte) consists of seven cells.

Figure 26-4 represents an enlarged ovule sectioned to show the internal structures. One of the cells at the micropylar region is the egg, or female gamete, and the other two are **synergid cells.** The two nuclei in the center are **polar nuclei,** and the other three structures are **antipodal cells.** As is quite obvious, the megagametophyte[2] of the

[1] Some variations occur in different flowers, such as *Lilium,* but the structures subsequently discussed in this section are basically alike.

[2] In many texts the terms nucellus and embryo sac are used in referring to the megasporangium and megagametophyte respectively. These are terms which were utilized for such structures before the realization that they were homologous with structures in lower (simpler) plants. In this text the more descriptive terms are used to emphasize homologies and comparable structures.

flowering plants is reduced much beyond that of any other group of plants. Many morphologists suggest that the synergids may be homologous to the archegonia of the simpler plants, structures which are not really present in the angiosperms. The antipodals possibly represent the vegetative cells of the gametophyte. Both groups of cells merely degenerate and disappear after fertilization occurs.

Figure 26-4. Mature ovule (longitudinal section) showing the structures of the megagametophyte.

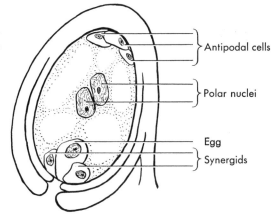

Antipodal cells

Polar nuclei

Egg
Synergids

26.4 Development of microspores and microgametophytes

As the stamen matures, the cells of the central portion of the anther become quite distinct from the peripheral cells; the former are the microsporocytes (microspore mother cells) (see Figure 26-5). As a result of the disorganization and absorption of surrounding cells, eventually many such microsporocytes are located within a chamber, the microsporangium, and each anther is composed of four microsporangia. Each diploid microsporocyte undergoes meiosis producing four functional haploid microspores, which lie freely in the microsporangium as a result of further gradual extension of the surrounding sterile tissue. The microspores undergo a mitotic division, but no walls separate the two resultant cells which are both retained within the wall of the microspore. The smaller cell is the **generative cell,** the larger one is the **tube cell;** the entire structure is a **pollen grain,** or young male gametophyte. At this stage of development, the anther usually splits open (dehisces) along a vertical line between the two pollen chambers on each side of the filament, thus releasing pollen grains.

26.5 Pollination and fertilization

345

The transfer of pollen from the anther to the stigma, **pollination,**

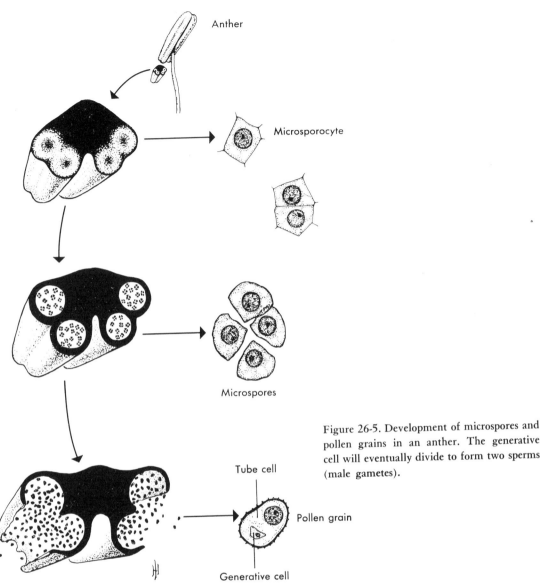

Anther

Microsporocyte

Microspores

Figure 26-5. Development of microspores and pollen grains in an anther. The generative cell will eventually divide to form two sperms (male gametes).

Tube cell

Pollen grain

Generative cell

is accomplished in a variety of ways but most usually by wind currents or by insects (see Section 26.10). The surface of the stigma is covered with a rather viscous secretion, and the pollen grains adhere to this material. The tube cell produces a long extension, the **pollen tube,** which projects through one of the thin areas of the pollen grain wall and grows down through the tissues of the stigma, style, and ovary toward the ovule. Although the pollen grain contains some food material, most of the food utilized in the growth of the pollen tube undoubtedly is obtained from the tissues of the pistil. The generative cell divides mitotically, producing two male gametes, or sperm; at this stage of development, the structure may be considered to be a mature male gametophyte (Figure 26-6). The sperm are carried within the

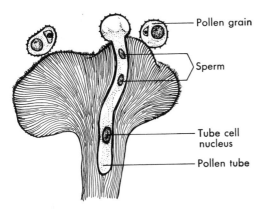

Pollen grain

Sperm

Tube cell nucleus

Pollen tube

Figure 26-6. Pollen grains on a stigma. One pollen tube is growing through the tissues of the stigma and style; the sperm are carried within this tube.

pollen tube to the ovule, where entrance is usually through the micropyle.

The pollen tube penetrates to the egg and ruptures, thus liberating the sperm within the female gametophyte. One of the sperm fuses with the egg.[3] The resultant diploid zygote undergoes many mitotic divisions as it develops into a multicellular embryo. The second sperm fuses with *both* polar nuclei. This *triploid* (3N) nucleus undergoes many mitotic divisions; eventually the resultant triploid nuclei are

[A]

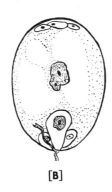

[B]

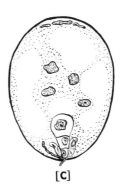

[C]

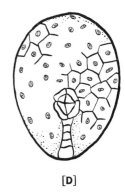

[D]

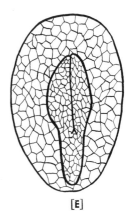

[E]

Figure 26-7. Fertilization and the development of the embryo and endosperm. **A**: One sperm is fusing with the egg in the lower portion of the figure as the other sperm is approaching the fused polar nuclei; the pollen tube is degenerating. **B**: Fusion of one sperm with polar nuclei forming the triploid endosperm nucleus. **C**: Endosperm nucleus has divided twice mitotically; zygote developing into the embryo. **D**: Formation of cell walls around the nuclei of the endosperm. **E**: Embryo (with two cotyledons) surrounded by the multicellular, triploid endosperm tissue.

delimited by cell walls and form a multicellular food storage tissue, the **endosperm.** The antipodal cells and synergid cells of the female gametophyte and the tube cell of the male gametophyte disintegrate (see Figure 26-7). The term "double fertilization" is used to emphasize the

[3] Pollination and fertilization are not the same; the former always precedes the latter.

fact that two sperm are involved, a condition restricted to the Angio-spermae.

26.6   The seed

As in the Gymnospermae, the ripened ovule containing an embryo is a **seed.** However, an important distinction exists with regard to the food storage tissue. In the gymnosperms the enlarged female gameto-phyte tissue functions in this manner, while in the angiosperms an entirely new type of tissue develops. Not only is this a new type of tissue with regard to its method of development, but it is also com-posed of cells which have three sets of chromosomes (triploid, 3N). As the embryo develops, it receives nourishment from the endosperm. In many seeds most, if not all, of the endosperm has been utilized by the developing embryo, so that the mature seed contains nothing but remnants of this triploid tissue.

The integuments grow and harden, forming the **seed coat.** Although the micropyle is closed as a result of integumentary growth, in most seeds the location of this area is visible as a slight depression. The **hilum** is a scar on the surface of the seed which indicates the point of attachment of the ovule to the ovary. Figure 26-8 represents longitu-dinal sections through a kidney bean seed in which the endosperm has disappeared and a castor bean seed in which the endosperm forms the bulk of the seed. In both types the embryo, or immature plant, is read-ily distinguishable. The seed actually consists of tissues of the original generation as well as those of the new generation, although the game-tophyte tissue (megasporangium) is usually digested away by this time.

The embryo consists of a short axis with one or two attached cotyle-

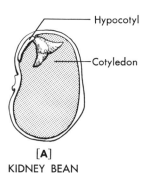

[A]
KIDNEY BEAN

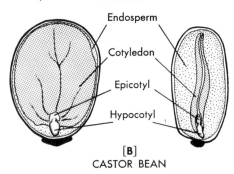

[B]
CASTOR BEAN

Figure 26-8. Longitudinal sections through seeds. **A:** Kidney bean. The endo-sperm has been utilized and food is stored in the cotyledons; one cotyledon has been removed so that the hypocotyl and epicotyl are visible. **B:** Castor bean. The endosperm is the bulky storage tissue; **two** views to show the sheet-like cotyledons.

dons. The portion above the point of attachment of the cotyledons is the **epicotyl,** or **plumule,** which becomes the stem system of the new plant as the seed germinates. The lowest portion of this axis is the **radicle,** which becomes the root system. The area between the epicotyl and the radicle is the **hypocotyl,** a transitional zone consisting of a stem-like mass of tissue which elongates in some seeds during germination. The **cotyledons** are usually food storage organs which digest and absorb food from the endosperm and which may function as leaves after germination. In seeds, such as the kidney bean, food is stored in the cotyledons; in those similar to the castor bean, food is stored in the endosperm.

SEED GERMINATION

The other parts of the seed may enlarge greatly as a result of absorbing water, but the embryo is really what is growing when a seed germinates. As is true of any living organism, growth will not occur unless moisture, oxygen,[4] and a suitable temperature are available. Sufficient food and minerals are stored in almost all seeds, so that these factors are not important for germination. They are, however, additional essential factors which must be present for continued growth of the seedling once it has become established. A source of light for photosynthesis enables the young plant to manufacture its own food as soon as leaves have developed.

As water is absorbed by a seed, the inner tissues swell more rapidly than the seed coats, resulting in a rupture of the latter. The penetration of water also results in tissues becoming hydrated, and enzyme activity is tremendously enhanced. Foods, stored in the cotyledons or the endosperm, are digested and utilized as the embryo grows. The radicle emerges first, grows rapidly downward through the soil, and develops into the root system. In some seeds the hypocotyl elongates, carrying the cotyledons above the surface of the soil, where they may function as green leaves. This is especially true of plants, such as the castor bean or squash, where the cotyledons are very leaf-like; the cotyledons of the garden bean are much more storage organs than leaves, even though they are exposed upon germination (Figure 26-9). In other seeds, such as the pea, the hypocotyl does not elongate, and the cotyledons remain in the soil (Figure 26-10). The epicotyl rapidly develops into the above-ground shoot system of the new plant. The plant is now established and able to absorb water and minerals as well as to manufacture its own food. The cotyledons eventually wither and die.

349

[4] The anaerobic organisms, of course, are exceptions to this.

Figure 26-9. Germinating seeds and young seedlings. **A:** Squash, in which the cotyledons are lifted out of the ground and function as green leaves for a brief period. **B:** Garden bean, in which the cotyledons are lifted out of the soil—but they are bulky storage organs and do not function as leaves.

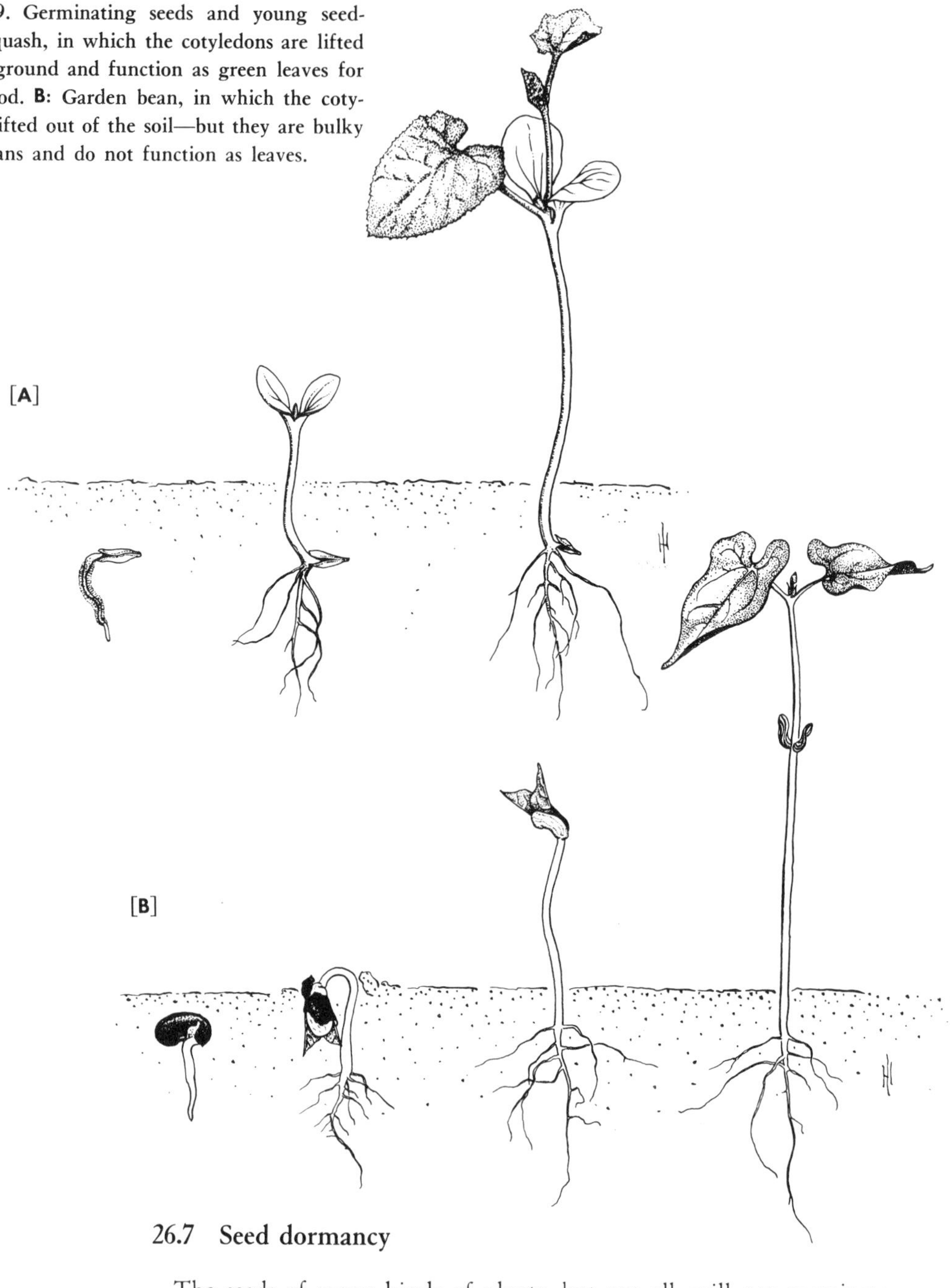

[A]

[B]

26.7 Seed dormancy

The seeds of many kinds of plants, but not all, will not germinate immediately even when placed in an environment conducive to growth, a condition known as **dormancy.** The seeds are viable, however, and after a period of a few weeks to a few months, germination will occur. Factors which bring about dormancy are related to the seed

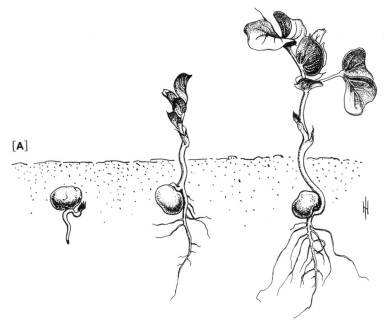

[A]

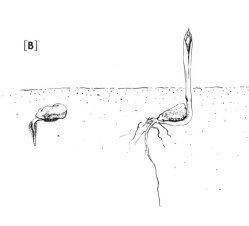

[B]

Figure 26-10. **A**: Germinating pea seed and young seedling; the cotyledons remain in the soil. **B**: Germinating corn grain; this is really a fruit (caryopsis) in which the seed coat is fused with the ovary wall.

itself, and the dormant period is one in which gradual changes take place which eventually allow for growth of the embryo. This condition is particularly advantageous in enabling progeny to withstand adverse environmental conditions. For example, if seeds germinated as soon as mature, many young seedlings in northern climates would be exposed to injuriously low winter temperatures. A similar situation would obtain in areas where rainfall is seasonal; seedlings might be exposed to conditions of dangerously low rainfall if they germinated immediately. Seeds are much more resistant than are seedlings and would withstand adverse conditions during dormancy, germinating later under favorable environmental conditions.

In some seeds (e.g., alfalfa, vetch, clover) dormancy results because the seed coat is impermeable to water; in others (e.g., many composites and grasses) the seed coat is impermeable to oxygen; in still a third group (e.g., many common weeds, such as mustard), the seed coat is mechanically resistant and prevents expansion of the enclosed tissues. In all such cases where the seed coat is involved, gradual changes result in the seed coat eventually becoming permeable or less resistant. Damage to the seed coat, as by abrasion, will have the same effect and may occur when the seed is blown about or washed about among rough soil particles. Once such changes have occurred in the integuments, the seed will germinate quite readily if conditions are favorable (as indicated in the previous section).

In some types of seeds, dormancy is not a result of the permeability or resistance of the seed coat; the embryo will not grow even if the seed coat is removed. Such seeds are considered to have dormant embryos. In some cases (e.g., iris, red oak, ash), inhibiting substances have been shown to be present, and these materials gradually disappear during the period of dormancy. In others the specific cause of dormancy is not known, although the environmental conditions which break dormancy have been ascertained in many instances. The seeds of apple, peach, dogwood, and pine require a period of low temperature of from two weeks to three months before the seeds will germinate; a number of grass seeds require alternating temperatures to break dormancy. One of the most interesting treatments to increase the percentage of germination has been discovered in the case of some varieties of tobacco and lettuce seeds. Exposure to light greatly increases the number of seeds which eventually germinate. In all of the treatments indicated, the seeds must be moist for the treatment to be effective. The explanations involved in an understanding of dormancy and the breaking of dormancy are not yet available. Much additional investigation is essential in this relatively unknown phase of botany.

26.8 The fruit

As the ovule develops into a seed, the ovary portion of the pistil sometimes increases enormously in size and develops into the **fruit,** a ripened ovary bearing one or more seeds. The seeds are enclosed [5] and not naked as was true of the seeds in the Gymnospermae. The

[5] The word Angiospermae is derived from two Greek words which mean "covered seed."

stimuli which bring about such growth of the ovary are secretions from the pollen tube and from the developing seeds. (The possible nature of these secretions will be discussed in the next chapter.) The tremendous growth entailed is made more meaningful when one realizes that a peach, a string bean, a pea pod, and a watermelon all develop from ovaries no more than two to ten mm. in diameter, hundreds of times smaller than the mature fruit. This is a considerable drain on the food supply of the plant, and vegetative growth frequently ceases as the fruits mature.

Pinching off, or pruning, flower buds will result in larger flowers and fruits developing from the remaining buds as a result of the extra food supply available to the latter. Such thinning out is a common practice among amateur gardeners as well as among professionals. In fact, if perennial plants are not thinned, flower and fruit production may be quite irregular from year to year. A year in which a very large yield is obtained is quite likely to be followed by a year with a relatively poor yield. The amount of food utilized in fruit production during the first year results in such little vegetative growth or in the storage of such low food reserves that the development in the subsequent year is greatly curtailed. Besides pruning, various sprays can be used to bring about flower and fruit drop with its concurrent thinning. Commercial fruit tree growers, especially, utilize a spray program for this purpose.

FRUIT TYPES

Many kinds of fruits, which develop in various ways are to be found. They may be composed of one or more pistils, with or without including adjacent parts of the flower, and dry or fleshy; they may or may not be dehiscent. The great diversity in fruits makes difficult the devising of a classification which will include them all. However, a few of the more common fruits are described below, with examples of each. Remember that, botanically speaking, the term "fruit" is very specifically defined, while "vegetable" is not; the latter may, or may not, also be a fruit.

Fruits are generally divided into four large groups, which may each then be further sub-divided: simple, aggregate, multiple, and accessory fruits. A **simple fruit** is one which develops from a single ovary. Most angiosperm fruits are of this type. An **aggregate fruit** is formed from a group of ovaries produced in a single flower, as in raspberries and

Figure 26-11. Grape (*Vitis*), a typical berry; the pericarp is soft and fleshy.

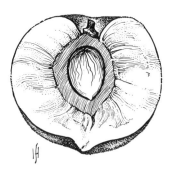

Figure 26-12. Peach (*Prunus*), a typical drupe. The exocarp is a thin skin, the mesocarp is fleshy, and the endocarp is extremely hard.

blackberries. A **multiple fruit** is composed of the ovaries of a cluster of flowers which are borne on the same stalk, as in the mulberry, fig, and pineapple. An **accessory fruit** consists of one or more ovaries together with additional tissues, usually the calyx or receptacle or both, as in the strawberry, apple, and pear.

The female portion of the flower shows great diversity (see Section 26.10), and fruits also could be expected to be of various kinds. Simple fruits are frequently sub-grouped on the basis of the characteristic appearance of the mature **pericarp,** or ovary wall, which sometimes becomes differentiated into three distinct layers: the **exocarp** (outermost), **mesocarp,** and **endocarp** (innermost). A **berry** (Figure 26-11) is a fruit in which the pericarp becomes soft and fleshy at maturity, as in the grape, tomato, citrus fruits (lemon, orange, etc.), and date. In a **drupe** (Figure 26-12) the exocarp is a thin skin, the mesocarp is the fleshy pulp, and the endocarp is extremely hard (the pit), as in the cherry, plum, peach, and olive. A **legume** (Figure 26-13) consists of a single dry (or leathery) carpel which splits along two sutures, as in the bean, pea, clover, vetch, and acacia. A **capsule** (Figure 26-14) consists of dry fused carpels which open in various ways, as in the lily, poppy, and tulip. An **achene** is a dry, indehiscent, one-seeded fruit formed from a single carpel, as in the sunflower and dandelion. A **nut** is similar to an achene but is formed from fused carpels and has a very hard pericarp, as in the oak, chestnut, and beech. The **grain,** or **caryopsis,** is a dry one-seeded fruit in which the seed coat is fused with the ovary wall, as in corn, wheat, oats, and other grasses.

Fruit classification is in just as much a state of flux as is general plant classification. No one system is completely adequate in all respects. For example, although a blackberry is usually considered to be an aggregate fruit, a small portion of that fruit consists of the pulpy

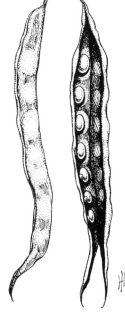

Figure 26-13. Bean (*Phaseolus*), **a typical** legume. It is a single dry carpel which splits along two sutures.

receptacle or stem tissue. Some botanists would prefer the term aggregate-accessory in this instance. For most purposes, however, the classification utilized in this text is quite suitable. Remember that not all fruit types, but merely the most common ones, have been included. Remember, also, that common names are not necessarily botanically correct. The student might consider, in the light of this statement, which of the following is actually a berry: blackberry, strawberry, mulberry, or grape. The term "nut" is used just as indiscriminately: peanuts are legumes; Brazil nuts, pine nuts, and beechnuts are all seeds; almonds, coconuts, pecans, and walnuts are all drupes.

Figure 26-14. *Yucca,* **a typical capsule. It consists of dry fused carpels.**

26.9   Seed dispersal

The tissues of the seed and the fruit increase the survival possibilities of the progeny by the protection which they afford to the embryo. In addition to this, various modifications of the seed, and frequently the fruit, facilitate the dissemination of the embryo. Such seed dispersal may result in the seed germinating in a more suitable environment than that in which the parent plant is located. The new environment might be less suitable, of course, but in either case the progeny are distributed at some distance from their point of origin. This in itself is advantageous, helping to prevent over-crowding and the attendant deleterious effects of shading and competition for water and minerals.

Although the production of large numbers of seeds aids in the propagation of a species, this factor should not be assumed to be the most important criterion for the successful establishment of a plant. The really important factors are the ability of the plant to grow in diverse environments and the facilities of the plant for dispersal to these various environments. Bermuda grass (*Cynodon dactylon*), for example, will spread with nauseating rapidity by means of runners. Even if the flowers are trimmed by mowing a lawn before seeds are mature, this will not retard the progress of this grass to any great extent. In fact, although many flowers are produced, very few seeds actually mature; vegetative propagation is the rule in this plant.

WIND DISPERSAL

One of the most important agents in the dissemination of plants is wind. In some instances the seeds are so light that they can be carried

Figure 26-15. Examples of plants that are dispersed by the wind. **Upper left:** Hairy seed of milkweed (*Asclepias syriaca*). **Lower right:** Hairy fruit of dandelion (*Taraxacum officinale*); individual fruits are shown being blown away from the dense cluster which is typical of this plant.

great distances. This is true of the orchids, whose seeds are so tiny as to appear like specks of dust; several hundred thousand weigh approximately one gram. In other plants the seeds or fruits have hair-like appendages or wings which tend to keep them suspended in the air, often for considerable periods of time. The seeds of the common milkweed (*Asclepias syriaca*) have hairy appendages, while the fruit of the dandelion (*Taraxacum officinale*) bears a hairy parachute (Figure 26-15); the hairs have a similar function, although a dissimilar origin. One also discovers winged seeds and winged fruits. In the former the wings are outgrowths of the seed coat, as in members of the Bignonia Family (Bignoniaceae; example, *Jacaranda ovalifolia*)

(Figure 26-16A). The fruit of the maples (*Acer* spp.) has two wings, each of which grows from the back of a carpel (Figure 26-16B); the seeds of pine (see Section 25.2) are also winged.

Figure 26-16. Examples of plants that are dispersed by the wind. **A**: Winged seed of *Jacaranda ovalifolia*. **B**: Winged fruit of maple (*Acer*).

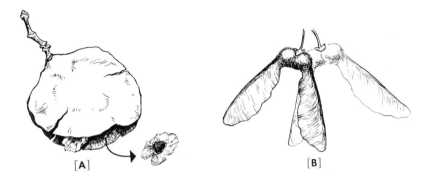

[A] [B]

ANIMAL DISPERSAL

The other agent of most importance in the spread of seed plants through the world is the animal population, including man. The fruits of some plants have hooks or spines which become entangled in the hair of various animals (or in the clothing of humans) and then are carried about, eventually dropping off as the animals brush against objects (Figure 26-17). The seed may then germinate if the environment is suitable. Some seeds or fruits may be carried considerable distances, even though they do not possess such spiny protuberances, by being located in mud or earth which adheres to the feet of animals, especially wading birds. The mud may be shaken loose or drops off as it dries.

Many fruits are edible, such as grape (*Vitis* spp.), cherry (*Prunus serotina*), and *Pyracantha* berries. These attract birds and other animals, which may spit out the pits or swallow them. The seeds are usually resistant to digestive enzymes and pass through the animal virtually undamaged. The fecal material excreted with the seeds may actually be beneficial to the growth of the resultant seedling. Remember that bird manure, usually from chicken farms, is an excellent

Figure 26-17. Examples of plants that are dispersed by animals. **A**: Cocklebur (*Xanthium*). **B**: Fruit of unicorn plant (*Martynia*).

[A]

[B]

source of nitrogen when used as a fertilizer. Birds quite likely are responsible for carrying seeds over natural barriers, such as water. Nuts and nut-like fruits are carried about by rodents and are frequently abandoned without being eaten. Oak (*Quercus* spp.), hickory (*Hicoria* spp.), and beech (*Fagus* spp.) are usually scattered in this fashion.

Man in his travels throughout the world has played an exceedingly important role in the dissemination of plants. He has purposely carried with him the crop plants, grazing plants, and ornamentals which he prefers. However, he has also, usually unknowingly, carried seeds and fruits of weed plants along with him. Such weeds, in competition with crop plants, result in tremendous economic losses. Millions of dollars must be expended each year in an attempt to control weed growth, and additional millions of dollars are lost as a result of decreased crop yields due to weed competition.

ADDITIONAL DISPERSAL MECHANISMS

Water acts as an agent of dispersal for some kinds of plants. The seeds and fruits of various aquatic plants float and may be carried about by water currents. Rainfall may wash seeds about, and receding floods may strand seeds in likely spots, where germination then occurs. If these are seeds of a non-aquatic plant, they will not remain viable if submerged in water too long. However, most seeds are capable of germination after submersion of one to several days. Probably the most outstanding .example of a water-dispersed plant is the mangrove (*Rhizophora mangle*). The fruits of this tree are carried great distances by ocean currents, and the plant is now well-distributed along tropical shores.

A few types of plants have modifications which result in a mechanical seed dispersal. The drying-out of various layers of the ovary wall at different rates may result in such strains that a very rapid rupture of some of these tissues results in the forcible ejection of seeds. This frequently occurs in the fruits of the violet (*Viola* spp.), sorrel (*Oxalis* spp.), and witchhazel (*Hamamelis* spp.). In the squirting cucumber (*Ecballium* spp.), osmotic pressures build up as the inner tissues of the fruit ripen until the tensions are such as to forcibly extrude the mucilaginous contents and the seeds through a small rupture in the leathery outer layer of the fruit. These forces, which develop osmotically or upon drying, are frequently sufficient to cast seeds several feet away from the parent plant.

Tumbleweeds, such as *Amaranthus albus* and *Salsola kali* var. *tenuifolia,* effect seed dispersal in an interesting manner. The bushy plant breaks off near the surface of the soil and is rolled along open ground by the wind. Seeds and fruits are dislodged during this tumbling process which may carry the plant for considerable distances.

26.10   Diversity in flowering plants

In the early discussions of the flower in this chapter, many aspects were somewhat simplified for the sake of clarity. Anyone who has taken even a cursory glance around a flower garden or at flowering plants in the fields and woods is immediately made aware of the tremendous diversity of such organs. Certain structures, which have been discussed as parts of generalized and complete flower, may be missing or greatly reduced. But in addition to this, parts may be fused, or the insertion (attachment) of structures may be various. A few examples may help to emphasize the great differences which obtain from flower to flower.

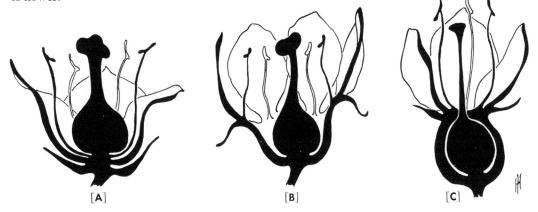

[A]   [B]   [C]

Figure 26-18. Position of the ovary. **A:** Hypogynous flower; the ovary is superior. **B:** Perigynous flower, superior ovary. **C:** Epigynous flower with the ovary inferior; the basal portions of the floral parts fuse around the ovary.

POSITION OF THE OVARY

Most flowers have ovaries which are termed **superior,** i.e., they are above the place of attachment of the other floral parts. Figure 26-18A represents an **hypogynous** flower with such an ovary as could be found in the buttercups (*Ranunculus*), grasses (*Poa*), and morning-glories (*Ipomoea*). In **perigynous** flowers the receptacle forms a cup-like structure around the superior ovary, with the stamens, petals, and sepals on the rim of the cup (Figure 26-18B); such flowers are found in the apple (*Malus*), rose (*Rosa*), and cherry (*Prunus*).[6] The **inferior** ovary

[6] The genus *Prunus* includes plums, peaches, and apricots in addition to cherries; all are perigynous.

of an **epigynous** flower is enclosed by the receptacle (Figure 26-18C), and the other floral parts are attached above the ovary; such flowers are found in the *Iris*, honeysuckle (*Lonicera*), and composites (*Aster, Zinnia, Helianthus,* or sunflower, *Taraxacum,* or dandelion).

PARTS FUSED OR IRREGULAR

In many kinds of flowers various of the floral parts may be fused to form tubular or bell-shaped structures. The bluebell (*Campanula rotundifolia*) has fused petals as well as fused sepals; in *Hibiscus* the filaments of the stamens also are fused, forming a tube around the pistil; in the Compositae (sunflower family) the anthers are fused as a cylinder around the pistil, but the filaments are free. The most common examples of irregular flowers, those which are not radially symmetrical, can be found in the snapdragon family (Scrophulariaceae), the bean family (Leguminosae [7]), and the orchid family (Orchidaceae). Many other examples could be given, but those listed should be sufficient to indicate the great diversity within flowers.

WIND POLLINATION VS. INSECT POLLINATION

As comparisons are made with regard to flower structures, basic similarities become evident among wind-pollinated flowers and among insect-pollinated flowers. Just as evident are certain basic differences between these two groups of plants. Such similarities and differences revolve particularly about the flower, its structures and numbers.

In general, wind-pollinated species tend to bear many, rather small, inconspicuous flowers. The petals are frequently much reduced and not colorful, whereas the stamens are quite numerous and conspicuous. By the very nature of the pollinating agent, those plants which happened to develop the type of flowers mentioned would tend to reproduce and survive more readily. Relatively large amounts of pollen are essential because of the rather inefficient mechanism involved. Large, showy structures would be of no advantage and could be of considerable disadvantage by forming wind barriers, thus interfering with pollen distribution. The oak (Fagaceae), willow (Salicaceae), and grass (Graminae) families are all wind-pollinated.

Those plants which are insect-pollinated tend to have flowers in which the petals are quite colorful and conspicuous and in which nectaries are present. Both of these structures attract a variety of insects.

---

[7] Included in the Leguminosae are: peas, *Pisum sativum;* beans, *Phaseolus vulgaris;* peanuts, *Arachis hypogaea;* alfalfa, *Medicago sativa;* clover, *Trifolium;* sweet peas, *Lathyrus odoratus;* etc.

Frequently the presence of fused petals forces the insect to crawl toward the nectary, which insures its brushing along stamens and pistils. Examples of insect-pollinated flowers are found in the bean, snapdragon, orchid, and mint (Labiatae) families.

The sunflower family (Figure 26-19) is rather interesting, because it is insect-pollinated and yet produces large numbers of small flowers. However, the flowers are arranged in clusters, generally called **inflorescences;** each "sunflower" or "daisy" is not a single flower but is one such compact cluster. The outer flowers, or ray flowers, each have one conspicuous strap-shaped petal which attracts insects, since the group together is conspicuous. The inner flowers, or disc flowers, are small and tubular. Thus, no one flower is really very attractive, but the cluster of flowers, termed a **head** in this case, creates a very pleasant appearance. Due to the compactness of arrangement, one visiting insect pollinates many flowers.

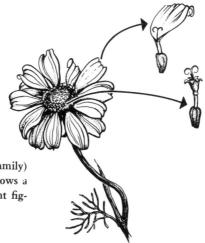

Figure 26-19. Composite (sunflower family) inflorescence. The upper right figure shows a ray flower enlarged, and the lower right figure shows a disc flower enlarged.

SELF-POLLINATION AND CROSS-POLLINATION

Flowers may be variously modified to insure either self-pollination or cross-pollination. The latter type is much more advantageous,[8] and the greater number of plants have flowers which are usually cross-pollinated. However, self-pollination does occur in oats (*Avena*), wheat (*Triticum*), and violets (*Viola*). In some plants, such as the willows (*Salix*) and poplars (*Populus*), cross-pollination must occur because they are dioecious, with the stamens and pistils occurring on

[8] Review Chapter 17 on Genetics if necessary.

different plants. In others the same flower contains both male and female parts, but these mature at different times, thus preventing self-pollination.

DICOTYLEDONAE AND MONOCOTYLEDONAE

The Angiospermae are divided into two subclasses, the Dicotyledonae and the Monocotyledonae, on the basis of differences within the flower and seed structures as well as within the leaf and stem structure. As is indicated by the name, the dicotyledonous plants are those in which two cotyledons are present in the embryo. In addition to this, the flower parts are in whorls of four or five or their multiples, the leaves are net-veined (reticulate venation), the vascular tissue of the stem is in the form of concentric cylinders or in bundles which form a ring, and a cambium is present. The monocotyledonous plants have but one cotyledon in the embryo, the flower parts are in threes, leaf venation is usually parallel, vascular bundles are scattered in the stem, and a cambium is almost always lacking.

Obviously, then, from the previous paragraph, the clearest distinctions between the two subclasses are in embryo and flower structures. The other characteristic differences will be true for almost all plants, but exceptions to these are somewhat more frequent. Some palms, for example, have leaves in which the venation is certainly not parallel, even though these plants are monocots. Although the distinction between a monocot and a dicot is not as sharp and clear as had been thought earlier, they are very useful taxonomic groupings.

26.11 Primitive and advanced flowers

The great differences which occur among the Angiospermae are a result of evolutionary processes. Although this topic will be discussed in considerable detail in the next chapter, the evolution of the flower will be mentioned at this time, while the involved structures are fresh in mind. This is such a well-illustrated example of evolution within a group that this section should be reviewed after the chapter on evolution has been completed.

The general trend of evolution of the flower has been toward a gradual shortening and compaction of the axis (receptacle). Primitive flowers (e.g., buttercup, *Ranunculus; Magnolia*) have an elongated receptacle, whereas advanced flowers (e.g., sunflower, *Helianthus;* dandelion, *Taraxacum;* orchid, *Cattleya*) have a very short, blunt receptacle. This shortening has resulted in a number of changes in the structure and arrangement of the flower parts, changes which can be observed quite readily when examining a variety of flowers.

CHANGE FROM SPIRAL TO CYCLIC ARRANGEMENT OF THE FLOWER PARTS

In the primitive *Magnolia* flower, the parts are arranged spirally; the stamens, for example, are of an indefinite number attached in a spiral fashion to the axis. In the advanced *Iris* flower, the parts are arranged in a whorl or cycle; the stamens are definite in number (three), and all are attached at the same level.

REDUCTION IN THE NUMBER OF CYCLES

The most advanced flowers always have only four cycles of parts, that is, one each of sepals, petals, stamens, and carpels (pistils). *Trillium* or *Lilium* (lily) have flowers of a moderate degree of advancement; all of the parts are arranged in cycles, but the stamens are in two cycles.

UNION OF PETALS

In primitive flowers the petals are separate, whereas they are fused or joined in most advanced flowers. The bluebell (*Campanula rotundafolia*), for example, has flowers in which the fused petals (a **sympetalous corolla**) form the distinctive feature from which the name is derived.

UNION OF CARPELS

In primitive flowers, such as the buttercup, each carpel forms a pistil. In advanced flowers, such as the lily, several carpels fuse to form a single pistil. In many of the most advanced types, the outer sets of parts are attached to the carpels and seem to be inserted at the top of the ovary, the epigynous condition mentioned in the previous section.

IRREGULARITY OF PARTS

In primitive flowers all parts of a set, such as the petals, are alike. In some of the advanced flowers, as in the bean family (Leguminosae), the various petals are quite dissimilar.

26.12 Importance of the Class Angiospermae

The flowering plants are undoubtedly the dominant members of our present-day flora and are found in almost all land and shallow water environments. Man's most important crop and forage plants—the plants of greatest economic value—are angiosperms. The major uses of wood have been discussed in Section 7.6, and the reader should review these.

Man's basic food supply depends upon the cereals (rice, *Oryza sativa;* wheat, *Triticum vulgare* and *T. durum;* corn, *Zea mays;* oats, *Avena sativa;* rye, *Secale cereale;* and barley, *Hordeum vulgare*) and grasses. Most of the cereals are eaten directly, but they may also be fed to livestock, which are then eaten. The forage grasses, of course, are consumed indirectly by man. Of those plants just mentioned, rice is used by more people than is any other food; probably half of the world's population, mainly in the Asiatic countries, consumes this plant. Cereals, especially barley and corn, are also frequently used in the production of alcohol and alcoholic beverages.

The reader might also review Section 9.6 for discussions of various fibers and chemicals obtained from flowering plants. Of the former, the most important are undoubtedly cotton, linen (flax), and hemp. Many synthetic fabrics are now produced, but most of these utilize cellulose (a plant product) as a base. The following are but a few of the materials obtained on a commercial basis from flowering plants: alcohol, acetone, acetic acid, tars and resins, tannins, oils, gums, and dyes. Rubber and cork are obtained from certain trees: *Hevea brasiliensis* and *Quercus suber,* respectively. Various drugs and beverages are also obtained from angiosperms: quinine, morphine, strychnine, digitalis, and ephedrine; tea, cocoa, and coffee.

Many other plant parts than those already mentioned are useful to man. Entire volumes have been written concerning edible seeds, fruits, rhizomes, tubers, etc.; thus this brief discussion is intended merely to emphasize the economic importance of the Angiospermae and not to list all of the uses to which these plants have been put. The reader should refer to a text on economic botany for further details.

26.13 Evolutionary advantages featured in the Angiospermae

As in the Gymnospermae (Section 25.4), the gametophytes develop within protective tissues and are not directly exposed to the environment. However, the Angiospermae are in a much more favorable condition with respect to the female gametophyte and the embryo than are the gymnosperms. The ovules of the former plants are enclosed within an additional mass of tissue, the ovary, which affords much protection to the developing gametophytes and eventually the embryo, as well as frequently aiding in the dissemination of the mature seed. Just as the seed habit is considered to be a major evolutionary advance, so is the development of the fruit considered to be exceedingly significant. The production of a fruit and the various modifications which aid in seed dispersal are the two factors which are most important in establishing the Angiospermae as the dominant plants of today. Some of the modifications leading to vegetative reproduction (e.g., runners, rhizomes, tubers, bulbs) are somewhat important, but sexual reproduction and its resultant variations are much more significant when examined from an evolutionary viewpoint.

In the angiosperm a well-developed storage tissue, the endosperm, results from fertilization. This is sometimes referred to as "double fertilization" because one sperm fuses with the egg and a second sperm fuses with the polar nuclei. This is a misnomer, but the important point is the formation of an additional storage tissue which is more efficient than that in the gymnosperms (Section 25.2).

Only one egg is present in an ovule of the flowering plant. This insures a greater supply of food for the developing embryo, since the single embryo thus has no competition, as was the case in the gymnosperms. In the latter several archegonia and eggs may be produced by the female gametophyte.

The evidence is not clear as to the ancestors of the flowering plants. They probably evolved from a primitive group of gymnosperms or from the psilopsids, but additional evidence must be obtained before any definite statement may be made.

26.14 Comparison of life cycles

In Figure 26-20 is represented the generalized life cycle of a flowering plant. This should now be compared with the life cycles of representatives from the various groups of the plant kingdom which have been studied.

Certain general observations should be clear when examining these life cycles. An ever-increasing dominance of the sporophyte phase is

Figure 26-20. Life cycle of a flowering plant (word diagram).

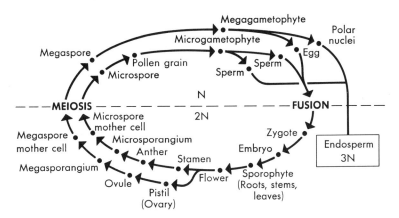

evidenced in the more complex plants, correlated with a general reduction in size of the gametophyte and its eventual dependence on the diploid sporophyte. As a result of these changes, the delicate gametes and gametophytes are more and more protected in the advanced plant groups. The dissemination of a species depends more and more upon the distribution of fruits and seeds and the movements of spores, especially microspores or pollen grains. These spores are much hardier than are gametes. The large sporophyte development is, thus, a great advantage—many spores are produced.

Summary

1. Angiospermae produce specialized structures, the flowers, in which enclosed seeds develop. They are the dominant members of the world's flora.

2. A complete flower has the following parts: sepals, petals, stamens, and at least one pistil. Microspores are produced in the anther portion of the stamen; the stalk is termed the filament. The pistil consists of the stigma at the tip, an elongated style, and the enlarged ovary at the base; one or more ovules are contained within the ovary. In some plants one or more of the floral parts may be absent.

3. A single megasporocyte in the ovule develops into four megaspores as a result of meiosis; three of the megaspores degenerate. Mitotic divisions of the functional megaspore result in the production of the megagametophyte: an egg, two polar nuclei, synergid cells, and antipodal cells.

4. Many microsporocytes in the anther produce microspores by meiotic divisions. The microgametophytes which develop from these spores are transported to the pistil in a variety of ways (pollination). Two sperm are produced as the pollen tube grows down the tissues of the pistil.

5. One sperm fuses with the egg, forming a zygote; the second sperm fuses with both polar nuclei, eventually forming the endosperm (a triploid storage tissue). The zygote develops into a multicellular embryo.

6. The ovule enlarges, the integuments harden, and the resultant structure is the seed. The seed may be dormant for a time. Upon germination, the cotyledons may be carried up and out of the soil. The cotyledons may also function as leaves for a short time.

7. As the ovule develops into a seed, the ovary increases enormously in size and forms the fruit. Flowers and fruits are of many different kinds.

8. Seeds and fruits may be variously modified, a factor which fre-

quently assists in seed dispersal. Wind, animals (including humans), and water are the most important agents of dispersal.

9. The Angiospermae are divided into two subclasses, the Dicotyledonae and Monocotyledonae. The former have two cotyledons present in the embryo, the flower parts are in multiples of four or five, the leaves are net-veined, and a cambium is present. The monocotyledonous plants have one cotyledon in the embryo, the flower parts are in threes, leaf venation is usually parallel, and a cambium is usually lacking.

10. Primitive flowers have the following general characteristics: spiral arrangement of floral parts, separate petals and carpels, and regularity of structures. Advanced flowers usually have a cyclic arrangement of parts, fused petals and carpels, and irregular or dissimilar parts.

11. The flowering plants, in addition to their aesthetic values, are our most important food and forage plants. Many fibers are obtained from the Angiospermae; so also are cork and rubber. Drugs, beverages, and other commercial products of various sorts (alcohol, acetone, tars, resins, dyes, etc.) are also obtained.

12. The enclosing of the seed within the fruit greatly increases the possibility of survival in diverse environments. The well-developed storage tissue surrounding a single embryo may also be considered advantages which enabled Angiospermae to become the dominant plants of the world.

REVIEW TOPICS AND QUESTIONS

1. Discuss, with the aid of a word diagram, the general life cycle of a flowering plant with regard to alternation of phases, general chromosome number, fertilization, and meiosis.
2. Indicate the similarities between the life cycle of a flowering plant and that of a moss, a fern, and a pine.
3. Indicate the differences between the life cycle of a flowering plant and that of a moss, a fern, and a pine.
4. Describe the development in a flowering plant of a sperm, starting with a microsporocyte. Indicate where each structure develops and whether it is haploid or diploid.
5. Describe the development of the megagametophyte, starting with the megasporocyte. Indicate where each structure develops and whether it is haploid or diploid.
6. Diagram a complete flower, and label all parts.
7. Define the following: carpel, incomplete flower, imperfect flower, monoecious, endosperm, epicotyl, hypocotyl, and fruit.
8. Describe in detail what happens when a dry (viable) seed is placed underground and watered. Assume that you have a garden bean seed, and conclude your discussion with the fully established seedling.

9. Discuss at least four mechanisms for seed dispersal, indicating the advantages which accrue to plants having such mechanisms.
10. Define the following, and give an example of each: simple fruit, accessory fruit, berry, nut, hypogenous flower, perigynous flower, and epigynous flower.
11. Compare the general structure of a wind-pollinated flower with that of an insect-pollinated one.
12. Discuss the functioning of those structures which have made it possible for the Angiospermae to obtain their prominent position in the flora of the world.
13. List at least ten ways in which the flowering plants are important economically.

SUGGESTED READINGS

Eames, A. J. *Morphology of the Angiosperms*. New York: McGraw-Hill, 1961.

Foster, A. S., and E. M. Gifford, Jr. *Comparative Morphology of Vascular Plants*. San Francisco: Freeman, 1959.

Fuller, H., and O. Tippo. *College Botany*. New York: Holt, 1954.

Gibbs, R. D. *Botany, An Evolutionary Approach*. Philadelphia: Blakiston, 1950.

Hill, A. F. *Economic Botany*. New York: McGraw-Hill, 1937.

CHAPTER 27

Evolution

27.1 Evolution

The idea that all organisms are descended from past organisms from which they differ more or less is one of the broadest concepts in biology and has influenced many fields outside of biology. **Evolution** most simply means descent with change and implies that all organisms are more or less related one to another. Presenting this idea in a logical way, we shall first examine the general evidence which leads to the acceptance of an evolutionary concept. Then we can consider several theories which eventually led to the modern formulations of this process. Finally, then, we shall be able to examine more specifically evolution within the plant kingdom in the light of the discussions of various plant groups in the preceding chapters.

27.2 Geological evidence

The earth has undergone a tremendous physical evolution. In some areas land masses have risen from the sea and in others have sunk beneath the oceans. The recent (1960) calamitous earthquakes in Chile are examples of earth movements; so also is the sudden appearance of the massive volcano Paricutin in Mexico during 1943. The processes which caused changes in the past are causing them today, but human time scales are too short for recording the many changes which have occurred since the earth's beginning. Estimates of the age of the earth vary from two-and-one-half to four billion years, depending upon the method of estimation, but three billion is the consensus at the present time.

The most accurate determinations of geologic ages are based upon known rates of decomposition of radioactive materials. Such breakdown occurs at a uniform rate and is independent of temperature, pressure, light, or other environmental factors. By determining the ratio of radioactive materials to their breakdown products, we can estimate the length of time during which the original material underwent decay. Some difficulties with this technique have yet to be worked out, so our estimates tend to be a little conservative. However, the earth very likely is older than three billion years. In fact, each new estimate pushes the age further and further backward.

These changes which have occurred emphasize the tremendous environmental variations to which living organisms must have been subjected. Some of the many different kinds of individuals could well have been better adapted to a new environment than were the parental types. The time involved is so enormously great that changes could have been taking place very slowly as well as rapidly.

27.3 Paleontological [1] evidence

The concept of evolution is probably best substantiated by the existence of fossils. Basically, a **fossil** is any trace of a former living thing and may be of several types:

1. Intact specimens or parts of them. These are sometimes found embedded in amber, in tar pits, or in localities where decay has been prevented (e.g., in bogs which are relatively toxic).

2. Molds, casts, or impressions. The shape of the organism is retained, but none of the original plant (or animal) material remains.

3. Compressions. These consist of carbonized plant material more or less in the original shape but greatly compressed.

4. Petrifactions. The plant parts are infiltrated or replaced by mineral substances; the structure is preserved.

5. Accumulated products. These are structures, such as reefs, composed of the secretions of living organisms, or incomplete decay products, such as oil and coal.

The finding of such remains or indications of the one-time presence of living organisms enables biologists to deduce much concerning the changes which have occurred during past eras. The age of the fossil is determined by the location of the rock stratum in which it is found and/or by radioactive measurements. In general, the deeper the stratum, the older the fossil; earth upheavals or lowerings must be interpreted with care, of course. The radioactive measurements are made using rock samples or portions of the fossil itself (carbon-14 dating). Whereas the rock strata indicate more relative ages, radioactive dating

[1] Paleontology = the study of ancient life.

Table 27-1. Geologic Time Scale

Eras	Periods	Millions of Years from Present	Major Developments in Plant Life as Shown by Fossil Record
CENOZOIC	Quarternary	Present to 2	Extinction of many trees through climatic changes. Increase in herbaceous flora.
	late Tertiary early	2 to 60	Dwindling of forests; climatic segregation of floras. Rise of herbaceous plants.
			Development of many modern angiospermous families. Rise and world-wide extension of modern forests.
MESOZOIC	Cretaceous	60 to 125	Angiosperms gradually become dominant, some modern angiospermous types represented. Gymnosperms decline.
	Jurassic	125 to 185	Earliest know angiosperms. Cycads and conifers dominant; primitive gymnosperms disappear.
	Triassic		Increase of cycads, ginkgo, and conifers. Disappearance of seed ferns.
PALEOZOIC	Permian	185 to 309	Waning of arborescent clubmosses and horsetails. Early cycads and conifers.
	Carboniferous		Extensive coal-forming forests of giant clubmosses, horsetails, and seed ferns. Primitive gymnosperms.
	Devonian	309 to 381	Early vascular plants: psilophytes, primitive clubmosses, horsetails, and ferns. Early forests of arborescent clubmosses.
	Silurian		Algae dominant. First direct evidence of land plants.
	Ordovician	381 to 600	Marine algae dominant. Possibly first land plants.
	Cambrian		Some modern algal groups established.
PROTEROZOIC	600 to 1,500		Bacteria and simple algae.
ARCHEOZOIC	1,500 to 4,000		No fossils known; possibly unicellular algae.

371

Source: Victor A. Greulach and J. Edison Adams, *Plants, An Introduction to Modern Botany* (New York: John Wiley and Sons, 1962), as adapted from Eames and with the permission of the publisher.

presents us with more nearly an exact time scale. In some cases the fossil records are quite complete, while in others they are not. This is not too strange when one considers what happens to organisms when they die—decay occurs. An organism (or portion of it) must be protected quickly from decay in order for it to be preserved. Such protection may occur in swamps and bogs due to a low oxygen content or toxic materials which decrease or prevent bacterial action, in rapidly silting streams and lakes, in tar pits, and in glaciers.

One finds, on examining fossils, that the flora and fauna of the earth are constantly changing; new types of plants and animals arise, flourish, and sometimes become extinct. The general sequence of evolutionary change from organisms of very simple structure to more complex organisms is well-substantiated; the older remains are the more primitive. The evidence for the presence of bacteria and some of the more primitive algae is mostly indirect because of their extremely small size and simplicity of structure. Table 27-1 is a comparative chart, based upon available knowledge, of geological and paleontological history and indicates the environmental changes which occurred and the organisms which were present during the various periods.

27.4 Biogeographical evidence

Plant geographers frequently point out that many types of plants are widely distributed and that others are quite restricted in occurrence. Also, different kinds of plants are found growing in areas which are widely separated but which have similar environments. Such observations indicate that the environment alone cannot explain distributions of organisms. If areas containing similar species are isolated from each other by various barriers, such as mountain ranges or bodies of water, these organisms are quite likely to develop along divergent lines and become very different from one another. The occurrence of variants is a haphazard phenomenon, after which the environment will act as a selective agent in perpetuating those individuals which are best able to survive under the existing conditions.

Darwin was greatly impressed by the flora and fauna of the Galapagos Islands, a group of small islands about 600 miles west of Ecuador, South America. Here he found certain organisms (e.g., the giant tortoise and marine iguana) not found elsewhere; he also found that tortoises from different islands in the group were distinguishable. This was an example of areas only 50 to 60 miles apart which had differing organisms, a clear case of divergent development. However, Darwin's investigation of the finches was what provided him with his first insight as to the mechanisms involved in the origin of species. He found

thirteen distinct species of these birds varying in both beak structure
and habit—some fed on fruits, some ate seeds, and others hunted for
insects. These all had to be descendants of a common ancestor which
had migrated from the mainland. The absence of other land birds as
competitors enabled the finches to evolve in many directions—directions which would not be available to them in a populous area, where
the finches are restricted to very narrow niches. As a result of his
observations, Darwin became aware of the importance of both environment and competition as factors in evolution (see also later in
this chapter and Section 17.4).

27.5 Taxonomic evidence

Plants and animals are classified mainly with regard to their similarities and dissimilarities of structure. The kinds of organisms thus
become arranged in various groupings which indicate relationships.
The greater the structural resemblances, the more closely related are
the organisms. A dog and a wolf are more closely related than a dog
and an antelope; peas and beans are more closely related than peas
and roses. If organisms are closely related, they must have a common
recent ancestor. Those organisms which are quite dissimilar can be
related only very distantly with a common ancestor ages ago. Relationship (common ancestry) is the simplest valid general explanation
of similarity of organisms.

Related organisms have similar basic structural patterns. One example of this is the flower, which is characteristic of one large group
of plants (Class Angiospermae). Subdivisions of this group exist with
regard to the particular kind of flower, but the members of this group
are certainly more closely related to each other than they are to plants
which bear cones rather than flowers. The homology of vertebrate
appendages (e.g., wing bones of birds and finger bones of man) is
another example of structural relationships. Even more basic than these
examples is the cellular structure of all living organisms.[2]

27.6 Embryological evidence

In many cases the early development of organisms may be very similar, even though the mature individuals are quite different. The early
stages of a moss gametophyte (the protonema) and a fern gametophyte (prothallus) are alga-like in appearance and tend to indicate that
algae were ancestors to these plants. More vivid evidence of embryological similarities can be found among animals. In the very early

[2] The viruses are notable exceptions.

stages of development, when only a roundish mass of cells is present, one animal embryo is almost impossible to distinguish from another. Even somewhat later, when the head and other regions are clearly visible, many animal embryos look very much alike. At this stage, the human, pig, chick, and shark have many points of similarity. The human embryo even has gill lobes and a tail, both of which disappear before birth. These various similarities during the development of organisms certainly is indicative of relationships between them.

27.7 Evidence from comparative physiology

Just as structural patterns exist, so do basic chemical patterns in organisms. Photosynthesis, chlorophyll, respiration, cytochromes, adenosine triphosphate (ATP), deoxyribose nucleic acid (DNA)—the presence of these and similar materials and processes attests to general relationships among organisms. In a more restrictive sense, we may consider the resins, such as turpentine, of the pines (Pinaceae), the essential oils of the mints (Labiatae), and the latex found in the spurges (Euphorbiaceae); these materials are less widespread than, for example, chlorophyll and indicate closer relationships.

As is the case with animals, certain proteins are characteristic of plant groups. The more nearly alike the proteins, the closer is the relationship. Conversely, plant groups that are not closely related tend to have quite different protein characteristics.

27.8 Evidence from genetical studies and domestication

These studies have provided a source for evolutionary change. The hybrids between species are occasionally sufficiently self-fertile to become new species. Evidence for this can be found in the California pines. A cross between *Pinus jeffreyi* and *P. coulteri* produces mostly sterile hybrids which have no future. The cross between *P. jeffreyi* and *P. ponderosa* produces some fertile hybrids, but they are poorly adapted. The cross between *P. jeffreyi* and *P. ponderosa* var. *scopulorum* probably resulted in the production of a successful (fertile) hybrid now known as *Pinus washoensis,* which grows near Lake Tahoe. This is apparently a new species which arose as a hybrid.

New species have been shown to arise from a multiplication of the original basic chromosome number, usually as a result of the failure of one cell division during meiosis. The diploid gametes then produce a tetraploid zygote. Such multiplication of basic chromosome sets occurs naturally or may be induced by colchicine, and the individuals are polyploid.[3] Polyploids usually look different from the original plant and are not capable of inter-breeding with it—thus, a new species may arise. Polyploids are often larger and more desirable than diploids. Many cultivated lilies, petunias, snapdragons, and blackberries are polyploid.

In the genus *Clarkia* are several well-substantiated cases of fertile hybrid species which developed when polyploid individuals arose. For example, *C. similis* combines gene sets from *C. modesta* (8) and *C. epilobioides* (9); the numbers in parentheses refer to the normal gametic chromosome number. The hybrid, having a diploid number of seventeen, would be sterile; with an uneven and non-homologous number of chromosomes, pairing (synapsis) could not occur. A doubling of the chromosome number resulted in the fertile hybrid with the even number of thirty-four; the gametes, of course, contain seventeen chromosomes.[4] Similar results possibly may be obtained with other sterile hybrids by using colchicine to double the chromosome number.

Domestication is really evolution under more or less controlled conditions, with man, instead of the natural environment, determining which individuals will survive and reproduce. This was mainly a hit-or-miss proposition until the 1900's, when the field of genetics opened up tremendous possibilities in plant and animal breeding. Without an understanding of genetics, the procedure was merely to keep the seeds of the "best" plants, hoping that such seeds would develop into equally good offspring. In many instances this was quite successful, especially over rather long periods of time. However, if several pairs of genes or multiple alleles or dominance is involved, the progeny will be quite diverse. The concept of inheritance being determined by particles (genes) enabled one to predict results, to estimate possibilities, and to plan an accurate series of breeding programs. The results since 1900 have been astounding.

Plant breeding programs, with their genetical basis, are generally concerned with developing plants which have one or more of the following characteristics: (1) increased yields (quantity), (2) better quality, (3) shorter growing seasons, (4) disease resistance, and (5) the ability to grow in diverse environments. During the past fifty years, for example, the average yield of wheat (*Triticum aestivum*) has in-

---

[3] There are various kinds of polyploids: triploids, tetraploids, pentaploids, and so on.

[4] Additional information concerning *Clarkia* may be found in "The Genus Clarkia" by Harlan Lewis and Margaret Ensign Lewis, *University of California Publ. in Botany*, Vol. 20, No. 4 (1955), pp. 241–392.

creased from twenty bushels per acre to forty, and that of corn (*Zea mays*) from ten bushels per acre to thirty. Some of these increases are due to modern agricultural practices, but most of the increases are a result of new varieties. The many varieties of apples are good examples of man's efforts to produce quality products. At first the improvement of the apple (*Malus sylvestris*) consisted largely of the selection of chance seedlings, and this is even true today, the Golden Delicious being a prime example. The Cortland variety, however, is an example of the results of controlled breeding which is being carried on with significant results. European grape varieties based on *Vitis vinifera* were unsuccessful in North America due to a lack of resistance to low temperatures in the north and various diseases in the south. Hybrids between native American species and the European grape are of better quality than the native grapes and retain the resistance of the native types.

Possibly one of the best examples of the use of a breeding program is the work which has been done with the resistance of wheat to a fungus disease. The wheat plant is one of the most important food plants in the world, especially in the Western hemisphere. Unfortunately, the yield is greatly reduced by various diseases, with wheat rust (organism: *Puccinia graminis* var. *tritici*) the major culprit. The only economically feasible method of controlling this disease is by using resistant wheat varieties. In many agricultural experiment stations, wheat-breeding programs are a continuing project, because the rust organism produces new varieties as a result of sexual reproduction. Varieties of wheat which are resistant one season may be attacked by new rust varieties within a few years. Here, then, is an example of man-made evolution attempting to maintain an advantage over natural evolution.

Domestication has resulted in the production of various species from a common ancestor. The wild cabbage (*Brassica oleracea*) has produced cauliflower, kale, kohlrabi, and brussels sprouts, in addition to the cabbage itself. One might also list the many kinds of dogs, horses, and chickens which have resulted from man's efforts. In all of these, conscious selection by man has preserved those types in which he was interested. Darwin, himself, was impressed by this great variety of domestic plants and animals.

27.9   Lamarck's theory

376

Lamarck was the first (1809) to suggest that all species had descended from other fewer species by gradual changes. He realized the importance of close and distant relationships as a result of his studies of comparative anatomy and the difficulties he encountered in clearly defining a species. He understood evolution as a dynamic process, continually occurring and leading to increasing complexity and specialization. These were accurate and excellent ideas, but his theories as to the method of evolution have not been accepted.

Lamarckian evolution is frequently termed evolution through the transmission, or lack of it, of characteristics gained or lost by use or disuse—the inheritance of acquired characteristics. As new needs or wants arise, these tend to cause new parts or organs to develop. The use of a structure increases its development and so produces a variation which is transmitted to subsequent generations. Similarly, disuse tends to cause structures to disappear. In this way variations great enough to be considered a new species are built up. Lamarck emphasized the development of structures *in order to* accomplish some end. The long neck of the giraffe must have been acquired by generations of giraffes stretching for foliage in trees; long legs must have been developed in certain animals in order for them to escape enemies; keen sight must have developed so that the animal could find its prey.

Experimental evidence was readily accumulated which refuted Lamarck's ideas. Acquired characteristics are not inherited as long as they have no effect on the genes. The environment does, of course, greatly influence the development of an individual, but such development is not inherited. The children of weight lifters are not born with bulging muscles; cutting off the tails of mice for many generations does not produce progeny without tails. One of the simplest experiments to demonstrate environmental influences on the individual and to refute Lamarckianism is to grow plants of the same genotype under different environmental conditions: sufficient vs. insufficient water, light vs. shading, sufficient nitrogen vs. lack of nitrogen, and so forth. Many differences in size, shape, and color will result. If these plants are capable of producing seed (self-pollination), seeds from the different-appearing plants, grown under uniform conditions, will develop into plants which are all the same. The genetic make-up alone determines the *capabilities* of the organism, while the environment may influence the actual growth of an individual. A similar situation obtains in humans existing on a diet insufficient in certain vitamins, for example. The individual is capable of normal growth if he receives the required nutrients; without the essentials his growth and development is abnormal (e.g., a lack of vitamin D results in rickets; a lack of vitamin C results in scurvy).

In recent years Lysenko, a Russian plant breeder, claimed to have produced heritable acquired characteristics. We cannot in this book detail the mass of evidence in opposition to this claim.[5] Suffice it to say that independent workers in other countries have never been able to duplicate Lysenko's experiments. In fact, all of the data which such investigators have obtained are opposite to those of Lysenko. Needless to say, his claims have not been accepted.

27.10   Darwin's theory

Darwin was a naturalist who correlated his immense powers of observation with an idea gained from Malthus' "Essay on Population" (1798) in devising a concept of evolution which is accepted in modified form by biologists today. Darwin observed the many variations of plants and animals and collected many of them, particularly during his voyage around the world aboard H.M.S. *Beagle* from 1826 to 1835. (This was partially discussed in Section 27.4.) His ideas are frequently incorporated in the phrase, "The theory of natural selection, or the survival of the fittest."

Darwin's observations led him to the idea that inheritable variations of all kinds and of various degrees, but mostly small, occur in all organisms. He acknowledged Malthus' statements that the reproductive potential of any organism is limitless, leading to overproduction or an overabundance, and that the actual numbers of organisms was not increasing. This indicated a keen competition among organisms, which produced a natural selection, acting on small variations and resulting in the survival of those individuals best fitted (adapted) to the environment. This survival is based upon the better-adapted individuals leaving proportionately more offspring, thus increasing the prevalence of the favorable variations. The continued operation of this natural selection over long periods of time produces forms sufficiently different to be called new species.

In Darwinian terms those giraffes which happened to develop with long necks could obtain more food than their short-necked brethren and thus would have a better chance of surviving in that environment. The difference in approach between this statement and that by Lamarck is so important it should be stressed. Lamarckian thought is that the long neck developed *in order to* guarantee survival, while the Darwin concept implies that survival was possible *because* the long neck *happened* to develop. In other words, many variations occur at random, and the environment determines which variants are suitable. Of course, many gradations of adaptability exist.

[5] Conway Zirkle, *The Death of Science in Russia* (Philadelphia: Univ. of Pennsylvania Press, 1949). This is an excellent discussion of the results when political doctrine governs science.

Darwin gave full credit to Lamarck and others for initiating the theory of evolution, but his own careful observations added such a tremendous amount of detail that he is really considered to be the person who developed most thoroughly the basis of our modern concept of evolution. His concept of the method of selection was quite different from Lamarck's, of course. However, Wallace, entirely independently of Darwin, reached the same conclusion concerning natural selection. In fact, Darwin's *The Origin of Species by Means of Natural Selection* (1859) was published as a result of the article Wallace submitted. Darwin since his voyage had been compiling his data and writing—he had shown a rough draft of this material to various friends as early as 1844—but had spent about twenty years in the effort. With the arrival of Wallace's paper, friends persuaded Darwin to submit his article along with that of Wallace to the Linnaean Society (one of the foremost scientific societies of the day) for publication. The more massive amount of data accumulated by Darwin, as well as the fact that his project had been well underway since about 1835, earned for him fame throughout the world, whereas Wallace is known mainly to biologists (and not to all of them, either). Independent discovery of basic ideas is nothing new. If the data are present, the theory will eventually be suggested by someone. Newton did not manufacture gravity, and Einstein did not produce relativity. These were basic ideas which would have had to be developed eventually. Fortunately, the world produces intelligent men who perceive concepts more readily than do most of us.

Darwin's ideas concerning evolution, one must realize, do not explain the *source* of variations. He assumed that variations occurred and that natural selection took place among these. We are indebted mainly to de Vries for an understanding of how variations develop.

27.11 De Vries' theory

In 1901, de Vries, a Dutch botanist, proposed his mutation theory of evolution as a result of his studies of the inheritance of a species of evening-primrose (*Oenothera lamarckiana*). He observed that individuals with new types of flowers occasionally developed, that these changes were inherited, and that some of the new individuals were sufficiently different from the parent type to be considered new species. The sudden changes which resulted in new kinds of plants were called mutations. Later evidence supported the idea that mutations are chromosomal changes, thus influencing hereditary characteristics.

One of the important aspects of sexual reproduction is the production of variability in the offspring as a result of re-combinations of different kinds of genes. The origin of a different gene, or a new allele, as a sudden unpredictable change of an existing gene is termed **mutation.**[6] Neither Darwin nor Mendel had any idea of such changes; they just assumed that variations existed.

Usually mutations are of minor effect, recessive, and harmful, although occasionally dominant and major changes may be brought about. That mutations tend to be harmful and recessive is not really strange: the living organism is a highly complex system, and even small changes may disrupt a whole sequence of events—one non-standard bolt may prevent an entire machine from functioning properly. Also, life has existed for a considerable length of time. Mutations have occurred throughout this period, and "natural selection" by environmental conditions would have resulted in perpetuating the more favorable of these changes. Mutations occurring at the present time have probably occurred in the past and have been selected *against*.

The gene may be pictured as a complex organic molecule, one of a chain of such molecules which comprise the essential part of a chromosome (see Sections 17.3 and 17.4). Mutations could then consist of rearrangements of the atoms of the molecule as a result of internal or external forces. X-rays, infra-red rays, cosmic rays, ultraviolet light, heat, and various chemicals serve to increase the rate of natural mutations. In the absence of such external forces, mutations probably occur at the rate of one gene per million genes each generation, although this will vary considerably with regard to different organisms as well as with different genes. A particular gene may vary in several ways, resulting in multi-allelic forms, or the mutant may revert back to the original. The changes are at random, as are the genes which may mutate. Artificial methods (e.g., X-rays, mustard gas) are utilized to increase the rate at which mutations occur, so that they may be studied more readily, but such treatments do not change the kind of mutations which occur, nor do they enable one to predict the mutant which arises; the occurrence is still at random. (Radiations and mutations have a direct correlation: a little radiation produces few mutations, while much radiation produces many mutations.)

Some mutations are not inherited. For example, the navel (seedless) orange is a result of a mutant in a bud. Obviously, since seeds are not produced, such a mutation cannot be transmitted to progeny. However, vegetative propagation by means of cuttings or grafts serve to

---

[6] The term "mutation" is sometimes used to refer to any chromosomal change, while the term "gene mutation" is used in referring to changes in genes. The changes observed by de Vries were actually cases of polyploidy and chromosome aberrations, but many cases of gene changes were subsequently investigated. The more common practice is to use the term mutation as done in this text.

perpetuate such desirable plants. Somatic mutations, those occurring in vegetative cells, are not inherited but may be visible as variations in flower color or shape, leaf size, etc. These may not be advantageous to the plant (the seedless orange for example), but they may be desirable to man, who aids in their survival. This is also true, of course, with inherited mutations which would die out except for man's interference.

The idea suggested by de Vries was actually a modification of Darwin's theory of natural selection. The latter emphasized an unbroken, gradually merging series of variations. De Vries believed that new forms, often sufficiently distinct to be called new species, appear suddenly, repeatedly, and unpredictably in the ordinary course of reproduction. These new forms (mutants) breed true. That is, in reproduction they produce organisms like themselves, except when another mutation occurs. Mutations are of all kinds and of various degrees and frequently result in quite large and distinct changes. The competition resulting from overproduction produces a natural selection (as suggested by Darwin) which results in the survival of those mutants best fitted to the environment.

27.12   The modern concept of evolution

The considered judgment of biologists today is that from a single original form of life, or from a relatively few original forms, of very simple organization, other forms of greater complexity and diversification have in some manner been developed; that from these forms still others, mostly of greater complexity but sometimes of simpler organization, have been developed in the same manner; that this process has continued at varying rates but without interruption from the time of the beginning of life and is still going on; and that all organisms, both extinct and living, both plant and animal, have arisen in this way.

Studies of plant fossils have emphasized this developmental change from simple organisms to complex ones. The oldest layers of rocks, at least two billion years old, have no evidence of plant remains (see Table 27-1), but in rock strata of the Proterozoic Era, which was about one billion years ago, evidence of bacteria and algae has been found. During the Paleozoic Era, besides the algae, the first true land plants and eventually seed plants developed. Great beds of coal were formed during the Carboniferous period of this era, probably 250 million years ago. Later, during the Mesozoic Era, the gymnosperms flourished, the angiosperms appeared, and the gymnosperms began a marked decline. Although the first angiosperms appeared about 120 million years ago, their rapid and diverse evolution is shown especially in the fossil specimens found in the Cenozoic layers; during this era of 60 million years or so, the angiosperms have emerged to attain their present dominant place among the flora. All of this information has been obtained by a careful study of rock layers and the fossils they contain. Those fossils located in rock levels of more recent origin are the more complex; the older the fossil, the simpler the organism.

Although progressive evolution is the most conspicuous trend, examples exist of **retrogressive evolution** in both the plant and animal kingdoms. The parasitic mode of life, wherein structurally simple organisms have developed from more complex ancestors, is considered to be of this latter type. **Parallel evolution** refers to the common evolutionary pattern of different plant groups and may result in plants which are morphologically similar. Parallel evolution of this latter type is sometimes called **convergent evolution** and is shown clearly in the xeromorphic characteristics of the cactus and some members of the spurge family; *Agave* (amaryllis family) and *Aloe* (lily family), have developed similarly.

SEQUENCE OF EVENTS IN EVOLUTION

Variations are produced by chance mutations, and these variations are re-combined at random by sexual reproduction. Many of the variants will be less fitted to the existing environment and will die, but others may arise which are better adapted and will survive and may completely replace the parental type by leaving more offspring. In the latter case, the parental type becomes an extinct group. If the environment gradually changes, a few of the new genetic combinations may be better adapted to the different environment than was the original organism, and more of the new types will survive. If environmental changes are sufficiently prolonged or severe, the original plant will become extinct, and the new type will become normal.

An example of evolution due to environmental conditions within the last 100 years can be seen in the change of the peppered moth (*Biston* sp.) from its normal light color to a black coloration. Occasional dark mutants were first collected about 100 years ago in Great Britain. Since the moths rest on tree trunks during the daytime, the dark ones are much more easily seen by birds and eaten. Thus they become eliminated, even though they are hardier than the normal. In the smoke-grimed industrial areas, however, the "normals" no longer match their surroundings as well as do the "blacks," which thus have a selective advantage. As a result, the dark forms have now almost entirely replaced the light forms in England, whereas the light forms are still the predominant members of the population in Scotland

and other rural areas. This situation is completely understandable in terms of our evolutionary concepts.

Isolating two or more segments of an interbreeding population encourages their evolution into distinct species. When variations occur anywhere in the original population, they can spread entirely through that population by means of sexual reproduction. When such variations occur in isolated segments, they cannot spread to other segments. Similar mutants are not likely to occur in the various segments; also possible is that the environments of the isolated segments will be somewhat different, thus favoring different variants. If the period of isolation is sufficiently prolonged, the original species may develop into two or more species. So many hereditary differences will have accumulated during this period that the genes of the various forms will not combine readily. Natural selection will tend to intensify the differences, distinct species will evolve, and interbreeding may eventually become impossible. Isolating mechanisms may be geographic (oceans, mountain ranges, etc.), temporal (differences in flowering time or reproductive cycles), or genetic (incompatibility of gametes, sterility).

Optimum conditions for evolution appear to be small, semi-isolated populations. Such populations are isolated enough to develop independently and differently and yet close enough to receive occasional "transfusions" of new variability from adjacent populations.

27.13 The pattern of evolution

A schematic diagram (Figure 27-1) of evolutionary development emphasizes the fact that this is not a straight-line process but resembles more the branches of a tree; thus the term "family tree." Variations

Figure 27-1. A schematic diagram of evolutionary development.

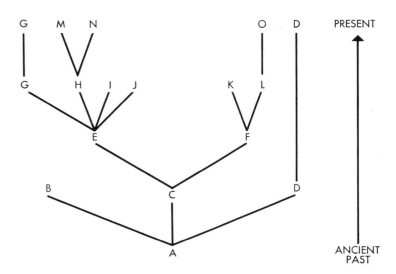

may persist for a short or long time, depending upon possible environmental shifts and other variants. In the diagram, the original organism **A** of an ancient age gives rise to **B, C,** and **D. B** becomes extinct and gives rise to nothing, whereas **D** persists unchanged to the present time. **C,** on the other hand, eventually develops into two different groups, **E** and **F.** Group **E** gives rise to **G, H, I,** and **J,** while group **F** produces **K** and **L. G** persists unchanged. **H** gives rise to **M** and **N. I, J,** and **K** become extinct, while **L** develops into **O.** The groups living at the present time are **G, M, N, O,** and **D;** the other groups are found only as fossils. In this representation **M** and **N** are closely related, with a recent common ancestor **(H),** and are rather similar morphologically, though different enough to be distinct species. **M** and **D** are very dissimilar, although related distantly through an ancient common ancestor, **A. D** and **O** might look very similar because of similar adaptations, but they are only distantly related **(A).** This could be an example of parallel evolution (e.g., *Agave* and *Aloe*). Only a small portion of the total number of individuals evolved exist at any one time, the remainder having become extinct. Without extinctions, classification would be extremely difficult because of the lack of gaps in the range of variations.

When a new basic series of adaptations, such as the flower, arises and becomes established, the group remains small during establishment and early development. Many variations on the original structure are developed as the group becomes dominant and exploits many environments. A group may decline as a new group with a better basic adaptation arises. The group may also decline if it becomes overspecialized and cannot adapt to changes in the environment. The *Yucca* [7] is potentially over-specialized. A few of the older species usually persist after a new group becomes dominant. If an organism finds itself in a suitable environment, it may remain unchanged to the present. The blue-green algae are probably such primitive organisms which arose ages ago.

[7] The styles of *Yucca* (Spanish bayonet) flowers are hollow, with the stigmatic surface at the lower end of this tube. Pollination is accomplished when the female Yucca-moth (*Pronuba*) collects a ball of pollen from the stamens and stuffs this pollen down the tubular style. The moth then drills a hole through the ovary with her ovipositor (egg-laying device) and lays eggs among the ovules. The moth larvae develop within the ovary and feed upon the developing ovules. Enough ovules are present so that some are almost always left as seeds. The larvae bore out of the ovary and form cocoons in the soil, and the adult emerges at about the time that the *Yucca* flowers. Note that the *Yucca* can be pollinated only in this fashion and the moth larvae can use only *Yucca* ovules for food; thus, the plant and the animal share a complete interdependence. Such over-specialization is quite likely to result in extinction of both organisms.

Evolution can be discussed from two points of view. First, we can indicate that the gradual change from the simple to the complex by the accumulation of additional traits as we examine representatives from the primitive bacteria to the modern flowering plants. A second approach is to discuss each general advantageous characteristic separately, indicating the manner in which the simple and then the complex plants solved the problem of survival.

In the first approach we may list important descriptive features of an organism which differentiate it from simpler types but which are also partially descriptive of all the more complex types. In other words, the traits listed for one type of organism would be found in all of the more complex types, but not in any of the simpler forms. If the great groups of plants are arranged in order of complexity starting with the simplest, we find that, in general, any group will display the principal characteristics of all the groups above it, together with certain new characteristics peculiar to itself. Hence in the Angiospermae we found all the fundamental characteristics of all the lower groups. Such a listing of characteristics affords an excellent over-all view of the increasing complexity of organisms when comparing types which were present early in the period of time encompassing life on earth with those that were present more recently. Now that various groups within the plant kingdom have been covered, we can discuss more readily some of the specific modifications and adaptations which form the basis for our concept of evolution.

The second approach is more general, in that we select an advantageous feature, such as the protection of reproductive parts, and examine the various types of organisms with an attempt to ascertain with what degree of success they have accomplished the task.

INCREASING COMPLEXITY IN THE PLANT KINGDOM

Remember that the characteristics which are listed occur in most organisms within the group but not necessarily in all. Also, some groups have a range of organization from simple to complex.

I. Schizomycetes (bacteria). These are considered to be the most primitive of living plants, and they have certain traits which are characteristic of plants in general:

1. Protoplasmic membranes and cell walls.
2. Growth and cell division.
3. Metabolism.

385

II. Chlorophyta (green algae). Actually, most of the algal groups have the new characteristics enumerated below in addition to the three traits above. The green algae are utilized as the type organism because they are more closely related to the flowering plants.

4. Chlorophyll and associated pigments in chloroplasts, photosynthesis.
5. Multicellular organization, a nucleus in each cell.
6. Sexual reproduction, meiosis, fusion of gametes.
7. Alternation of phases, diploid and haploid.

III. Bryophyta (mosses and allies). Even though these plants are considered to be a side-branch of the plant kingdom, they do indicate a position more advanced than the algae and less complex than the ferns. These are the simplest of the land plants and have the following features:

8. Epidermis with a cuticle and stomata.
9. Multicellular sex organs, antheridia and archegonia.
10. An embryonic stage which is protected by tissues of the preceding generation.

IV. Filicineae (ferns). The additional features found in the ferns are significant for a terrestrial existence:

11. Independent sporophyte.
12. Leaves, stems, and roots as part of the sporophyte.
13. Vascular tissue.

V. Gymnospermae (pines and associated forms). These plants add to the features which are advantageous to existence on land:

14. Heterospory and the associated two types of gametophytes.
15. Very large sporophyte and dependent gametophytes.
16. Pollination.
17. Seeds.

VI. Angiospermae (flowering plants). These plants possess all of the traits mentioned above, plus others which indicate that the angiosperms are truly the most complex plants:

18. Vessels.
19. Ovary, which matures as the fruit.
20. Endosperm.
21. Flower.

The list of fundamental features could be expanded, depending upon the wishes of the individual making a similar list. All of the specific characteristics of the various plant groups were not utilized, nor was every plant group afforded a position in the listing. For example, we could quite logically list "heterospory" under the Lycopsida and then follow with the gymnosperms. However, the principle is the same, and a simplified scheme was utilized.

GENERAL EVOLUTIONARY TRENDS

After the discussion of plant groups in preceding chapters and the listing of specific features of plant groups to indicate evolutionary accumulation or complexity in the foregoing pages, we can now indicate how certain problems of existence were solved (or partially solved) by different plant groups.

Protection of reproductive parts. Sexual reproduction is exceedingly important to an evolutionary process because of the variations which are produced in the offspring. In considering the life cycle of any plant, one discovers that the gametes are the most sensitive, or the least resistant, structures with regard to environmental factors. These sex cells never develop thick walls. To do so would be very disadvantageous (why?), and such plants would soon die out; they would not be able to compete successfully with other plants. The gametes, whether isogametes or egg or sperm, are bounded by a thin membrane but by no other protective structure. As a result, their survival would be enhanced if they were retained within a gametangium (or similar structure) as long as possible before fertilization, or if fertilization took place within such a structure.[8]

I. CHLOROPHYTA [9]

1. *Ulothrix*. This plant is selected as one of the simplest multicellular organisms exhibiting sexual reproduction. Motile isogametes are liberated into the surrounding water. No protection exists prior to and at fertilization, except for the brief period during which the gametes are developing in the gametangium. The isogametes and the resulting zygote are at the mercy of the environment.

2. *Oedogonium*. In this plant one discovers oögamy. Only the sperm are really exposed to the environment as they swim to the egg, which is retained within the wall of the oögonium. Not only is the egg somewhat protected by a cell wall, but it also contains a considerable amount of stored food. As a result, the zygote is adequately nourished as well as protected by the oögonium wall; fertilization occurs within the oögonium.

---

[8] If necessary, the student should review the various plant groups which are discussed in the rest of this section.

[9] Again, the green algae are utilized because they probably gave rise to the complex land plants.

II. Bryophyta

3. The moss plant is one of the simplest in which multicellular sex organs, the antheridia and archegonia, are found. The importance of such sex organs is that the gametes are protected by a layer of cells rather than a single cell wall, as in *Oedogonium*. The sperm are, of course, still liberated and swim to the egg, but the latter remains within its protective jacket of cells. The zygote and resulting embryo are also sheltered for a time.

III. Filicineae

4. The ferns are quite similar to the mosses, except that the base of the archegonium is embedded within the vegetative portion of the gametophyte in the former. The egg is contained within this basal portion, and the additional tissues are undoubtedly beneficial to its chances of survival.

IV. Gymnospermae

5. In pines, the development of ovules and the seed habit resulted in tremendous advantages to the gametes and to the progeny. The gametes are protected by the gametophyte, and the reduced gametophytes are in turn protected by the tissues of the sporophyte. The female gametophyte and its eggs are never really exposed. The male gametophyte, but not the male gamete, is exposed for a short time. The sperm is actually brought to the egg; the male gamete no longer swims to the egg. In addition to this protection of the gametes, the young plant (embryo) is sheltered within the seed. Dormancy also becomes possible with seed production, and this is again an advantageous condition for the new generation.

V. Angiospermae

6. In the flowering plants one finds a situation similar to that in pines, plus the added protective feature of ovules enclosed within ovaries. The gametophytes are further reduced and protected. Many fruits not only afford additional protective layers but also aid in dispersing the seed.

Increased diversity. The simplest plants, the types which were first present on earth, are unicellular and exhibit little diversity.[10] The plants which developed later show increasing diversity, a multicellularity

[10] This is always a debatable point. *Euglena* (of the Euglenophyta) has considerable diversity as compared with *Micrococcus* (of the Schizomycetes), even though both are unicellular. However, our simplified discussion is still valid. We must merely decide where to draw the line in the comparisons. We could just as easily discuss evolution within a group, such as a single phylum or class, as in the broader view of a kingdom.

resulting in specialization and a division of labor. Without such specialization large land plants would not develop. These plants require
supporting tissues and conducting tissues, as well as others. One type
of cell or one type of tissue alone could not possibly be sufficient for
these diverse functions. Compare, for example, the conducting and
supporting cells of the xylem with the food manufacturing cells of
the leaf mesophyll. Elongated cells with thick walls are essential in a
supporting function, whereas such structures would be detrimental to
cells carrying on photosynthesis. Gaseous exchange in the latter, for
one thing, makes it imperative that the cells be thin-walled and that
there be much intercellular space, a condition efficiently handled by
the leaf mesophyll. The most complex plants, then, are multicellular
and, more than that, consist of specialized types of cells which perform
certain functions and not others; the summation of the inter-related
functions of the various tissues is the resultant whole plant. This specialization results in the efficient performance of the various functions
of the plant, including reproduction.

I. CHLOROPHYTA

1. *Chlamydomonas.* This plant is a single-cell type, in which no
great specialization is possible. Relatively few gametes and spores are
produced.

2. *Ulothrix* and *Oedogonium.* These are multicellular plants having
both vegetative and reproductive cells. The plants are larger than
Chlamydomonas, many more gametes and offspring are produced,
and this provides more material for natural selection and evolution.
No longer does one type of cell carry on all functions of the organism.
The sporophyte is unicellular, however.

II. BRYOPHYTA

3. The mosses produce a fairly large multicellular gametophyte and
also a more specialized sporophyte. Both of these structures have localized areas devoted to the production of gametes or spores, providing
large numbers of offspring and the possibility of variations. Also, the
central cells of the gametophyte are slightly modified as conducting
cells. This increases the efficiency of food and water transport, without
which a small size or a water habitat is mandatory.

III. FILICINEAE

4. In ferns the large sporophyte with its vascular tissue and many
spores results in a dispersal of the species to various environments.
Spores are more resistant than gametes and are better able to withstand
the difficulties inherent to dissemination. Even if large gametophytes
with vascular tissue had developed in some groups, they probably

would not have been nearly as successful as those plants in which diversification was emphasized in the sporophyte. Natural selection would undoubtedly favor the sporophyte development.

IV. Gymnospermae

5. In pines the exceedingly large sporophyte results in the production of enormous numbers of easily dispersed spores, and only the microspore (pollen) is exposed. The differentiation of separate male and female gametophytes provides a greater efficiency of gamete formation. The emphasis upon sexual reproduction provides additional material for variations in offspring. A well-developed root system and vascular tissue are also advantageous to the survival of the sporophyte, which in turn protects the gametophytes.

V. Angiospermae

6. The flowering plants provide highly efficient mechanisms of pollination, and sexual reproduction is more certain. The leaf structure is very effective in exposing photosynthetic cells to those factors which are essential to food manufacture. Vascular tissue in these plants is more efficient than in the pines as a result of the development of vessels in the xylem. The angiosperms, thus, are the most successful of plants, and one finds that they inhabit almost every environment of the earth.

Retention of water. This is a problem restricted to land plants. Without some means of water retention, land plants could not exist; water would evaporate, and the individual cells would rapidly die.

I. Bryophyta

1. Moss plants can exist on land because of the cuticle and cuticularized spores which developed. The cuticle greatly retards water loss from the exposed surfaces. The lack of organized vascular tissue and the necessity of water for fertilization (why?) prevented the mosses from developing to any large size.

II. Filicineae

2. The development of vascular tissue, well demonstrated in the ferns, was the big evolutionary step which made possible the existence of large land plants. Although the cuticle retards water loss, it does not stop transpiration completely, especially with the presence of stomata in the epidermis. Diffusion of water (osmosis) through parenchyma-type cells is far too slow to supply above-ground portions of a plant with water, except in the case of small plants such as the mosses.

III. Gymnospermae and Angiospermae

3. These land plants have various modifications and adaptive struc-

tures which make existence possible in very dry areas: thick cuticles, sunken stomata, water storage tissues, reduced leaf surfaces, etc.

Summary

1. Evolution means descent with change and implies that all organisms are more or less related one to another. All organisms are descended from past organisms. This concept is based upon much evidence of various sorts.

2. The vast physical changes occurring during the earth's history have resulted in so many and such radical environmental changes that organic evolution must have occurred for living organisms to have survived.

3. The discovery of fossils, traces of former living organisms, emphasizes the general sequence of evolutionary change. The older fossils are basically of much more simple structure than are the more recent fossils or the dominant organisms of the present.

4. The wide distribution of some plants, the restricted distribution of others, and the different kinds of plants growing in similar environments which are widely separated—all indicate that variations are haphazard phenomena which are acted upon selectively by the environment.

5. Basic similarities and differences between plant groups are found by a study of embryological development and chemical patterns in living organisms. Recently, genetical studies have shown that new species may arise as hybrids between existing species or as a result of the multiplication of the original basic chromosome number.

6. Lamarck's ideas concerning evolution were based upon the inheritance of characteristics which were gained or lost by use or disuse. Darwin's observations led him to suggest that of the variants which arose, those that survived were the ones best fitted to the environment. This did not explain the source of variations. De Vries suggested that variations arose as sudden unpredictable changes in existing genes. Biologists basically agree that mutations bring about changes and that these changes, and variations in general, are perpetuated and expanded by sexual reproduction. The complex plants and animals of the present are descended from much simpler organisms which existed ages ago, some of which may still exist.

7. Optimum conditions for evolution appear to be small, semi-isolated populations. Such populations are isolated enough to develop independently and differently and yet close enough for occasional interbreeding to occur.

8. In examining the various groups of the plant kingdom, one is

impressed with the increasing complexity of those plants in the higher groups, which are of relatively recent origin, as compared to those plants of ancient origin. Three evolutionary trends of great importance, which have reached their highest development in the flowering plants, are protection of reproductive parts, diversity, and retention of water.

REVIEW TOPICS AND QUESTIONS

1. Discuss what is meant by the term "evolution." Indicate at least five kinds of evidence supporting the concept of evolution.
2. Compare Lamarckian and Darwinian evolution. Discuss the kind of evidence which tends to refute some of the ideas of Lamarck. What suggestions by Lamarck are acceptable to our modern concept of evolution?
3. What was the contribution of de Vries to the concept of evolution? In what way did his ideas differ from those of Darwin? In what ways did de Vries agree with Darwin?
4. What is meant by "retrogressive evolution"? Give an example.
5. Discuss why semi-isolated, but not completely isolated, populations afford optimum conditions for evolution. What is the significance of "isolation"?
6. Why is "plant breeding" sometimes called "man-made evolution"?
7. Compile a descriptive list showing how the haploid spores, produced as a result of meiosis, are afforded greater and greater protection with the increasing complexity of plant groups. Starting with the simplest, list each plant group and describe the structures which afford protection to the spores.
8. Discuss the causes of evolution.
9. What are fossils? Describe the various kinds of fossils. Why is the fossil record incomplete? (In other words, why are some groups not found as fossils? Why isn't the record of ancient relationships more exact? Why aren't we certain, from examining fossils, which organisms are descended from which primitive ones?)
10. What is the significance of sexual reproduction as far as evolution is concerned?
11. Since the bacteria are considered to be extremely primitive organisms, why have they not been replaced by more complex groups?
12. Bearing in mind the general similarities among the life cycles of mosses, ferns, and flowering plants, describe (with the aid of word diagrams, labeled diagrams, or general descriptions) the evolutionary trends shown in the following: (a) relative sizes of the gametophyte and sporophyte phases, (b) dependence and independence of the two phases, and (c) dependence of the sexual process on water.

SUGGESTED READINGS

Blum, H. *Time's Arrow and Evolution*. Princeton: Princeton Univ. Press, 1951.

Crow, J. F. "Ionizing Radiation and Evolution," *Scientific American,* 201 (September 1959), 138–160.

Dobzhanski, T. "The Genetic Basis of Evolution," *Scientific American,* 182 (January 1950), 32–41.

———. "The Present Evolution of Man," *Scientific American,* 203 (September 1960), 206–217.

Dodson, E. O. *Evolution, Process and Product.* New York: Reinhold, 1960.

Eiseley, L. C. "Charles Darwin," *Scientific American,* 194 (February 1956), 62–72.

Huxley, J. *Evolution in Action.* New York: New American Library, 1957.

Janssen, R. E. "The Beginnings of Coal," *Scientific American,* 179 (July 1948), 46–51.

Kettlewell, H. B. D. "Darwin's Missing Evidence," *Scientific American,* 200 (March 1959), 48–53.

Lack, D. "Darwin's Finches," *Scientific American,* 188 (April 1953), 66–72.

Lessing, L. P. "Coal," *Scientific American,* 193 (July 1955), 58–67.

Muller, H. J. "Radiation and Human Mutation," *Scientific American,* 193 (November 1955), 58–68.

Ryan, F. J. "Evolution Observed," *Scientific American,* 189 (October 1953), 78–83.

Simpson, G. G. *The Meaning of Evolution.* New Haven: Yale, 1949.

Shull, A. F. *Evolution.* New York: McGraw-Hill, 1951.

Stebbins, G. L. *Variation and Evolution in Plants.* New York: Columbia, 1950.

———. "Cataclysmic Evolution," *Scientific American,* 184 (April 1951), 54–59.

CHAPTER 28 ·

Growth

and Flowering

28.1 Growth

The term "growth" refers to two basic factors of a plant's development: (1) an increase in the number of cells as a result of cell division, and (2) an enlargement and maturation of existing cells accompanied by an increase of cellular components. No sharp distinction exists between these phases of growth, but to consider them separately is useful. Remember that when a cell divides, even if the volume of the two resultant cells does not total more than that of the original, some increase in cellular components always occurs. The new cell wall which forms and the duplicated chromosomes which are produced during cell division are examples of additional components which were not present in the original cell. However, the greatest increase of cell material occurs during the enlargement and maturation of the cell.

Meristematic tissues, cell division, and general areas of cell enlargement have already been discussed in previous chapters. In those discussions growth was considered on the basis of an increased length and, sometimes, diameter of the plant as a result of tissue development. Also stated was that for growth to occur, various factors are required: food, minerals, water, a suitable temperature, and usually oxygen. In addition to these, investigations over the last 40 to 60 years have shown that growth regulators are also necessary.

28.2 Growth regulators

The term **growth regulators** is used in referring to those organic compounds, other than nutrients, present in minute quantities, which promote, inhibit, or otherwise modify growth, development, or differentiation of plants. A **hormone** is a growth regulator which is produced in one part of the organism and elicits a response at some other location in that organism. In other words the hormone, which is essential for growth, is produced in one area, while the actual growth response occurs elsewhere in that plant. In animals hormones are produced in and secreted from the discrete glandular [1] structures, but such glands are not present in plants.

An important class of plant growth hormones are called **auxins,** and the principal naturally-occurring one which has been extracted from plant material is **indolyl-3-acetic acid** (indoleacetic acid). All auxins are basically similar, and they are all organic acids. Although not all have been examined, a sufficiently great variety of plants have been found to contain auxins so that botanists agree that auxins are probably universally present, with the principal centers of auxin synthesis being apical meristems, buds, young leaves, and young flowers.

One of the characteristics of hormones is that they exert regulatory effects upon metabolism when present in only minute quantities. This makes very difficult the extraction of sufficient material for chemical analyses, and the existence of various hormones is frequently inferred from the occurrence of various physiological reactions rather than from the isolation of a specific compound. Much more information has been gathered with regard to auxins than with regard to other hormones, and the former will be discussed in some detail in the next section.

If plant tissues are cut, various parenchyma cells at the site of injury usually become meristematic, forming a cork cambium and eventually cork. If the freshly-cut tissue is immediately rinsed with water, very few cell divisions occur. If some tissue is removed, ground into a paste, and smeared onto the rinsed (cut) surface, cell divisions do occur. In at least one case, a compound called **traumatic acid,** which acts like a **wound hormone,** has been extracted. Several such wound hormones may exist, but additional investigation is necessary to clarify the situation.

In recent years **kinins** and **gibberellins** have been undergoing considerable investigations as additional plant growth regulators. The former, of which **kinetin** has been identified, appear to be general growth regulators. Kinins have been obtained from yeast, coconut milk, apple fruit extracts, and many other plant materials. They may be important in maintaining protein contents in the plant. The gibberellins were first observed in connection with the bakanae disease of rice in Japan. *Gibberella fujikuroi,* the causal fungus, produces sev-

[1] A gland is any organ of secretion, such as the adrenal, thyroid, and pituitary glands in humans.

eral gibberellins, of which the most familiar is **gibberellic acid.** The best-known effect of gibberellin is that of increasing the elongation of stems. In fact, the Japanese investigators noted that diseased seedlings grew unusually tall before they died and referred to such as "foolish seedlings" (bakanae). In recent years gibberellins have been isolated from various plant parts, and evidence is accumulating that they are, indeed, naturally-occurring plant regulators. Investigations indicate that the gibberellins have a multiplicity of effects on flowering, germination, and dormancy. These various facets will be discussed in subsequent sections.

28.3 Auxins

As is true so frequently, the presence of a growth factor or a hormone was postulated before auxin was isolated, just as the vitamins in the human diet were known to be essential before any of them had been isolated. The presence of such materials is inferred from the physiological reactions which occur in the presence, or absence, of certain tissues or extracts. Darwin, as early as 1880, had shown that seedlings bent toward the light only if the tips were exposed and that such bending resulted from greater growth on the non-illuminated side of the stalk. He exposed grass seedlings to a unilateral source of light and noted that they curved toward the light source. When he covered the tip of the seedlings with lightproof caps, no bending took place. The control seedlings, those without coverings, responded as before (Figure 28-1). This indicated that some influence must be transmitted from the tip downward. Although no further explanations were forthcoming until 1910 and later, in the light of our *present* understanding of hormones the work of Darwin would imply the presence of a hormone—a material produced in the tip of the seedling which elicits a response (curvature, or differential elongation) in the stem below. Such a material would fit well into our present definition of a hormone.

Boysen-Jensen's investigations (1910–1913) stimulated other botanists to explore further this field of plant curvature toward a source of light.[2] He decapitated the seedling, placed a bit of gelatin on the stump, replaced the tip on the gelatin, and found that curvature toward light ensued just as with intact seedlings (Figure 28-2). The substance diffused from the tip through the gelatin to the stump. If the tip is not replaced, curvature does not result.

---

[2] The layman "explains" (?) the bending of a plant toward a source of light by stating that the plant is seeking the light which it requires for food manufacture (photosynthesis). This is, of course, not an explanation. No plant consciously seeks anything.

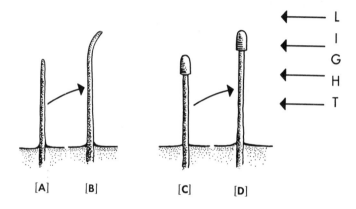

Figure 28-1. Darwin's experiment. **A, B**: Control seedlings bend toward a light source. **C, D**: Seedlings with lightproof caps over the tips do not bend.

Figure 28-2. Boysen-Jensen's experiment. **A, B**: Control seedlings bend toward a light source. **C, D**: Seedlings decapitated, gelatin placed on the stump, the tip replaced. The treated seedlings also bend.

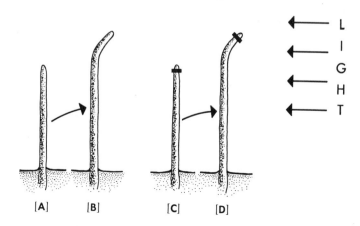

Most of the information about plant hormones has been obtained from experiments using the coleoptile of grasses, chiefly oats (*Avena*). The **coleoptile** consists of a leaf-like, cylindrical structure with a conical top, which encloses the developing leaves of the germinating seed. Early in the development of the seedling, the parenchyma cells of the coleoptile stop dividing, and all subsequent growth is by cell elongation. The coleoptile serves as an excellent organ for the study of the cell enlargement phase of growth.

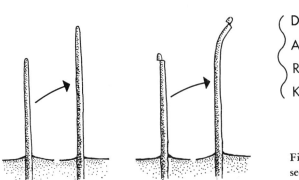

[A]   [B]   [C]   [D]

Figure 28-3. Paal's experiment. **A, B:** Control seedlings grow but do not bend in the dark. **C, D:** Seedlings decapitated and tips replaced eccentrically. Such seedlings bend in the dark, away from the side upon which the tip is placed.

Paal (1918) demonstrated that if a freshly-severed coleoptile tip is replaced on the stump eccentrically, more growth results on that side, even though this is done without illumination (Figure 28-3). Eventually Went showed in 1928 that a growth substance diffused into agar [3] if excised tips are placed thereon for a short time. He then cut the agar into small blocks which, when placed eccentrically on decapitated coleoptiles, caused curvatures of the coleoptiles; they could be used in place of the severed tips. Controls, utilizing plain agar, elicited no response (Figure 28-4). The degree of curvature was found to be proportional, within limits, to the concentration of the hormone in the agar blocks. This is still the basis for the method of determining the concentration of these growth substances in tissues. No chemical test is sensitive enough to determine the presence of plant growth hormones in the minute amounts [4] which elicit responses. Thus the biological techniques must be utilized. Actually, not until 1931 was this plant growth hormone isolated and found to be indolyl-3-acetic acid.

28.4   Phototropism

The investigations mentioned in the previous section really resulted because botanists were curious as to why a plant bent toward a source

[3] Agar is a polysaccharide with a gelatin-like consistency when dissolved in hot water and allow to cool.

[4] It has been calculated that 1 mg. of auxin is capable of bringing about a 10-degree curvature in 50 million decapitated coleoptiles. This number would make a row of coleoptiles, standing closely side by side, nearly 50 miles in length. A similar 10-degree curvature in one coleoptile would be brought about by approximately 5×10^{-11} gm.

of light. The cells on the non-illuminated side were soon shown to elongate more than those on the illuminated side. Auxins stimulate such elongations. By illuminating excised tips from one side, a greater concentration of auxin was found to accumulate in agar beneath the non-illuminated side of the tip. This, then, was the explanation for stem curvature toward a source of light; the higher concentration of auxin on the darker side stimulated greater elongation. Growth responses resulting from external stimuli are termed **tropisms.** Since the stimulus in this case is light, the term used is **phototropism** (photo = light). Considerable evidence supports the suggestion that light stimulates a transverse, or horizontal, diffusion of auxin toward the darker side. This results in a higher concentration of auxin on the one side and greater elongation of the cells on that side.

28.5 Geotropism

For a great many years, biologists had observed that when a plant is placed in a horizontal position, the stem curves upwardly, the shoot eventually resuming its normal upright position. Once phototropism was explained on the basis of auxin concentrations, **geotropism,** the growth response due to gravitational stimulus, was soon shown to be due to a similar asymmetric distribution of auxins in the plant. Consid-

Figure 28-4. Went's experiment. A: Coleoptile tips are placed on agar, and later small blocks of this agar are placed on one side of cut coleoptiles; bending of the coleoptiles results. B: Plain agar blocks do not elicit a bending response.

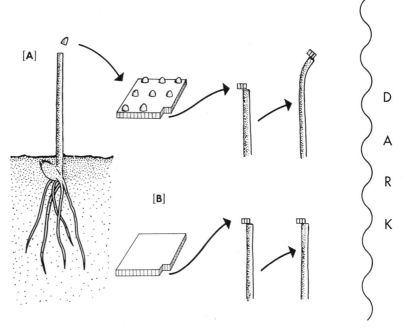

D

A

R

K

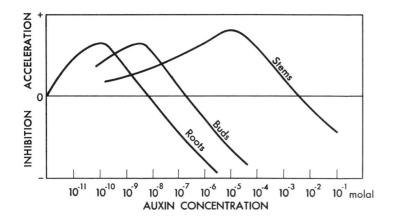

Figure 28-5. The inhibition and growth promotion of different organs as a function of auxin concentration. (From K. V. Thimann, *The Action of Hormones in Plants and Invertebrates.* New York: Academic Press Inc., 1952.)

erably more auxin accumulates in the lower side as compared with the upper side of a coleoptile which has been placed in a horizontal position. This stimulates a greater elongation of those cells on the lower side, and the coleoptile tends to grow upwardly to an erect position.

The foregoing explanation is satisfactory in explaining the negatively geotropic response of shoots; it is not sufficient for an understanding of the positively geotropic response of roots in bending toward the source of stimulus (down, in this case). Fortunately, the work of Thimann (Figure 28-5) demonstrated that shoots are accelerated in their growth by concentrations of auxin which inhibit root growth. Auxins accumulate in the underside of both roots and shoots placed in a horizontal position. While this induces a more rapid growth of the underside of stems, the concentration of auxin is such as to inhibit growth of the underside of roots. As a result, stems tend to grow up and roots tend to grow down, both as a result of asymmetric distribution of auxin.

28.6 Gibberellins

These compounds are more complex than the auxins. Various of the gibberellins have been found in diverse plant groups, including angiosperms, gymnosperms, ferns, and *Fucus* (one of the brown algae, Phaeophyta), and they are probably of universal occurrence.

Gibberellin will not cause curvature in the *Avena* coleoptile as auxin will. Lateral transport of the former occurs very rapidly, and the compound is rather uniformly distributed in the coleoptile; elongation, but not curvature, will result. This is one way of differentiating auxins from gibberellins. The basic test for the latter utilizes dwarf maize (corn). These plants are very stunted in growth as compared with normal maize plants. Increasing concentrations of gibberellin applied to the dwarf maize result in increasing growth responses as a result of cell enlargements and division; $\frac{1}{1000}$ of a microgram (a microgram = one millionth of a gram) of gibberellin can be detected in this manner. These maize plants do not respond to auxin treatments.

Gibberellins and auxins frequently bring about similar responses in plants. These and other growth regulator responses will be discussed in subsequent sections.

28.7 Kinetin

This material is more complex than the auxins but not as complex as the gibberellins. Not too much is known about kinetin's role in plant functions, since the study of this compound is really just beginning. It has been found in coconut milk and in various fruits, but its actual distribution in plants is yet to be clarified.

Kinetin promotes cell expansion in some tissues but inhibits such growth in others. It has no effect on dwarf maize or on coleoptile curvature. The differentiating test for kinetin-like compounds consists of culturing tobacco pith (parenchyma) cells in a nutrient solution. If kinetin and auxin are added, a growth response is evidenced; no response occurs with kinetin, auxin, or gibberellin alone. The initiation of buds or roots from a callus derived from tobacco pith can be obtained by regulating the ratio of auxin to kinetin.

If an excised leaf is floated on water plus kinetin, it stays green, succulent, and healthy. Similarly treated leaves, but without kinetin, shrivel and die. We can even treat one portion of a leaf with kinetin and cause it to remain green and healthy, while the other portion withers and dies. This peculiar response to kinetin is called the Richmond-Lang effect. If amino acids are added to the water in which treated leaves are floating, these amino acids tend to accumulate only in the treated portion of the leaves. Protein synthesis appears to be increased by kinetin treatment, and, at the same time, protein degeneration is decreased.

28.8 Additional effects attributed to growth regulators

Most of the discussion thus far has concerned the influence of auxin on cell elongation, and this is what was emphasized in the early work with plant growth regulators; existing cells were stimulated to increased enlargement when treated with indolylacetic acid. Very rapidly, however, great ramifications with regard to processes influenced by auxin and gibberellin became evident. In addition to this, many chemicals which do not occur in plants have been found to act as

401 ॐ

growth regulators. As a result, commercial preparations of plant growth regulators frequently are not naturally-occurring products but compounds which are more active or which may be obtained more readily and with less expense than the naturally-occurring auxins or gibberellins.

GROWTH INHIBITION

Almost everyone knows that removing the terminal bud of a shoot results in a bushier plant. This is commonly done with such garden flowers as chrysanthemums. The bushier appearance results from the growth of lateral buds which are normally inhibited by the presence of a terminal bud. This influence of a terminal bud in suppressing the growth of lateral buds is termed **apical dominance.** If the excised terminal bud is replaced by agar blocks containing auxin, the lateral buds will not develop. If the auxin-containing blocks are removed, the dormant axillary buds start to grow; controls of plain agar do not inhibit such growth. Although the mechanism of lateral bud inhibition is not clear, auxin produced in the terminal bud has been proved to be largely responsible. However, both gibberellin and kinetin also influence the development of lateral buds, auxin appearing to function almost like an on-off switch. If the concentration of auxin is above a certain amount, the lateral buds do not grow. If the concentration is below this amount, kinetin will produce a stimulation of the laterals. Gibberellin seems to stimulate only those buds which are about ready to grow.

Auxin has also been shown to be involved in preventing the separation of abscission layers in the petioles of leaves, flowers, and fruits. Normally when a leaf blade is removed, petiole abscission soon follows, probably as a result of diminished auxin supply (usually available from the blade). If auxin is applied to the cut petiole, abscission is considerably delayed. Synthetic auxins, such as naphthaleneacetic acid, are used in dusts or sprays to delay the premature drop of certain fruits, especially apples. Pre-harvest drop of apples often causes large losses to growers, because the crew of pickers cannot work around the orchard rapidly enough or because the apples fall before they are sufficiently ripe. The McIntosh variety of apple is especially susceptible to premature fruit drop and is one in which auxin spray programs are very important.

PARTHENOCARPY

The development of fruits from unpollinated flowers occasionally occurs, as in banana, navel orange, seedless grape, and seedless grapefruits. Such **parthenocarpic** fruit can be produced in some plants by treating the pistils with auxins, usually indolebutyric acid, or gibberellins. Although edible seedless fruit have been produced in this manner in strawberry (*Fragaria* sp.), eggplant (*Solanum melongena* var. *esculentum*), cucumber (*Cucumis sativus*), and squash (*Cucurbita maxima*), the most satisfactory results have been obtained with tomato (*Lycopersicon esculentum*). Under natural conditions most fruits are produced by the development of the ovary brought about by auxin introduced from the pollen or by auxin synthesized in the ovary as a result of a stimulus introduced from the pollen. Treatment of flowers with growth regulators merely provides a supply of these materials without the presence of pollen.

ROOT INITIATION

In many kinds of plants, stems, leaves, and even roots may be severed from the parent plant and used for propagation. This vegetative propagation by the use of cuttings is frequently very useful in perpetuating desirable characteristics, such as disease resistance, quality, yield, and vigor. The offspring are identical with the parent plant; no possibility exists of genetic change, because sexual reproduction (gamete fusion) is not involved. Also, by using cuttings, much more rapid growth is obtained than by using seed; a saving of time from two to four years in obtaining a mature plant may be realized. This is quite significant to the nurseryman and gardener.

Treatment of stem, leaf, and root cuttings with any one of several plant growth substances frequently results in a stimulation of root formation. Auxin-treated cuttings root more rapidly and have a greater profusion of roots than the untreated. Dipping cuttings into dusts or solutions of such substances as indolebutyric and naphthaleneacetic acids, however, does not necessarily ensure the production of roots. Auxin is only one of several factors which may be limiting the process, and careful attention must be given to water, light, temperature, humidity, and the general condition of the cuttings. Also, some kinds of plants are difficult to root and do not respond to hormone treatments. Gibberellin generally inhibits the formation of adventitious roots.

CELL DIVISION

Recent evidence indicates that regulators are involved in cell division also. Auxin and gibberellin have been shown to stimulate cell division, and kinetin has a similar effect on the cells of some tissues. The influx of cambial activity during the spring appears to be due to the increasing production of auxin by terminal meristems, buds, and

403

developing leaves, all of which show increased activity at this time of year. Gibberellins may also influence cambial activity.

WEED CONTROL

As work with growth regulators progressed, some of the naturally-occurring substances were synthesized in the laboratory, and eventually new compounds with similar properties were synthesized. The latter are not found in plants, but may be cheaper, more effective, or easier to manufacture or use. By this time, scientists had found that whereas low concentrations of some of these compounds would stimulate growth, larger amounts were toxic and killed the plant. Besides the effects already noted, these materials had great influences on cellular metabolism, high concentrations appearing to be disruptive of general metabolism.

Some of the synthetic growth regulators affected certain types of plants more than others, thus suggesting the possibility that weeds might be eradicated by *selective* sprays. Chemical weed-killers had been in use for many years, but these were compounds [5] which generally killed all vegetation; they were directly toxic to the cells with which they came in contact. Differential killing with these materials is basically a result of differences in the permeability of the cuticle; if the material penetrates to the cell, the cell is destroyed. Herbicidal plant regulators, on the other hand, are highly effective at concentrations which do not directly destroy cells with which they come in contact. The killing appears to be due to greatly increased respiration, an acceleration of cell enlargement, and a disruption of phloem tissue as a result of excessive development of parenchyma in the phloem region. These hormone herbicides are selective: many broad-leaved plants (dicotyledons) are extremely susceptible, while narrow-leaved monocotyledonous plants are highly resistant. This selectiveness has not yet been explained.

Fortunately, most of the common weeds are broad-leaved. This makes possible the use of something like 2,4-D (2,4-dichlorophenoxyacetic acid) to destroy weeds without injuring grasses. Such regulators are transported throughout the plant and are very effective in eradicating plants like dandelion (*Taraxacum officinale*) and morning-glory (*Ipomoea purpurea*) which have extensive root-storage systems. The chemical weed-killers mentioned in the previous paragraph would destroy the above-ground portions, but sprouts would subsequently

[5] Some of these all-purpose vegetation-destroying chemicals are still used in special cases: ferrous sulfate, sulfuric acid, arsenical preparations, aromatic fractions of fuel oils, etc.

emerge from the undestroyed roots. The weed-killing activities of materials like 2,4-D have nothing to do with their auxin-like properties but are probably secondary effects. Not all auxins can be used as weed-killers; indolylacetic acid and indolylbutyric acid, for example, are not effective.

An interesting note is that this practical application of one phase of botanical research was totally unexpected. No one could have guessed that an investigation concerned originally with phototropism would eventually lead into the extremely important field of weed control. Because certain investigators were interested in a fundamental plant phenomenon, the practical problem of killing weeds is much nearer a solution. This is really the way in which many practical problems become solved; fundamental research with the general aim of increasing knowledge is always the foundation for the solution of practical problems.

28.9 Flowering

In previous chapters the general structure, growth, and development of the flowering plant was discussed. All of these plants undergo a period of vegetative development before flowers are produced, the length of this period varying greatly. Some trees may grow for years before any flowers develop, whereas flowers appear on some annual herbs in a few weeks from the time of seed germination. Since about 1920, the stimulus which initiates flowering has been the subject of considerable investigation and speculation. About this time Garner and Allard began publishing the results of their investigations, which demonstrated that flower production was influenced by day length. Subsequently, other investigators added temperature as another environmental factor which affected flowering.

PHOTOPERIODISM

Flowering plants can conveniently be arranged in three general groups (Table 28-1) with regard to the duration of the light period (**photoperiod**) required for flowering: (1) "long-day" plants, which will flower only if exposed to day-lengths longer than a critical amount, (2) "short-day" plants, which will flower only if the duration of the light period is shorter than a critical length, and (3) "day-neutral" plants, which appear to be unaffected by day-length and flower readily over a wide range of photoperiods. Varietal differences exist with regard to the critical day-length, and a "short-day" species may flower if the light exposure is less than 13 hours or 15 hours or 17 hours, depending upon the variety used. This is true, for example, in soybean (*Glycine soja*): the Biloxi variety flowers if the day-length is less than 13 hours and remains vegetative if the day-length is prolonged beyond this amount; for the Peking variety the critical period is 15 hours, and it is 17 hours for the Mandarin variety. All of these soybean varieties will flower at about the same time if the day-length is 12 hours or less. Under these conditions, the duration of light is less than the critical period for all of the varieties. Differences in flowering would be noticeable only when the day-lengths are prolonged.

Table 28-1. Examples of Well-Known Plant Species which Are Short-Day, Long-Day, or Day-Neutral with Regard to Their Flowering Behavior

SPECIES	COMMON NAME	CRITICAL DAY-LENGTH (Hours)
Short-Day Plants *		
Xanthium pennsylvanicum	Cocklebur	15 to 15.5
Glycine soja var. Biloxi	Soybean	14 to 16
Cosmos sulphureus var. Klondike	Cosmos	12 to 13
Nicotiana tabacum var. Maryland Mammoth	Tobacco	13 to 14
Chrysanthemum indicum var. Queen Mary	Chrysanthemum	14 to 14.5
Euphorbia pulcherrima	Poinsettia	12 to 12.5
Long-Day Plants †		
Anethum graveolens	Dill	11 to 14
Hyoscyamus niger (annual variety)	Henbane	10 to 11 (22°C.)
Spinacea oleracea	Spinach	13 to 14
Hibiscus syriacus	Rose Mallow	12 to 13
Day-Neutral Plants ‡		
Lycopersicon esculentum	Tomato	
Zea mays	Corn	
Fagopyrum esculentum	Buckwheat	
Antirrhinum majus	Snapdragon	
Nicotiana tabacum var. Java, etc.	Tobacco (most varieties)	
Capsicum annuum	Chili Pepper	
Cucumis sativus	Cucumber	

* Short-day plants flower only when the illumination is shorter than the critical day-length.
† Long-day plants flower only when the illumination exceeds the critical day-length.
‡ Day-neutral plants flower under a wide range of day-lengths.

Source: James Bonner and Arthur W. Galston, *Principles of Plant Physiology* (San Francisco: W. H. Freeman and Co., 1952), by permission of the publisher.

Another complicating factor with regard to flowering is that both "short-day" and "long-day" plants may flower when exposed to a 12-hour photoperiod. This appears to be rather strange but is readily explained. The critical day-length of most "short-day" plants is about 14 hours, while it is approximately 10 hours for "long-day" plants. Thus, a 12-hour day-length is less than the critical for the one group and more than the critical for the other group, and both flower. Obviously, then, "short-day" and "long-day," when used in reference to flowering, do not imply a particular length of time. The terms refer to the fact that flowering occurs if the photoperiod is shorter or longer than a critical amount. The number of photoperiodic cycles required to induce flowering differs from one species to another and frequently from one variety to another within a species. In a few types, one or two exposures to the correct photoperiod is sufficient to induce some flowering, although a greater number of flower primordia will be initiated with a greater number of photoperiodic induction cycles.

Gibberellin treatment can substitute for the photoperiodic stimulus required of many long-day plants which form rosettes. Plants like carrot, cabbage, and henbane (*Hyoscyamus*) produce a whorl of leaves (a rosette), and then the flower stalk emerges from the center after an appropriate stimulus. The flowering response to gibberellin treatment may be an indirect effect.

Although photosynthesis and the resultant accumulation of food reserves are essential to flowering, the photoperiodic stimulus which brings about the initiation of flower primordia does not function through the photosynthetic process. The light intensity which is sufficient to produce flowering may be so low as to be unimportant photosynthetically. Also, while red wave-lengths are very effective, blue wave-lengths have the least influence on flowering. Besides, "short-day" plants can be prevented from flowering by prolonging the day-length. The same treatment would increase the amount of photosynthetic material produced by these plants.

As Hamner first pointed out, the terms "short-day" and "long-day" are somewhat misleading.[6] He found that if *Xanthium* (cocklebur, a "short-day" plant) is exposed to short photoperiods, flowering is inhibited when the *dark* period is interrupted by a brief flash of light. Figure 28-6 represents the situation as it occurs in *Xanthium*. Plants in Group B receive the same total amount of light and dark exposure as the plants in Group A, but those in B do not flower as a result of the interruption of the dark period. If the flash of light (actually a five-minute flash is sufficient) occurs near the beginning or near the end of the dark period, as in groups C and D, flowering is reduced but not inhibited. Even when the dark period is increased to 12 hours, flowering is inhibited by a brief flash of light. These and similar results have indicated that the dark period is very important. Thus, although the terms "short-day" and "long-day" are so well established

[6] For this reason the two terms have always been used within quotation marks.

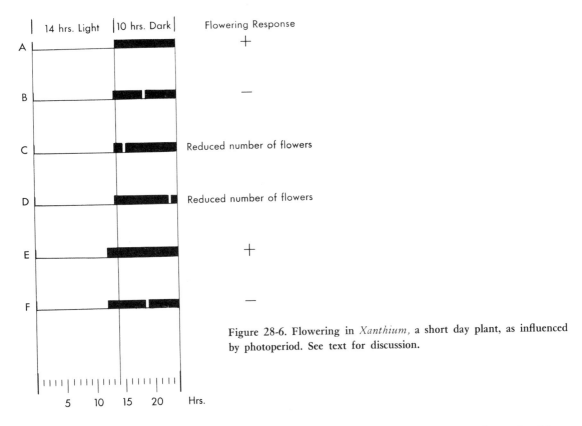

Figure 28-6. Flowering in *Xanthium,* a short day plant, as influenced by photoperiod. See text for discussion.

in the literature that they will undoubtedly be retained, we should re-examine their meanings and re-define them. For a "short-day" plant to flower, the *continuous* dark period must exceed a certain length; in the case of a "long-day" plant the longest dark period must be shorter than a critical length. Because our 24-hour days include periods of light and dark as the sun rises and sets, a "short-day" plant flowers when undergoing short days and long nights.[7] We must merely remember that both the light and dark periods are important.

The geographic distribution of plants is governed in part by their photoperiodic responses. Since the length of the daylight period increasingly varies from season to season in latitudes increasingly north or south of the equator, "short-day" plants cannot compete too well beyond 50° latitude, because the growing season in such regions is restricted to the time of year during which long days prevail. Also, sexual reproduction of plants requiring longer than a 13-hour light

<hr>

[7] Some botanists have suggested using "long-night" rather than "short-day" and "short-night" instead of "long-day." This is probably more logical. In either case the understanding of photoperiodism, rather than the peculiar terminology, is important.

exposure cannot be accomplished in the tropics. The "day-neutral" group of plants can grow in either locality. In the temperate zones all three groups of plants flourish because of the varying day lengths, but they flower during different seasons. In general the "long-day" plants bloom in late spring or early summer, while the "short-day" species bloom in early spring, late summer, or early autumn. Of the latter group, those which grow rather rapidly and can withstand chilly weather will bloom early; the majority, however, tend to bloom during the latter portion of the growing season.

THE TEMPERATURE FACTOR

Recent investigations have demonstrated that temperature influences flowering in some kinds of plants. Most biennials will flower only after exposure to relatively low temperatures, the condition which exists between their two seasons of growth. During the first season, growth is normally vegetative. After over-wintering, these plants produce flower-stalks and eventually seeds. For example, celery (*Apium grave-oleus*) remains vegetative at 16°–21°C. If the plants are exposed to temperatures of 5°–16°C. for ten to fifteen days, flowers and seeds will be produced. Thus, this biennial can be converted to an annual by manipulating the environment. Such induction of flowering by low-temperature treatment of seeds or plants is called **vernalization.** Occasionally, weather conditions are such that late cold spells in the spring may cause celery to go to seed during its first season of growth. This is a loss as far as the farmer is concerned, since he is interested in the stalks (petioles) and not in the seed. Gibberellin treatment can substitute for the cold-temperature stimulus in rosetted plants.

The White Boston variety of lettuce (*Lactuca sativa*) is stimulated to flower by relatively high temperatures. If the temperature remains below 15°C., heads, but no flowers, will be produced; at 16°–27°C., no heads will be produced, and the plants will flower rapidly.

Night temperature, especially, appears to have an influence in reinforcing the effect of the photoperiod. In general, the number of flower primordia increase if the night temperature during photoperiodic induction is high rather than low.

28.10 Flowering hormone

Most botanists are convinced that flower initiation is a result of a hormonal influence, and the tentative name **florigen** has been assigned to this unknown material. Even though the hormone has not been isolated, a vast amount of evidence that it exists has been gathered.

Albeit the evidence is somewhat indirect, this situation was also true of the vitamins before they were isolated.

The young, fully-expanded leaves are the structures which perceive the photoperiodic stimulus, which is then transmitted to the growing point. This was demonstrated by exposing the buds to one photoperiod and the leaves to another. Flowering resulted only when the leaves were exposed to the correct light duration. In some plants, when one branch is exposed to an induction period, flowering occurs throughout the plant, indicating that some material was transmitted from the one branch to the rest of the plant. The stimulus is also transmitted through a graft union. These data all imply the presence of a hormone—a material produced in one part of the organism (i.e., the leaves) and which elicits a response in other parts (i.e., the meristems). In 1961 came a report that florigen had been isolated; these results are still preliminary, but the hormone will most assuredly be isolated some day. The difficulty probably arises from the fact that the material is used up during the flowering process and from the probability that extremely minute amounts are effective.

In spite of the fact that "short-day" and "long-day" plants flower under differing photoperiods, the hormone responsible for flower initiation is in all likelihood the same in these two groups of plants. If a "short-day" variety is grafted to a "long-day" variety, flowering can be initiated in both plants under either type of photoperiod. The hormone must be the same, although the internal mechanism which utilizes this material probably differs substantially.

Further investigations with regard to florigen promise to be of tremendous value. A future where man can govern whether or not a given plant will flower is not too inconceivable. In fact, this can be done with many plants at the present time. For example, chrysanthemums normally bloom in the fall, as do many "short-day" plants. They can be made to bloom in mid-summer by covering the plants during the afternoon or morning, thus shortening the days and lengthening the nights. With florigen and "anti-florigen" compounds of the future, the same effect may be obtained by the use of economical sprays.

28.11 Phytochrome

Recent investigations have shown that inhibition of flowering, by interrupting the dark period in "short-day" plants, can be caused by red light of a wave length of 660 millimicrons (actually orange-red in color). This effect of red light can be counteracted by exposure to far red light of a wave length of 740 millimicrons. This is called the Red-Far Red reversible photo-reaction. The fact was obvious to investigators that some kind of a pigment must be involved, since light energy cannot be effective unless it is first absorbed. (A substance which absorbs visible light is a pigment.) In 1959 Borthwick and Hendricks finally demonstrated the presence of phytochrome.

Phytochrome appears to be a protein with a chromophore, or colored group. It occurs in two possible forms. P_R is the form of phytochrome which absorbs red light (660 millimicrons), and P_{FR} is the form which absorbs far red light (740 millimicrons). These forms are readily interconverted:

$$P_R \underset{740\,m\mu}{\overset{660\,m\mu}{\rightleftarrows}} P_{FR}$$

When P_R is exposed to red light, it is converted to P_{FR}; when P_{FR} is exposed to far red light, it is converted to P_R. In the dark a slow change from P_{FR} to P_R takes place. At least one of these forms is active. In cocklebur, and probably most short-day plants, flowering cannot occur unless P_R is present, and this is formed during the dark period. In long-day plants phytochrome has to be in the far-red-absorbing form.

We now can suggest an explanation for the results obtained with *Xanthium* when the dark period is interrupted with a flash of light (Figure 28-6). At the end of the light period, the phytochrome is in the far-red-absorbing form, due to the wave lengths of sunlight. Then follows a slow conversion of P_{FR} to the red-absorbing form during the subsequent dark period. P_R stimulates the formation of a flowering substance (FS, probably florigen), and, when enough FS has been produced, flowering is initiated. If the dark period is interrupted with red light, P_R is forced back to the P_{FR} form. If the exposure to red light occurs early in the dark period, sufficient dark period still remains to build up some P_R and FS; flowering will be reduced but not inhibited. If the exposure is near the end of the dark period, enough of the flowering substance has already been formed to provide for some flowering; FS is not affected by light. Figure 28-7 represents the interconversions of phytochromes and the resultant flowering response. The influence of phytochrome in the flowering of long-day plants has not been worked out as well as with short-day plants. Very likely the far-red-absorbing form of phytochrome is the active agent in long-day plants. Further investigations are necessary; our ideas with regard to "short-day" plants may have to be modified somewhat in the future as investigations proceed.

Phytochrome is also involved in seed germination in some plants. For example, lettuce seeds require an exposure to light for germination—this exposure usually need be for only a few seconds—in the dark they will not germinate. If exposed to red light, they germinate; if exposed to far red light, they will not germinate. Actually, a range

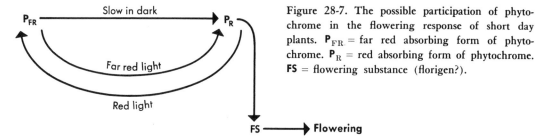

Figure 28-7. The possible participation of phytochrome in the flowering response of short day plants. P_{FR} = far red absorbing form of phytochrome. P_R = red absorbing form of phytochrome. **FS** = flowering substance (florigen?).

of red and far red light is involved, with the maximum responses at 660 and 740 millimicrons respectively. The same is true for the influence of light on flowering. Plants may be exposed alternately to red and then far red illumination. The wave length of the last exposure determines the response of the plant.

Phytochrome apparently is involved in a variety of processes in plants, including stem elongation. Future investigations will undoubtedly expand our knowledge of this interesting pigment.

28.12 Résumé

No plant growth regulator functions individually. The inter-actions of many regulators undoubtedly govern the growth, development, and differentiation of a plant. These inter-relationships, although essential to the normal functioning of complex organisms, greatly increase the difficulties encountered in attempting to study individual growth regulators.

Table 28-2 presents some of the characteristic effects of auxins, gibberellins, and kinins. In some aspects these three regulators are similar;

Table 28-2. Some of the Characteristic Effects of Auxins, Gibberellins, and Kinins

	Auxin	Gibberellin	Kinin
Cell elongation	+	+	+, − *
Cell division	+	+	+
Parthenocarpy	+	+	
Lateral buds	−	+	+
Root initiation	+	−	−
Abscission	−	0	0
Seed germination	0	+	+
Flowering of rosetted nonvernalized biennials and rosetted long-day plants	0	+	0
Richmond-Lang effect	0	0	+
Polar transport	Yes	No	No
Avena curvature test	+	0	0
Dwarf maize test	0	+	0

* + refers to stimulation, − refers to inhibition, 0 refers to no effect.

 412

in others they are quite different. Other plant growth regulators quite likely will be discovered in the future.

Summary

1. Growth consists of an increase in the number of cells and an increase of cellular components. Growth regulators are organic compounds which promote, inhibit, or otherwise modify growth, development, and differentiation of plants. A hormone is a regulator which elicits a response at some distance from where it is formed.

2. Known growth regulators are auxins, gibberellins, and kinins.

3. Auxins are identified by their effectiveness in causing curvature of oat coleoptiles. They are important in phototropism, geotropism, inhibition of lateral buds, inhibition of abscission, fruit development, stimulation of root initiation, and stimulation of cell division and growth.

4. Gibberellins are identified by their effectiveness in causing elongation of dwarf maize plants. They are influential in. stimulation of lateral buds, fruit development, inhibition of root initiation, and stimulation of cell division and elongation.

5. Kinins are identified by the tobacco pith test. They bring about stimulation of lateral buds, cell division, and cell elongation (in some tissues).

6. Some of the synthetic plant growth regulators are useful as selective herbicides.

7. In many plants, flowering is induced as a result of a photoperiodic stimulus; in others the stimulus is high or low temperature. For convenience, we divide plants into three groups on the basis of their response to photoperiodic stimuli: (1) short-day, (2) long-day, and (3) day-neutral.

8. Short-day plants flower only if the day-length is shorter than a critical length and if the dark period is continuous. Long-day plants flower only if the light period is longer than a critical length. Day-neutral plants flower over a wide range of photoperiods.

9. Certain wave lengths of light influence the conversion of phytochrome from one form to another. One of these forms stimulates the production of a flowering substance.

REVIEW TOPICS AND QUESTIONS

1. Distinguish between growth regulators and hormones.
2. Describe an experiment which could be used to determine whether or not auxin is produced by the ovary of an apple flower. Explain how the condition of the ovary may influence your results.

3. Explain the mechanism which brings about the geotropic response of stems and roots.
4. Describe in detail how you could prove that a differential concentration of auxin is responsible for phototropism.
5. An investigator isolates a growth factor from cucumber seedlings. Describe in detail what he should do in order to determine whether this cucumber factor is an auxin, gibberellin, or kinin.
6. Discuss at least five ways in which auxins influence plant growth and development.
7. Differentiate between short-day and long-day plants. What are day-neutral plants? During what time of the year do these three types of plants usually flower? How does day-length (photoperiodism) influence plant distribution?
8. Describe the experiment which demonstrated the importance of the dark period in flower induction.
9. Discuss the evidence which indicates the existence of a flowering hormone.
10. Discuss the manner in which phytochrome participates in flower induction of short-day plants.
11. Why does a brief flash of red light during the dark period prevent flowering in short-day plants? How does this response vary if the red flash is given at different times during the dark period?
12. Discuss at least six ways in which gibberellins influence plant growth and development.

SUGGESTED READINGS

Audus, L. J. *Plant Growth Substances.* New York: Interscience, 1959.

Avery, G. S., et al. *Hormones and Horticulture.* New York: McGraw-Hill, 1947.

Biale, J. B. "The Ripening of Fruit," *Scientific American,* 190 (May 1954), 40–46.

Braun, A. C. "Plant Cancer," *Scientific American,* 186 (June 1952), 66–72.

Greulach, V. A. "Plant Movements," *Scientific American,* 192 (February 1955), 101–106.

Hillman, W. S. *The Physiology of Flowering.* New York: Holt, Rinehart and Winston, 1962.

Jacobs, W. P. "What Makes Leaves Fall," *Scientific American,* 193 (November 1955), 82–89.

Leopold, A. C. *Auxins and Plant Growth.* Berkeley: Univ. of California, 1955.

Naylor, A. W. "The Control of Flowering," *Scientific American,* 186 (May 1952), 49–56.

Salisbury, F. B. "Plant Growth Substances," *Scientific American,* 197 (April 1957), 125–132.

———. "The Flowering Process," *Scientific American,* 198 (April 1958), 108–114.

Schoken, V. "Plant Hormones," *Scientific American,* 180 (May 1949), 40–43.

Weisz, P. B., and M. S. Fuller. *The Science of Botany.* New York: McGraw-Hill, 1962.

Went, F. W., and K. V. Thimann. *Phytohormones.* New York: Macmillan, 1937.

Populations and Their Problems

AT VARIOUS times throughout this text, the dependence of all organisms upon green plants for a food supply has been emphasized. The few chemosynthetic autotrophes which can manufacture their own food are insignificant as far as a supply of food for other organisms is concerned.[1] In order to understand more fully the basic relationships involved, we will undertake a discussion of factors which influence the numbers of individuals within a given population.

29.1 Population increase

To most biologists, and to many other individuals as well, the most serious problem facing us is the tremendous increase of the human population: not merely the large population which now exists on the earth, but the rate at which this population is increasing each year. Malthus was one of the first to point out that all populations have a tremendous capacity for increase because of the reproductive potential of organisms. Each plant or animal is capable during its lifetime of leaving large numbers of offspring upon the earth. Consider, for example, the enormous numbers of spores produced by puffballs, the amount of pollen which is liberated from pine cones on a single tree, or the large quantity of sperms and eggs secreted by spawning salmon. If all of the spores survived or if all of the eggs were fertilized and survived, each of these organisms (in pairs, possibly) is capable of producing progeny in such quantity that the earth would soon be clut-

[1] The reader should review Section 20.6 with regard to the importance of chemosynthetic bacteria.

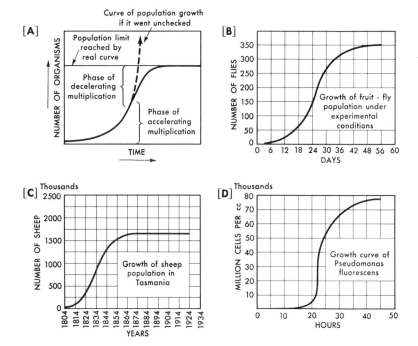

Figure 29-1. Curves of population growth. **A**: The broken line represents the potential growth of a population; the solid line represents the actual growth. **B**, **C**, and **D**: Growth curves of actual populations. (**A** and **C** from G. G. Simpson, C. S. Pittendrigh, and L. H. Tiffany, *Life, An Introduction to Biology*. New York: Harcourt, Brace & World, 1957. **B** from Raymond Pearl, *The Biology of Population Growth*. New York: Alfred A. Knopf, 1930. **D** from Otto Rahn, *Physiology of Bacteria*. Copyright 1932, Blakiston Div., McGraw-Hill, and used by permission.)

tered with their descendants. A similar situation would result in the case of organisms which reproduce more slowly, except that there would be a longer interval before these progeny would over-run the earth. Elephants reproduce rather slowly, starting at about thirty years of age and sometimes continuing until the age of ninety. But even at this slow rate, if all progeny reached their full life span, the descendants of a single pair would number over 18 million in 750 years. At the other end of the scale, one could examine certain bacteria which divide about every thirty minutes under ideal conditions. In twenty-four hours, a single bacterium could give rise to 2^{48} descendants if they all survived. This would be more than 281 trillion, weighing approximately 245 grams, or 10 ounces.[2] Although the number of individuals

[2] An average-size bacterium, such as *Escherichia coli*, weighs about 8×10^{-10} mg. Fluctuations in this figure depend upon age, kind of food, and amount of food.

is represented by an impressive figure, the weight of such a large number of bacteria may not appear to be very significant. However, if this rate of reproduction and survival continued for a mere thirty days, the weight of this mass of bacteria would be more than 130,000 tons. Possibly this is more impressive.

Populations obviously do not increase continually at the rate of which they are capable. Eventually, the rate decreases until the population stabilizes, because the number of individuals which can be supported by an environment is limited. Figure 29-1A represents the potential growth of a population as a broken line and the actual growth as a solid line. Figures 29-1B, 29-1C, and 29-1D are growth curves of actual populations; similar curves could be obtained from data of other populations. The limiting factors which bring about the stabilization of a population are: food supply and its resultant starvation, predators, parasites, and climatic conditions. Organisms retain the ability to reproduce rapidly, but only a small fraction of the offspring actually survive because of these limiting factors.

29.2 Human population

The problem of most vital concern to us is the future of human populations. Many demographers [3] have pointed out that the number of humans has been increasing with leaps and bounds, especially during recent generations. Since records were either not kept or were not very accurate before the 1800's, the estimates of early populations are not as valid as one would wish. Various ways of making such estimates have been suggested, and demographers are rather careful to be conservative under such conditions. Warren Thompson suggests the following data as an indication of population growth. Assuming that one million people lived on earth 10,000 years ago and 600 million in 1700, the average yearly increase was only 0.64 of a person per 1,000 of the population. From 1700 to 1950, a period for which the figures are understandably more accurate, the population increased to 2.5 billion; this is an average annual increase of 5.5 persons per 1,000. The factor primarily responsible for this sharp increase is the relatively rapid drop in the death rate, as a result of modern medical and sanitary facilities. Also, the average life expectancy has increased. Even now, however, the life expectancy at birth of at least one half of the present population is about 35 years, compared to 65 to 70 years in countries where modern preventive medicine has been applied; con-

[3] Demographers are those individuals concerned with the vital statistics (births, deaths, etc.) of populations; the term is usually used in reference to those concerned with human population.

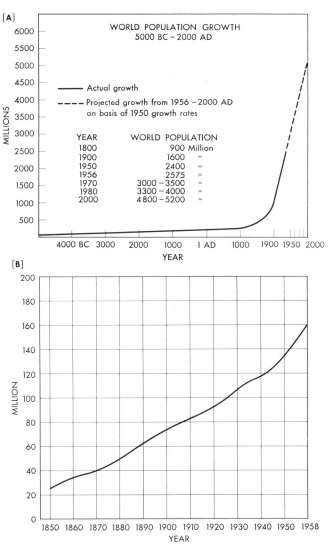

Figure 29-2. Curves of human population growth in various areas. **A**: World population growth. The size of the interval between 1900 and 2000 has been disproportionately lengthened to give a clearer presentation of past and projected population growth during the 20th Century. **B**: Growth of population in continental U. S. (*Source:* Years 1850–1950 from *Statistical Abstract of the United States, 1957,* U. S. Bureau of Census; years 1950–1958 from *Current Population Reports: Population Estimates,* Series P-25, Bureau of Census.) **C**: Population growth in Japan, U. S., U.S.S.R., India, and China. (*Source:* "The Future Growth of World Population," United Nations, Department of Economic and Social Affairs, 1958.) **D**: Population growth in South America. **E**: Population growth in Uruguay, an area with the lowest death and lowest birth rate in South America. (*Source: The Population of South America, 1950–1980,* U.N., 1955.)

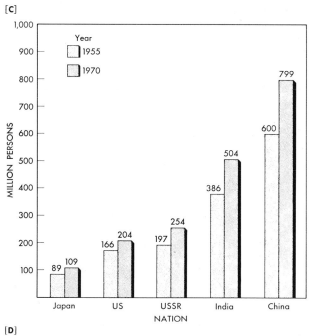

[C]

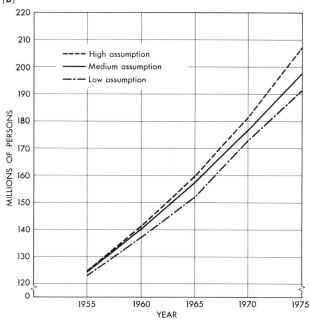

[D]

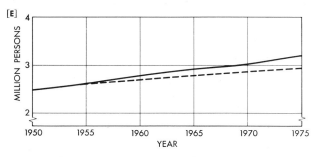

[E]

419 ࿊

sider what the population increase would be if such preventatives were in universal use.

Frank Notestein points out that the rate of growth of the human population is more than one per cent per year. Although this figure appears to be very small, no sustained population growth, even at a very low rate, could be maintained for very long. For example, a rate of one-half of one per cent maintained for another 2,000 years would leave less than four square yards of the earth's land surface for each person. The question is not merely one of food supply, but also of living space. An extreme example of population explosion is in Puerto Rico, where the birth rate is 40 per 1,000,[4] and the death rate is 11 per 1,000, resulting in an increase of 29 per 1,000, or almost 3 per cent per year. At this rate the population would double about every twenty-three years, if no emigration occurred. The population density in Puerto Rico is already 600 per square mile, as compared with 50 per square mile in the United States. Obviously, Puerto Rico cannot long contain this increase in numbers.

In Ceylon, that large island off the southeast coast of India, the population has nearly doubled since World War II as a result of malarial control. Birth rates have remained fairly steady, whereas death rates were greatly decreased by spraying malarial areas with DDT (a potent, residual insecticide). Similar actions aimed toward disease prevention and further efforts to establish greater sanitary facilities and cleanliness will undoubtedly bring about great decreases in death rates in many areas. The resultant population increases will be truly astounding, even more so than they have been already.

The present world population is about 3 billion, and it is increasing at a rate which will add in the neighborhood of one-half billion people in the next ten years (Figure 29-2). This increase is more than the total present population of the Western Hemisphere. The questions which surely must arise in everyone's mind are: "Where will these people live, and how will they obtain food?"

29.3 The food problem

According to nutritional experts of the World Health Organization, each individual requires approximately 2,500 cal./day to be adequately

---

[4] Demographers indicate birth and death rates in terms of the number of births or deaths for every 1,000 people. An annual birth rate of 40/1,000 means that each year the population is increased by 40 for every 1,000 people who were present the year before. If 250,000 people live in an area with such a birthrate, the population will be 260,000 the following year if all survived (250,000 × 40/1,000 = 10,000 births).

fed.[5] At the present time, more than two-thirds of the world's population is undernourished, by this standard. According to the 1955 report of Political and Economic Planning (PEP), *World Population and Services,* the number of underfed approximates 98 per cent in Asia, 93 per cent in Africa, 80 per cent in South America, and 44 per cent in Europe. Other estimates indicate that probably 20 per cent of the people in the United States are also undernourished.

Food production has increased in all countries of the world, but in most of them the increase has been less than the per cent increase of the population. In Pakistan, for example, a 20 per cent boost in food production since World War II has been cancelled out by the great population increase there. Today that country has 10 per cent less food per person than fifteen years ago. In many areas lack of conservation measures and over-cultivation without regard for a sustained-yield basis have resulted in the gradual loss of many formerly productive lands. Members of the Soil Conservation Service have estimated that over 280 million acres of farm and grazing land have been ruined or seriously damaged in the United States and that erosion is active on an additional 775 million acres. The development of good topsoil is a process which takes thousands of years, while its destruction may take place in a very few seasons as a result of poor land management. C. E. Millar [6] of Michigan State College points out (in 1948) that erosion has seriously curtailed average crop yields in his state, and that 25 per cent of Michigan land has lost two to three inches of topsoil. He indicates that a few crops, such as wheat and potatoes, have had an increase in yield but that the average yields of crops most generally grown are about the same as they were sixty years ago. Given the great advances in the agricultural sciences, these yields should be much greater.

Similar erosion problems, and the resultant impoverishment of the land, have occurred in every country of the world. Large areas of forest, farm, and grazing lands are no longer useful. The saddest feature of such destruction is that man has caused the entire situation by a lack of understanding of natural laws. This is one of the reasons that an understanding of the basic principles of plant distributions is so important.

[5] The term calorie refers to energy requirements and is used in a general way to indicate dietary needs. However, calories alone do not really measure nutritional needs. If the calories are predominantly provided by cereals and potatoes, a deficiency of essential vitamins, proteins, and minerals is very likely. Fewer than 2,500 calories per day is certainly insufficient, even though a greater caloric intake may not be qualitatively sufficient; therefore, the caloric content of foods can be utilized as an indication of an absolute minimum.

[6] Mentioned in Stanley A. Cain, "Natural Resources and Population Pressures," *Bios,* XXI, 4 (December 1950).

29.4 Food sources

Estimates vary, of course, as to the amount of land now under cultivation, the amount necessary to maintain a population at an adequate level of living, and the amount of land which could yet be utilized. Assuming rather conservative estimates, probably two-and-one-half billion acres are now under cultivation and another one billion acres could be brought into cultivation. With the present agricultural techniques, approximately two acres per person are required to sustain an adequate level of living. This means that the present world population (or possibly even twice the present number) could be supported if we make certain assumptions which may or may not be valid.

First of all, we must assume that some mechanism could be devised to distribute food in such a manner that areas with a surplus would supply areas with a deficiency. This is similar to farmers supplying city-dwellers. However, in the latter case the urbanites supply a variety of useful articles (e.g., cars, tractors, furniture, electrical appliances, etc.) to the farmer in return for this food. Would similar possibilities of exchanges exist between nations? At the present time, very few nations are able to fill their own needs with regard to food supplies; most nations import foods. England, a great industrial nation, imports approximately 60 per cent of its food. This indicates the illusion of those who believe that industrialization of nations will solve food problems. If all nations increased their industrial potential to the height enjoyed by England, the United States, and a few others, to whom would such nations turn for their food supplies? At the present time, only the United States, Canada, Argentina, New Zealand, and Australia do not need to import food, and the last-named is not in too good a position at the present time.

A second assumption in our attempt to support the world's population is that everyone will be willing to accept an "adequate level of living." Assuredly, this means raising the standards of the majority of people. Just as assuredly, it would mean the lowering of standards for most of the people in at least North America and Western Europe. Human nature is such that we will heartily support the raising of standards in general—our own as well as our neighbors'—but we will usually not support the raising of our neighbors' standards at the expense of our own. Probably very few individuals will be willing to accept any substantial lowering of their own level of living.

The third basic assumption is probably the most serious. Our *present* world population could be supported. Therefore, we must assume that the population of the world will not increase substantially or that food production will increase at the same rate that the population does. But populations are increasing at a tremendous rate, even though the rate is only approximately 1.5 per cent for the world as a whole. If the death rates in most of the world are reduced to those of North America or Western Europe, the rate of increase would be close to three per cent. Within a relatively short period of time, certainly during this century, there would be five billion people and only 3.5 billion cultivatable acres—an almost impossible situation with our present techniques. Also, as we have already noted, food production in general is not keeping pace with population increases.

AVAILABLE LAND

Much of the additional land which could be brought under cultivation consists of rather dry areas, including deserts, and tropic areas, with their excessive rainfall. In the former, the expense of irrigation would vary considerably, depending upon the distances from a source of water and upon the feasibility of converting sea water to fresh water. However, as food supplies become increasingly difficult to obtain, the question of expense will become less important, and undoubtedly more and more of these relatively dry areas will be utilized. In many areas of the southwestern United States, irrigation has made possible the production of tremendous crop yields.[7]

Cultivation of the tropics poses an entirely different problem. Here the difficulty is not moisture but the absence of minerals. The average individual finds the fact almost impossible to believe that most of the soils in tropical rain forests are impoverished—sadly depleted, or lacking, in minerals. Hundreds of years of rains and warmth have weathered and leached such soils to the point where mineral reserves are almost exhausted. Then what supports the luxuriant forest vegetation? The answer lies in the accumulation and decay of humus. This humus is continually replaced by the shedding over the ground of tons of leaves. As these leaves decay and participate in the formation of humus, mineral elements are released to the soil. This continues as the humus is decomposed. The forests, thus, are supported because they return considerable quantities of minerals to the soil. Once the trees are removed, the rapid decomposition of humus (which always occurs in such moist, warm areas) results in the production of minerals which are washed or leached out of the soil by the following rains. No replenishing of the humus takes place, and soils rapidly deteriorate to the point where they will no longer support much growth.

In many areas of the moist tropics, land has been cleared for the production of corn, beans, sweet potatoes, yams, and rice. For a few

[7] See Section 14.7 and Table 14-4.

years yields were substantial, until the humus gave out. The fields were then abandoned, and gradually the forest reclaimed the clearings. At the present time, the natives practice a system of shifting cultivation; as one field gives out, they move to a new area. This cannot be continued indefinitely. However, tropical forest areas can be used for the production of tree crops. Oil, rubber, palm, and cacao could be cultivated successfully by making use of an understanding of the basic reasons why trees are successful and removable crops are not.

Many areas which are not now cultivated present a tremendous problem as far as transportation is concerned. For such an area to be useful, food must be able to be transported from the region in which it is produced to the region where it will be consumed. In order to provide such useful transportation facilities, enormous amounts of money must be expended. The African and South American continents, immense lands which could be utilized more fully, present unique problems. In Africa, the geographical characteristics are such that most of the rivers do not afford the ease of transportation found on the Mississippi or the Amazon; waterfalls and rapids are constant barriers. On the other hand, the cataracts with their cascading waters can be used to produce hydroelectric energy. Just recently has advantage been taken of this situation. Also, more and more roads and railroad lines are being constructed. If all of these factors could be correlated with correct land usage, productivity within the African continent could be increased tremendously. But one must bear in mind that much of the energy which is obtained would be most useful if used in the production of nitrogen fertilizers. No amount of hydroelectric energy or transportation facilities can replace the minerals which are so sadly lacking in most of the moist areas of this great land.

In the Amazon basin of South America, that other great land mass to which people turn hopefully as a possible food-producing area, the flatness of the terrain produces problems quite distinct from those of Africa. The Amazon River and its great tributaries are used extensively for transportation; in fact, almost the entire population and its agriculture is concentrated adjacent to these rivers. During seasons of high water, motor launches can travel at least 3,500 miles up the Amazon from the coast without encountering any natural obstacles. During seasons of low water, travel is greatly curtailed; sand bars and tortuous avenues prevent any large vessels from navigating the river in many areas. The extreme flatness of this basin also brings about severe flooding when the torrential equatorial rains pour enormous volumes of water into the various tributaries from the Andes mountains to the sea. Farmers must then await the receding of flood waters before the next crop can be grown. No simple solution to this flooding problem seems to exist. Iquitos, Peru, is 2,300 miles from the Atlantic Ocean but only 350 feet above sea level; 1,000 miles from the Atlantic, the land is only 125 feet above sea level. Dams would not suffice; tremendous dikes and levees are needed. Roads and railroads are needed to service those areas not immediately adjacent to rivers. This would be an immensely difficult undertaking. It could be done. But will it be done in time?

29.5 The standard of living

The grade or level of subsistence and comforts in everyday life enjoyed by a community will be influenced by a number of factors, all of which may conveniently fall under one of three categories: (1) land area, (2) cultural management, and (3) population intensity.

The term **land area** is used to indicate that land which is used, or which can be used, productively. Industrial and residential land would be included, because the products of such land may be exchanged for food. However, as the demand for food increases, agriculturally productive land clearly becomes increasingly important. In the long run, then, we are really speaking of land which is suitable for cultivation or the raising of livestock.

The term **cultural management** is a more inclusive one. Here we must refer to various methods of agriculture, science, industry, medicine, and social organization which enables humans to derive greater benefits from nature than would otherwise be possible. This is really what places man ahead of other animals, and modern man ahead of ancient man. This is a facet of man's intelligence. Because of such management, the city-dwellers can be supported by the relatively few people who remain on farms and ranches in an industrialized country like the United States. Transportation and storage facilities make possible the use of advanced agricultural techniques in producing much more from land than could be utilized by the people working that land. The building of farm machinery is essential to such advanced techniques and is a part of the exchange between city and farm.

Population intensity refers to the actual number of individuals in a particular area. The rapidity with which such numbers are increasing has already been discussed. This factor has the greatest influence on the standard of living, and the effect is inversely proportional to the number of people.

The level of living of any people can be raised by increasing the land area or improving the cultural management of the community in question. Unfortunately, the earth is finite, limiting the possible expansion of land area. As we have seen, not much more land is available for cultivation. Also questionable is whether the additional land

425

placed in cultivation during any one year will counterbalance the productivity loss resulting from erosion during the same period. In the future, man will need to examine more thoroughly the possibility of obtaining additional food supplies from the oceans of the world (see the next section). Also unfortunate is that the techniques and facilities with which man obtains his wants and necessities are not advancing rapidly enough. In comparison with man's achievements previous to this century, amazingly rapid advances, especially within the last few decades, have been made; however, even such relatively rapid advances have not kept pace with our problems of erosion. In spite of tremendous strides in the agricultural sciences, yields have been increased in only some crops, whereas over-all yield has not been substantially increased. If our present rate of soil destruction continues, the situation will become worse, because our best lands are already in use. Much less erosion is needed to ruin a poor soil than to ruin a soil which was originally quite productive.

If the land area available to a community does not increase and if the cultural management increases but slowly, then the increase in population will result in a lowering of the standard of living. Except for possibly Ireland and France, the population of every country is expanding at a rate of one to three per cent annually. At the present time, there are many countries in which the population intensity is such that any possible improvement in the level of living is immediately cancelled by the increase in numbers even at the low rate of one per cent. After all, one per cent of one million is ten thousand; a country of 200 million people with a one per cent annual increase will have 202 million the next year. An enormous advance in cultural management is necessary to raise the standards of the existing population, as well as to provide for an additional two million people. Even the rapid advances of the last twenty years have not managed to do this, and whether advances in the future can be rapid enough is questionable.

The problem really revolves about finding food and facilities for the peoples of the world.

29.6 Optimistic possible solutions to the population problem

The previous portions of this chapter have been couched in a rather pessimistic vein, and justifiably so, in the author's opinion. This opinion is shared by many individuals, scientists and non-scientists alike, but certainly not by everyone. Opinions vary from the extreme pessimists who believe the matter is hopeless to those wonderful optimists who are certain that everything will work itself out advantageously.

I hope that I am somewhere between these extremes and will discuss
what I am convinced must be done to alleviate the difficult situation
now existing in the world.[8] The heading "optimistic possible solutions"
has been used simply because of the colossal difficulties which must
be faced in implementing these solutions even under the best of conditions, and because of the grave possibility that we have started too
late in trying to solve the population-food supply problem. Of course,
natural laws will eventually solve the problem for us, but I am sure
that no one favors starvation, even for others.

The goal of any procedures to be discussed as possible solutions to
the population problem is to raise the level of living. This is much
more difficult than lowering the death rate. Wiping out disease by
medical means and by improved sanitation entails expenditure of time
and money but is certainly within reach. Raising living standards is
highly complex and involves education, science (including agriculture,
industrial techniques, etc.), sociology, religion, and politics. These are
inter-related problems, with difficulties on every side. This is why immediate steps are so essential.

EDUCATION

If one feature is common to just about all problems, it is education.
No procedure could be functional, even without considering its possible success, unless educational facilities are vastly increased. This is
really the key to any solution. Such education must be world-wide in
scope. The activities of any one community could be negated if a
neighboring community were not similarly engaged. An excellent example is derived from the dust-bowl situation of the midwestern
United States. Farmers utilizing good land management were often
handicapped by the smothering soil blowing toward them from adjacent lands. If all of the individuals in this area had been aware of
the basic reasons which resulted in the development of the dust bowl,
all more likely would have adopted more sensible practices.

One of the basic difficulties which must be faced is that probably a
majority of the people in the world are not even aware that a problem
of food supply exists. Too frequently, people assume that a mere re-
distribution of the world's supply is all that is required to alleviate the

[8] These discussions do not take account of the difficult political situations existing in the world at the present time. Such situations are entirely out of my
sphere of capabilities, and I do not wish to become embroiled in political arguments. I will present my carefully considered opinions as to methods for solving
the "population-food supply" question. The implementation of some of these
solutions may be very difficult, if not impossible, at the present time, because of
political factors. I am well aware of this.

Figure 29-3. Mono Dam in Los Padres National Forest, California, completely filled with silt. Top: Upstream view. Bottom: Downstream view. (United States Forest Service Photos.)

suffering of untold millions. With education, the problem can be recognized and attacked on many fronts. But how does one approach an illiterate population? Without a tremendous increase in literacy, failure is certain. A majority of the people cannot be reached unless use can be made of the written word. The estimated illiteracy varies from less than two per cent of the population to at least 80 per cent in some countries. The first step, then, must be to increase literacy. After this, explanations and reasons and solutions must be discussed thoroughly. All of this must be done immediately.

The following discussions of procedures which might help to solve or at best alleviate much of our difficulties will assume that education of the people is being emphasized.

INCREASED CULTURAL MANAGEMENT

This complex category includes many technical advances which could be utilized now and suggestions which lend promise for the future. As was mentioned previously, any increase in the facilities included under cultural management would assist in improving a standard of living. Again, it is mandatory that achievements not be unilaterally applied.

Agricultural production. Many different techniques are used to produce food from the land, either as crops or as livestock. A great increase in production should be possible by the diligent application of modern technology and practices to all land areas. The use of fertilizers, machinery, and hybrid seed are only a few examples of factors which would influence production favorably. Modern agricultural practices also include crop rotation, fallowing, and the use of legume plants where possible. These are items which would bring about immediate results.

We must also think in terms of long-range plans. Plant and animal breeding programs must be vastly increased to provide organisms which can be utilized more efficiently in the diverse environments of the world. Basic research in genetics and physiology must be emphasized. Such investigations are the foundation for an understanding of plant and animal growth, distribution, and inter-actions. We cannot emphasize too strongly that any basic research in the biological sciences (which necessarily overlaps other fields, such as chemistry, physics, psychology, sociology, etc.) must be pursued with vigor. Although the data and concepts which result do not always appear to have practical applications, this should not alter our efforts. Any knowledge is important. Also, much basic research frequently has future applications of considerable significance.[9]

An increase in agricultural production refers to the increase per land area and not to an increased production per person. For example,

[9] Two excellent examples can be cited: weed killers and nylon. The former resulted from investigations which started with studies as to the curious curvature of plants toward light and led to the discovery of plant growth hormones, to chemically synthesized growth regulators, and finally to weed killers, after studies concerning respiratory effects of such materials were undertaken. Nylon resulted from investigations concerning polymerization, the chemical formation of large molecules from smaller ones; some of the polymers had thread-like characteristics. The discovery of chemical weed killers (such as 2,4-D) and nylon could not have been anticipated. They didn't even exist when the basic research was started.

the use of machinery could enable one man to do the work of five; if the yield remains the same, however, the only advantage obtained is that four men can relax while one works. The real need is to produce a greater sustained yield.

Conservation. The term conservation is most frequently used as synonomous with "prevent erosion and save wildlife." Much more is involved. Erosion control is certainly essential, but the building of dams to achieve this is only a partial measure. The most important feature in the struggle to retain our topsoil is to keep a vegetative cover on the ground, especially at the headwaters of our various streams and rivers. Grasses, shrubs, trees, and even weeds deflect the pounding force of rain, and their roots hold soil particles against the forces of wind and flowing water. Unfortunately, all the dams we may build not only hold water but also collect silt. As more and more silt collects, the effectiveness of the dam declines. Figure 29-3 is a photograph of a silt dam built upstream from a reservoir dam (in the mountains just north of Santa Barbara, California). The purpose of the smaller dam was to decrease the amount of silting in the reservoir, and there are several of these dams. As can be seen, the silt dam *was* rather efficient; the accumulated silt has reached the top of the dam. Of course, this dam no longer serves its function. Gibraltar Reservoir, downstream from the area in the photograph, is approximately 25 to 30 per cent filled in with water-borne soil. The task of removing such debris and silt from dams is prohibitively expensive, even if possible. Figures 29-4, 5, and 6 indicate the damage that results as soil is washed away by water.

Conservation also entails sewage disposal and the re-use of water, with the sludge being used as fertilizer. Complete sewage disposal plants will be commonplace in the near future, as the demand for water keeps expanding and the supply continues to diminish.[10] Industry requires water in fantastic amounts, and disposal plants are needed now to battle the problem of pollution from industrial wastes as well as from human wastes. Once again, we have an example of human folly. The way in which man wastes soil and water is disgraceful.

Conservation should also be thought of in terms of studying the possible uses of industrial by-products. In certain areas of Florida, orange rind, a waste product of the orange juice industry, is used as a dietary supplement for dairy cows. The enormous variety of prod-

---

[10] This is not to imply that the amount of rainfall is any less than it was. The greater the built-up areas, the less soil is available to act as a sponge in retaining water. The soil which remains after the topsoil is removed (by erosion) is coarser and has low water-holding capacity. Water tables are lowering in many areas as a result of excessive use, and many wells are going dry. All these factors result in less and less water being available.

Figure 29-4. Gullies cut into rolling land by rainfall. (Courtesy United States Department of Agriculture, Soil Conservation Service.)

Figure 29-5. Severe gully erosion. (Courtesy United States Department of Agriculture, Soil Conservation Service.)

Figure 29-6. A passing rainstorm produces severe erosion. (Courtesy United States Department of Agriculture, Soil Conservation Service.)

ucts now obtained from the peanut plant (*Arachis hypogaea*) exemplifies the possibilities involved: (1) oil for salads, margarine, soap, and lubricants, (2) the pressed cake for stock feed (exceedingly high protein content), (3) peanuts themselves or peanut butter as food, and (4) foliage as fodder. Much more research should investigate possible uses of by-products and waste materials.

Nothing has been said about conservation in terms of aesthetic appeals and the preserving of the wonders of nature. I do not mean to slight the importance of such conservation goals, but this phase of conservation involves other considerations than the basic problem of food supply and will not be covered in this text.

Food chains. Under this category are included two general items: (1) the shortening of existing food chains, and (2) the utilization of foods not now consumed or consumed only in relatively small amounts. Many of our feeding habits will probably have to be re-organized as food becomes less available as a result of increased numbers to feed. More and more plant food will be consumed directly and less animal food will be utilized; this, of course, refers to plants which are edible to humans. Any such elimination of the "middle-man" in a food chain greatly increases the amount of original food value which is available to humans.

Attempts are being made to find new food supplies. Two excellent possibilities have come to light: yeasts and algae. In some localities yeast plants are already being utilized as a dietary supplement because of their relatively high protein content and their supply of B vitamins. The sugar and nitrogen necessary for yeast growth can be obtained fairly inexpensively from acid digestions of cellulose or starch and from ammonium salts. With these materials and an initial inoculum of yeast cells in large tanks, tons of yeast plants per day can be obtained. Yeast cells will double their weight within a period of a few hours, and the final amount of yeast will depend upon the initial inoculum, the amount of food and minerals, the temperature, and the concentration of oxygen. One conservative estimate is that ten fermenting tanks could produce at least ten tons of yeast per day, starting with about 500 pounds of yeast per tank. This would be equivalent to approximately 150 head of cattle or 80 pigs per day.[11]

Various algae, especially marine forms, are now utilized for food or as cattle fodder. However, the most promising alga for future use is *Chlorella,* a unicellular member of the Chlorophyta. The environmental conditions under which *Chlorella* is grown can be varied to alter the composition of each cell. The protein content can be increased from 50 per cent to 80 per cent of the total dry weight, and fat content from the normal 7 per cent to 75 per cent. The taste of fresh *Chlorella* is similar to somewhat oily broccoli, while the bright green powder (dried algae) resembles lima beans. However, artificial flavorings could be added, or other algae might be found which will have a more suitable taste. Investigators have already prepared alga bread, rolls, noodles, soup, ice cream, and a sauce which tastes like soy sauce. The addition of *Chlorella* to rolls causes an increase of 20 per cent in protein, 75 per cent in fat, and a considerable enrichment of the vitamin A and C

[11] Taste or flavor is not being considered. Yeasts do not have an unpleasant taste, and they can be mixed with other foods. Also, there are varieties of yeast which produce the natural flavor of meat (*Torula utilis*) and the flavor of bacon. Additional flavors and condiments can certainly be utilized.

content. A tablespoonful of *Chlorella* powder is equivalent in food value to a one-ounce piece of steak, a comparison which emphasizes the possibilities of utilizing this plant as a dietary supplement. For example, mixing algae powder with tea produces a brew as nourishing as beef broth without materially affecting the taste.

At the present time, preliminary designs indicate that algae could be produced at a cost of about 35 cents a pound. This is low compared to one dollar or more a pound for steak, but high when compared to that of vegetable proteins like soybean meal or yeast at about 10 cents a pound. However, the cost might be lowered with changes in technology or by the use of cheap labor in Asiatic countries. Estimates actually range down to six cents a pound in certain areas. Besides, expense may become meaningless as food becomes ever more scarce. The suggestion has also been made, and tried with some success, that algae be grown in sewage-disposal ponds. The sewage requires large supplies of oxygen to become decomposed to harmless wastes, and the algae supply this oxygen. Considerable amounts of carbon dioxide, nitrogen, and other minerals on which algae thrive are made available as the sewage decomposes. When heat-dried or cooked, the sewage-pond algae are edible. If humans are aesthetically insulted by such food, the algae could be used to feed cattle.[12]

Humans have also never really utilized food from the oceans as fully as might be done. Almost all of the annual fish haul is from the Northern Hemisphere, and yet conditions in the Southern Hemisphere are equally suitable for fish. Circulation patterns of ocean currents, up-welling of waters from deep layers, and proximity of land are factors which result in the availability of mineral nutrients upon which phytoplankton [13] thrive. These plants are the "grasses of the sea" and provide food for zooplankton; both are food sources for various fishes, and the food chain in all its ramifications can eventually support humans to a much greater extent than it is now doing. Food supplies from the sea can certainly be increased by at least ten-fold, especially if humans are willing to consume a greater variety of fish than is now the case. Also, no reason exists why more plankton could not be concentrated and consumed directly, as is being done in some Asiatic countries.

[12] Many other uses can be found for this algal material. The oils may be extracted and used for fuel. Algae contain vitamins, oils for paints, sterols to make cortisone and other hormones, pigments for dyes, and probably hundreds of other items which might be useful.

[13] The drifting microscopic algae and the microscopic animals which feed upon them are called plankton; the plants are the phytoplankton, the animals are zooplankton.

Industrial potential and trade. Future industrial expansion of most nations should emphasize power supplies and raw materials. The exchange of factory products for agricultural products is a thing of the past. So many industrialized nations (e.g., United States, Great Britain, Germany, Japan, Canada) now exist that additional nations similarly oriented will result in surpluses of industrial products, with little hope of exchanging such materials for essential food supplies. As nations with food surpluses gradually build up their industries, with whom will other nations trade for food? Energy and power supplies, however, will be required in ever-increasing amounts as populations and industries increase, especially if living standards can be raised. Fossil fuels, such as coal and oil, are being depleted at a fantastic rate; expanding economies may very well result in the complete utilization of all known coal and oil supplies within 200 to 300 years. Within this span of time the need is incumbent upon us to find new energy sources. At the present time, atomic energy appears to be the only possible solution. However, so many technical difficulties are involved that industrial uses of such energy may not be available soon enough. The simple matter of shielding or protecting humans from atomic radiations may preclude utilizing atomic engines in many instances. For example, automobiles and airplanes would require such heavy shielding that they cannot be built at present. In order to allow additional time to search for solutions to such problems, atomic energy likely will be used at first exclusively to create electrical energy. Similarly, water power in many nations could be harnessed to provide electrical energy. With these new sources of electrical energy available, coal and oil could be transported to those areas where electricity is not suitable. This would conserve fossil fuels and might extend the supply for an additional 200 to 300 years.

Industry also requires a tremendous amount of raw materials, such as iron ore, tungsten, magnesium, boron, uranium, and many others. Vast supplies of these exist in many under-developed countries of the world. Such nations should increase their industrial potential, with mining as the primary goal. This would provide a basis for trade.

Industrialization as such does not solve the basic problem of providing sufficient food for a population. However, industrialization is essential for improving standards of living. This results not only from the material things which industry provides but also from the increased education which must necessarily accompany such expansion. The importance of education has already been discussed.

POPULATION STABILITY

Undoubtedly the only real solution to the population problem is the

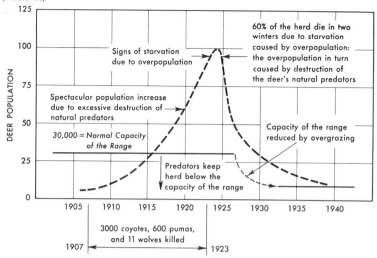

Figure 29-7. The history of the Kaibab deer. The dashed line is the graph of population numbers of the deer. (From Simpson, Pittendrigh, and Tiffany, *Life, An Introduction to Biology*. New York: Harcourt, Brace & World, 1957.)

maintenance of a stable population. Even if our cultural management increase could keep pace with our population expansion, which has not been possible thus far, populations will have to be stabilized eventually or there will be "standing room only" on the earth. At the present rate of increase, people standing shoulder-to-shoulder would cover the earth's land surface in another 700 years. Obviously this will not happen. Unfortunately, however, if populations are not stabilized in some humane way, starvation, war, and disease will do the job in an inhumane way.

Figure 29-7 represents a situation in nature which might be considered to exemplify this situation with which humans are faced. The original deer population on the Kaibab Plateau in Arizona was fairly stable as a result of predation and was well below the capacity which the vegetation could support. A campaign of extermination against the predators resulted in a greatly decreased death rate for the deer. (A similar result has been obtained in human affairs by advances in medicine and sanitation which have brought about rapidly declining death rates over recent decades.) Naturally, the deer population increased tremendously and far beyond the number which could be supported by the available vegetation. Starvation rapidly decimated the deer population until it stabilized at a relatively low figure. The range had been seriously damaged by over-grazing and could now support fewer animals than was originally possible. Unfortunately, the rapidly increasing numbers of humans have also been destroying soils for many generations, resulting in fewer really productive acres than was once the case. The future is not pleasant to contemplate in the light of examples from nature.

Methods of stabilizing populations are highly complex and involve all phases of human existence. Sociological, religious, psychological, and political aspects of the problem must be studied. The problem can be solved, and on a voluntary basis. The Scandinavian countries have a fairly stable population. Ireland and France have stable populations. Even Italy now has birth rates little above replacement levels in spite of relatively high birth rates in the south. One can hope that the solution is reached in time. Only with a stable population can we maintain a standard of living which we might consider adequate. With an increasing population, no matter how slow the rate, the future will bring malnutrition, starvation, disease, and poverty.

INCREASED LAND AREA

Enough has been said with regard to the availability of land to indicate that some increase is possible. Every effort should be made to utilize all available land. This utilization must be based upon sound land-use practices. Our knowledge of plant distributions, agricultural technology, environmental influences on soil fertility, genetics, pathology, storage, and transportation must be correlated for the most efficient methods of production. Surveys should be undertaken in an effort to ascertain whether production could be increased above present yields. Most of our efforts will be time-consuming and expensive, but necessary.

29.7 In retrospect

If we could utilize all known conventional agricultural techniques, including supplemental irrigation of land now under cultivation, we might be able to double food production. If new lands were brought into cultivation in a similar fashion and if the food sources of the seas were utilized to a greater extent, food production might be tripled. Improved plant and animal breeding programs would further increase this gain. Optimistically, it might be possible to increase total food production by a factor of five or six. With such an increase, a world population of probably three or four times the present number could be supported.[14]

[14] Harrison Brown is willing to estimate the much higher figure of 50 billion. However, his estimates are based upon one billion acres of algae farms, for one thing. If this food source is not utilized, his estimate of the population would be closer to 10 billion. This figure is approximately that which I would estimate as the maximum which could be supported.

However, one important factor remains—the space which is available for the population. Urban development continually removes land from cultivation, and this reduces food production. More important is the actual living space for an individual. No population can increase indefinitely, no matter how slow the rate. As Karl Sax so aptly put it, there would soon be "standing room only." Even the most optimistic estimates of food production cannot solve the problem of available space. This problem can be solved only when the population stabilizes.

Summary

1. All populations have a tremendous capacity for increase because of the reproductive potential of organisms. Such a rapid increase does not continue indefinitely, and eventually each population stabilizes. The factors limiting the size of a population are food supply, predators, parasites, and climatic conditions.

2. The human population is expanding very rapidly and has not reached stability except, possibly, in a few areas.

3. The large numbers of humans in the world and the continuing increase in numbers have created a serious food shortage. Expansion of modern technology to all countries and to all usable land areas would probably make possible the feeding of the present population of the world.

4. The standard of living depends upon the land available, upon modern technology (especially agricultural technology) and knowledge, and inversely upon the number of individuals which must be supported. The amount of land cannot be increased indefinitely, and technological advances have not been rapid enough in the past to keep pace with expanding populations.

5. The basic problem revolves around finding food, clothing, shelter, and other facilities for the peoples of the world. Many steps could, and should, be taken to alleviate this situation. Universal education, especially with regard to literacy, is the most important step and the one upon which all others depend. The initiation of modern agricultural methods in all areas, including conservation methods, should be undertaken immediately. New food sources must be utilized, and the length of food chains must be reduced. The industrial potential of various areas must be exploited more fully. Of utmost importance is the study of methods to stabilize populations. Even if food could be made available to an infinitely large population, the problem of space for the individuals of that population would remain.

1. Explain why no population continues to increase in numbers at the rate at which it is capable.
2. Discuss why the human population has increased much more rapidly during the last two hundred years than it has in all of the preceding years.
3. Discuss the factors which govern the standard of living of a population. What is meant by "standard of living"?
4. Explain why the soils of the moist tropics are usually not very productive after the first few years. Why can crops be grown successfully for the first few years?
5. Discuss the factors which you consider to be the most important to solving the population problem.
6. Why will a shortening of food chains enable us to feed more people with the available food?
7. Why are yeasts and algae considered to be excellent possibilities as new food sources?
8. Since industrialization will not solve the problem of food shortages, what is the importance of a country becoming industrialized? What form of industry would you suggest for those countries which are now primarily agricultural? If your answer varies with the location of the country, explain why.

SUGGESTED READINGS

Boner, H. A. *Hungry Generations*. New York: King's Crown Press, 1955.

Brown, H. S. *The Challenge of Man's Future*. New York: Viking, 1954.

Brittain, R. *Let There Be Bread*. New York: Simon and Schuster, 1952.

Cook, R. C. *Human Fertility: The Modern Dilemma*. New York: Wm. Sloane, 1951.

Deevey, E. S. "The Human Population," *Scientific American*, 203 (September 1960), 195–204.

De Turk, E. E. (ed.) *Freedom from Want*. Waltham, Mass.: Chronica Botanica, 1948.

Fairchild, H. P. *People, the Quantity and Quality of Population*. New York: Holt, 1939.

Hatt, P. K. (ed.) *World Population and Future Resources*. New York: American Book, 1952.

Naismith, G. "The Tidal Wave of World Population," *United Nations World,* Vol. 9 (1950).

Notestein, F. W. (ed.) *Demographic Studies of Selected Areas of Rapid Growth*. New York: Milbank Memorial Fund, 1944.

Osborn, F. *Our Plundered Planet*. Boston: Little, Brown, 1948.

———. *The Limits of the Earth*. Boston: Little, Brown, 1953.

Oser, J. *Must Men Starve?* New York: Abelard-Schuman, 1957.

Pearson, F. A., and F. A. Harper. *The World's Hunger*. Ithaca, N. Y.: Cornell Univ. Press, 1945.

Penrose, E. F. *Population Theories and Their Application*. Stanford Univ., Calif.: Food Research Institute, 1934.

Russel, J. *World Population and World Food Supplies*. London: Allen and
Unwin, 1954.

Sax, K. *Standing Room Only*. Boston: Beacon, 1955.

———. "The Population Explosion," *Headline Series,* No. 120 (November
1956), Foreign Policy Ass., Inc., New York.

Thompson, W. S. *Plenty of People*. New York: Ronald, 1948.

———. "Population," *Scientific American,* 182 (February 1950), 11–15.

———. *Population Problems*. New York: McGraw-Hill, 1953.

Vogt, W. *The Road to Survival*. New York: Wm. Sloane, 1948.

———. *People*. New York: Bartholomew House, 1961.

CHAPTER 30

The Beginning

Perhaps a chapter entitled "The Beginning" should be numbered *one* rather than *thirty*. However, any discussion as to the origin of life cannot be fruitful without an understanding of what one means by "life." We have accumulated many chapters of background material upon which we can now build a careful picture of life's beginning.

Various suggestions have been made by numbers of people who attempted to explain how life could have originated. No attempt will be made to include all hypotheses, but any theory must be conducive to careful scrutiny in the light of present concepts of physics and chemistry. We must also make the basic assumption that, if conditions are favorable for life, life will come into existence.

30.1 Autotrophe hypothesis

Since all organisms require food, we assume that the first organism must have been able to manufacture its own food supply. This would mean an entity similar to the photosynthetic or chemosynthetic organism of today (see Chapter 10 and Section 20.6)—an organism independent of other living organisms for its organic compounds (food). From this beginning would gradually (in a few millions of years) evolve organisms which could exist on the food so nicely manufactured for them. Such an autotrophe, however, requires a vast array of enzymes for the many syntheses necessary for life. Simple inorganic materials would have to be converted through many steps to the complex moiety we now know as protoplasm. With the increased study of cellular processes, we became more and more aware that autotrophic organisms are basically more complex than heterotrophic ones; more than likely, the former arose later in the evolutionary scheme of things.

30.2   Heterotrophe hypothesis

A heterotrophic organism forms its own structural components from preformed organic material (food), minerals, water, and oxygen. The first and last of these essential factors were the most difficult to obtain, since, at the earth's beginning, no oxygen gas molecules and no organic compounds were available. One of the important facets of the suggestion that heterotrophes were the first living things is an explanation of food formation which must have pre-dated "life."

The understanding of the relationship of one organism to another makes it clear that autotrophes are more complex physiologically or metabolically because of their ability to start with extremely simple substances, whereas the physiologically simpler heterotrophes start with substances already partially synthesized into cellular components. For example, a green plant readily produces proteins when supplied with water, minerals, carbon dioxide, and light. This is not true of a human, who must obtain either proteins or amino acids in order to form proteins. Many fewer reactions are involved in the human production of proteins, because the green plant has already done part of the work for us (i.e., the synthesis of amino acids). Since each step in the various metabolic processes is mediated by an enzyme, there must be more enzymes in the green plant. Hence, it is a more complex organism than a non-green one. A basic premise of the evolutionary concept is that simple organisms gave rise to complex organisms. Therefore, heterotrophes must have existed before autotrophes if the conceptual scheme of evolution is a valid one. With these thoughts as a starting point, any scheme concerning the origin of life must logically include the development of organic compounds first, then heterotrophes, and finally autotrophes, which really saved the day, as shall be seen later.

ORGANIC BEGINNINGS

Under special conditions, organic compounds can be produced from inorganic materials. Carbon readily combines with metals to produce carbides, and these latter frequently react with water to produce hydrocarbons (compounds of hydrogen and carbon) or with nitrogen gas to form cyanamides. Ammonia can result when cyanamides react with water. Such a mixture, when exposed to ultraviolet rays, which carry large amounts of energy, and high temperatures, results in the formation of amino acids—the basic building blocks of proteins, which are the main components of protoplasm. In this fashion a tremendously great variety of organic compounds could have been formed, resulting in the seas of the world becoming in effect a vast colloidal soup without life. The colloidal particles would come together in many instances to form clusters, or **coacervates,** held together by the electrical forces between them. The surfaces of these coacervates would differ much as the surface layer of water differs from the inner regions, a phenomenon referred to as surface tension and probably important in membrane structure.

Among the untold billions of colloidal particles and coacervates may have been some which were capable of utilizing less complex organic molecules in making duplicates of themselves in the manner that chromosomes reproduce. Such reproducing coacervates had a better chance of surviving as a type than would others. The slow accumulation of many changes over millions of years finally could have resulted in what is called "a living thing," which may have been very similar to a virus. Chemically, a virus consists of nucleic acid surrounded by protein, in other words, a nucleoprotein probably quite similar to a chromosome. The virus and the chromosome (or gene) obtain their substrate from the living cells in which they are found; the coacervate could obtain its substrate from the environment which abounded in organic molecules. Further changes probably resulted in an organism similar to the fermentative bacteria of the present.

EARLY FOOD PROBLEM

The increasing numbers of heterotrophic organisms brought about a food problem which had not existed before. In fact, as the food supply became increasingly scarce, survival began to depend more and more upon the ability of an organism to utilize a greater variety of foods or to synthesize its complex structure from simple molecules. Finally, after millions of years of changes, appeared some organisms capable of using the vast supply of inorganic compounds. These were probably similar to certain organisms living today: (1) the sulphur bacteria (see Section 20.6), (2) the nitrifying bacteria (see Section 20.6), and (3) the green plants (see Chapter 10). Sunlight is a source of much more energy than is available from chemical compounds, and thus the photosynthetic organisms became the dominant autotrophes of the world. The appearance of these organisms ended the danger of the exhaustion of the supply of organic substances needed by the organisms which could not get their energy directly from the sun. Photosynthetic organisms saved the day for the type of life which existed before that process developed; the former now supply all of the food material, as well as all oxygen, for all of the organisms in the world. Once oxygen became available, the much more efficient aerobic metabolism dominated the scene, as is indicated by the predominance of aerobic organisms in the world today. The increased energy made available by aerobic respiration resulted in the evolution of larger and more complex organisms than would have been possible with strictly fermentative (anaerobic) processes.

30.3 Earth's early environment

The foregoing paragraphs have presented suggestions as to how life could originate if certain conditions were present or available. If one examines evidence accumulated by geologists, biologists, astronomers, and others, general agreement is found concerning the earth's original environment and the changes which have taken place. It is also apparent that the environment was most certainly conducive to the formation of life.

As the hot mass which was our earth gradually condensed and cooled, great quantities of water vapor, carbon dioxide, nitrogen, and other gases evolved. With further cooling the water vapor condensed and formed oceans in which many materials were dissolved. Volcanic action and land upheavals brought carbides to the surface, resulting in the formation of hydrocarbons and cyanamides. Since oxygen and ozone were lacking, ultraviolet rays from the sun were not filtered out, and all conditions necessary for the formation of life were present.

30.4 Can life originate now?

A basic premise made early in discussing the origin of life was that when conditions are suitable for life, life will come into existence. The conditions are certainly suitable for life now, and yet life cannot possibly begin again. This apparent paradox comes about because the living organisms now present would consume new organic compounds before they could possibly evolve further. The time for life to originate was when no life existed, and further spontaneous generation on this earth is not possible.

The fact that life can no longer originate on Earth does not mean that such a beginning is impossible anywhere. The universe is vast, containing untold numbers of galaxies (like the Milky Way) with their myriads of stars and planets. The existence of other planets similar to the Earth revolving about their own stars or sun is not impossible. However, most conditions seem to be weighted against the existence of life on most planets. If the planet is too near its Sun, it will be too hot for life to exist; if it is too far away, it will be too cold. If it is much larger than the Earth, gravitational pull will retain too much atmosphere and result in a poisonous situation, as is found on Jupiter and Saturn. If it is much smaller, all atmosphere will have been lost, as is true of the Moon and Mercury.[1] Some astronomers feel that only Venus, Earth, and Mars of our own planetary system could possibly support life, that Mars is a planet where life has almost become extinct (possibly some scanty vegetation is left), and that Venus, though without life now, may be the home of life in the future.

30.5 Spontaneous generation

That spontaneous generation does not occur was difficult to demonstrate at first, and many years of controversy passed before Pasteur's famous experiment proved the matter conclusively. The appearance of maggots in putrefying meat was considered sufficient evidence that living creatures were generated spontaneously from non-living materials until Francesco Redi (1668), an Italian biologist, covered meat with gauze and prevented maggots from forming. This did not settle the controversy because the covered meat did become putrid, and the natural conclusion was that even if maggots did not develop from meat, bacteria did. Of course, Redi's experiments could have quashed the idea of spontaneous generation if von Leeuwenhoek's microscopes had not enabled biologists to see the extremely small bacteria which developed so profusely as the meat decayed. The arguments pro and con waxed hot and heavy for some 200 years more until Pasteur boiled various media in a flask which had a long swan-shaped, or S-shaped, neck. The flask was open to the air so that any "vegetative force" could still enter, and yet the curved neck prevented the relatively heavy bacteria and fungus spores from entering into the medium. No living organisms developed in such flasks after prolonged boiling and slow cooling. If the flasks were broken open or if dust were allowed to enter, microbes readily developed from those carried in the air. No doubt remained that, although spontaneous generation undoubtedly occurred millions of years ago when life originated, all organisms now develop from pre-existing organisms and all cells develop from pre-existing cells. This is one of the basic concepts of biology.

Summary

1. The autotrophe hypothesis concerning the origin of life suggests that those plants which could manufacture their own food must have been the first to develop. Since all other organisms now depend upon the autotrophes, this seemed to be a logical hypothesis. The fact be-

[1] For a discussion of atmospheres, velocities of escape, and velocities of gas molecules, see the book by H. Spencer Jones or other astronomy texts.

came evident, however, that these organisms are basically more complex than are the heterotrophes.

2. The heterotrophe hypothesis suggests that organic molecules developed first and that the heterotrophes, which eventually arose, could then utilize these compounds. In this view, the food for the organisms was available before the organism existed. The more complex autotrophes then developed from the pre-existing heterotrophes.

3. The origin of autotrophes allowed the heterotrophes to continue living.

4. Earth's early environment was conducive to the formation of organic molecules from simple inorganic materials. Spontaneous generation did occur at one time but is no longer possible.

REVIEW TOPICS AND QUESTIONS

1. Why is the autotrophe hypothesis of the origin of life not tenable?
2. How could a heterotrophic organism exist without autotrophes? Is this condition possible now? Explain what would happen if all autotrophic organisms died now.
3. What conditions are necessary before life could originate?
4. Explain why Pasteur had to cool his swan-neck flasks slowly rather than rapidly.
5. Explain why the evolution of an autotrophic type of metabolism was essential for the survival of life.

SUGGESTED READINGS

Adler, I. *How Life Began.* New York: New American Library, 1959.

Huang, Su-Shu. "Life outside the Solar System," *Scientific American,* 202 (April 1960), 55–63.

Jones, H. S. *Life on Other Worlds.* New York: New American Library, 1949.

Oparin, A. I. *Origin of Life.* Dover Books edition; New York: Dover Publications, 1953.

Vaucouleurs, G. de. "Mars," *Scientific American,* 188 (May 1953), 65–73.

Wald, G. "The Origin of Life," *Scientific American,* 191 (August 1954), 44–53.

Glossary

Abscission: dropping of leaves, fruits, or other plant parts, usually by the separation of cell walls in a zone at the base of a petiole or other structure.

Abscission layer: a zone of cells at the base of a petiole or other structure whose cells separate.

Absorption: the movement of substances into a cell.

Accumulation: the absorption of substances against a concentration gradient; requires respiratory energy.

Active absorption: same as *Accumulation*.

Achene: a dry, indehiscent, one-seeded fruit formed from a single carpel.

Adaptation: changes in an organism that result in it being better suited to an environment.

Adenosine diphosphate: ADP; a compound to which inorganic phosphate may be added to form a terminal high-energy phosphate bond. Respiratory energy is used in the formation of such bonds; the resultant compound is ATP.

Adenosine triphosphate: ATP; a compound containing high-energy phosphate groups which may be removed with the liberation of usable cellular energy. ADP is formed when such energy is made available.

Adsorption: the concentration of molecules or ions on the surfaces of solid particles.

Adventitious: structures arising in an unusual place.

Aerobic respiration: see *Respiration*.

After-ripening: metabolic processes that must occur in some seeds before germination will occur.

Agar: a gelatinous substance extracted from certain red algae (Rhodophyta); used as a solidifying agent in the preparation of nutrient media for the growth of microorganisms, and for a variety of other purposes.

Aggregate fruit: a fruit formed from a group of ovaries produced in a single flower.

Allele: one of the contrasting forms of a gene at a particular locus on a chromosome.

Alternate leaves: a leaf arrangement with a single leaf at each node.

Alternation of phases: the development of spore-producing structures followed by the development of gamete-producing structures in the life cycle of a plant; the cells of the former contain twice as many chromosomes as do those of the latter.

Amino acids: organic acids containing an amino group, NH_2; they are the units from which protein molecules are constructed.

Ammonification: the formation of ammonia during the decomposition of proteinaceous compounds by microorganisms.

Amylase: an enzyme which hydrolyzes (digests) starch to maltose.

Anabolism: the constructive phases of metabolism; syntheses.

Anaerobic respiration: see *Fermentation*.

Anaphase: that portion of nuclear division during which the chromatids of each chromosome separate and move to opposite poles, or a similar separation of homologous chromosomes (as in meiosis).

Angiosperm: one of the flowering plants; seeds are enclosed in fruits (ovaries).

Annual: a plant in which the entire life cycle is completed in a single growing season.

Annual ring: the amount of xylem formed during one year's growth.

Annulus: a ring of specialized cells around a fern sporangium.

Anther: the pollen-bearing portion of a stamen.

Antheridium: a structure in which sperms are produced.

Anthocyanins: water-soluble pigments found in the cell sap; usually reds or blues.

Antibiotic: a substance produced by living organisms (usually bacteria and true fungi) which destroys or inhibits the growth of other organisms.

Antibody: a substance, produced by the body, which destroys foreign bodies, invading organisms, or the harmful products formed by them; produced in response to an antigen.

Antigen: a foreign substance in the body of an organism that stimulates the formation of antibodies.

Antipodal cells: the cells, usually three, located at the end opposite the micropyle of the megagametophyte of angiosperms; functionless and vestigial.

Antitoxin: an antibody which neutralizes a toxin; the latter is the antigen.

Apical dominance: the influence of terminal buds in suppressing the growth of lateral buds.

Apical meristem: the meristematic tissue at the tip of a root or stem.

Apothecium: in Ascomycetes, a cup-shaped structure containing asci with ascospores.

Archegonium: a multicellular structure in which eggs are produced.

Ascocarp: in Ascomycetes, a structure in which asci are produced.

Ascogonium: the female gametangium of Ascomycetes.

Ascospore: a fungus spore produced in an ascus.

Ascus: in Ascomycetes, a sac-like structure in which ascospores are produced after nuclear fusion and meiosis.

Asexual reproduction: reproduction which does not involve the fusion of sex cells (gametes).

Assimilation: the conversion of nutrients into protoplasm.

Autotrophic: capable of manufacturing its own food, such as green plants.

Auxin: a growth regulator that promotes cell elongation.

Axil: the upper angle between a petiole and the stem to which it is attached.

Axillary bud: a bud borne in the axil of a leaf.

Bacillus: a rod-shaped bacterium.

Bacteriophage: a virus which attacks bacteria.

Bark: the tissues of a woody stem outside of the vascular cambium.

Basidiospore: a fungus spore produced on a basidium.

Basidium: in Basidiomycetes, a club-shaped structure on which spores are borne after nuclear fusion and meiosis.

Berry: a simple fleshy fruit.

Biennial: a plant which grows vegetatively the first year, produces seed during its second year, and then dies.

Binomial: the generic name and specific name of an organism taken together as its official name.

Blade: the expanded portion of a leaf.

Bract: a modified or reduced leaflike structure.

Bud: a much compressed embryonic shoot.

Bud scale: a modified protective leaf of a bud.

Budding: (1) grafting in which the scion is a single bud; (2) vegetative reproduction in yeast.

Bulb: a short, underground stem with fleshy leaves.

Bundle sheath: a layer of cells surrounding the vascular strands of a leaf.

Calorie: the amount of heat required to raise the temperature of one gram of water $1°C.$; it is useful as a measure of energy.

Calyptra: in mosses, a cap-like structure covering the apex of the capsule; it consists of the upper portion of the archegonium.

Calyx: collective term for the sepals of a flower.

Cambium: see *Cork cambium* and *Vascular cambium*.

Capillarity: the movement of water through tiny passages as a result of surface forces.

Capillary soil water: water held in the soil against the force of gravity; the water is retained in the spaces among and within the soil particles.

Capsule: (1) the sporangium of a bryophyte; (2) a simple, dry, dehiscent fruit formed from a compound pistil.

Carbohydrate: organic compound composed of carbon, hydrogen, and oxygen with the ratio of hydrogen to oxygen being $2:1$.

Carnivorous: meat-eating.

Carotenes: yellow to orange or red, carotenoid pigments found in plastids; one is a precursor of vitamin A.

Carpel: a floral organ bearing and enclosing ovules; a pistil may be composed of one or more carpels.

Catabolism: the destructive phases of metabolism in which organic com-

449 ॐ

pounds are broken down into simple substances, as in respiration and digestion.

Catalyst: a substance which regulates the rate of a chemical reaction without being used up in the reaction.

Cell: the structural unit of plants and animals; generally in plants this consists of protoplasm surrounded by a cell wall.

Cell sap: the solution in the vacuole of a cell.

Cellulase: an enzyme which hydrolyzes (digests) cellulose to glucose.

Cellulose: a complex carbohydrate formed from glucose; it is the chief component of the cell wall in most plants.

Centromere: that portion of the chromosome to which a spindle fiber is attached.

Chemosynthesis: the synthesis of organic matter utilizing energy made available by the oxidation of inorganic compounds, such as ammonia, nitrites, sulphur, etc.

Chemotropism: a growth movement induced by a chemical.

Chlorophylls: green pigments located in plastids; they are involved in photosynthesis.

Chloroplast: a formed body in the cytoplasm and which contains chlorophyll.

Chromatid: the term applied to one-half of a doubled chromosome before the two portions separate.

Chromatin: deeply staining nuclear material which forms the hereditary carriers of the chromosomes.

Chromonema: threadlike structure comprising part of the chromosome; it is composed of chromatin.

Chromoplast: a formed body in the cytoplasm which contains pigments other than chlorophyll; the color is often yellow or red because of the carotenes and xanthophylls.

Chromosome: structural bodies, frequently rodlike, in the nucleus; they are formed from chromatin and are the site of hereditary determiners or genes.

Cilium: short cytoplasmic projection which functions as an organ of motility.

Class: a group of related orders.

Cleistothecium: a closed spherical structure composed of hyphae and containing one or more asci.

Climax: the terminal community of a succession, which is maintained with little change provided the environment does not change significantly.

Coccus: a spherical bacterium.

Coenocytic: multinucleate; lacking cross walls.

Cohesion theory: a suggested explanation for the rise of water in plants; it is based upon the forces of attraction between water molecules.

Colchicine: an alkaloid which may induce polyploidy when applied to plant cells.

Coleoptile: a sheathlike structure covering the epicotyl of grass seedlings.

Collenchyma: a supporting and strengthening tissue in which the cells have irregular wall thickenings.

Colloid: a dispersion of particles ranging from 0.1 micron to 0.001 micron; the particles remain suspended and are usually large molecules or molecular aggregates.

Colony: a group of similar organisms living in close association, usually microorganisms; there is no division of labor.

Columella: the sterile central portion of a sporangium.

Community: an assemblage of organisms living together.

Companion cell: a narrow, elongated cell adjoining a sieve tube element.

Compensation point: the light intensity or temperature at which the rates of photosynthesis and respiration are equal.

Complete flower: a flower containing sepals, petals, stamens, and at least one pistil.

Compound leaf: a leaf in which the blade is subdivided into two or more parts.

Compound pistil: a pistil composed of two or more carpels.

Conceptacle: in certain brown algae, a cavity in which gametes are formed eventually.

Cone: a close aggregation of spirally arranged microsporophylls.

Conidiophore: a hypha which produces conidia.

Conidium: an asexual fungus spore produced at the tip of a conidiophore.

Conjugation: a type of isogamy in which one gamete moves toward another through a tube connecting the two cells.

Convergent evolution: the independent development of similar structures in groups of organisms that are only very distantly related.

Cork: a protective tissue in which the cell walls are suberized; formed by a cork cambium.

Cork cambium: a meristematic tissue which produces cork cells; also called phellogen.

Corm: a bulky, short, vertical, underground stem which stores food.

Corolla: the petals of a flower taken collectively.

Cortex: the tissue of a root or stem between the epidermis and the vascular tissue; composed primarily of parenchyma-type cells.

Cotyledon: the leaf of an embryo; also called seed leaf.

Crossing-over: the interchange of parts between chromatids of homologous chromosomes during meiosis.

Cross-pollination: the transfer of pollen from the anther of one plant to the stigma of another.

Cuticle: a waxy layer secreted by epidermal cells on their outer walls; composed of cutin.

Cutin: a waxy substance, rather impermeable to water.

Cutting: a severed plant part used for vegetative propagation; usually in reference to stems.

Cytokinesis: cytoplasmic division and the formation of a new wall.

Cytoplasm: that portion of the protoplasm exclusive of the nucleus and plastids.

451

Day-neutral plant: unaffected by day-length and flowers readily over a wide range of photoperiods.

Deciduous: (1) broad-leaved plants which drop their leaves at the end of each growing season; (2) parts which drop at the end of the growing season.

Dehydrogenase: an enzyme which removes hydrogens from certain organic compounds.

Denitrification: the conversion of nitrates into nitrogen gas by certain soil bacteria.

Deoxyribose nucleic acid (DNA): the nucleic acid found in the chromosome, combined with a protein as a nucleoprotein; it is involved in the transmission of hereditary characteristics.

Dicotyledonous plant (Dicot): a flowering plant characterized by two cotyledons or seed leaves in the embryo.

Differentially permeable membrane: a membrane which allows some substances to pass through more readily than others; some substances may not be capable of penetrating at all.

Diffuse root system: a root system in which the main roots are all about the same diameter and in which there is profuse branching.

Diffusion: the movement of molecules or ions from one location to another as a result of molecular activity.

Diffusion pressure: the net ability of a molecule or ion to diffuse as influenced by concentration, external forces, and temperature.

Digestion: the conversion (hydrolysis) of insoluble or complex substances into soluble or simpler substances.

Dihybrid cross: a cross (mating) between organisms differing in two pairs of genes.

Dioecious: having male and female reproductive organs on separate plants.

Diploid: having two sets of chromosomes, one set from one gamete and the second set from the other gamete of the two that fuse; the situation (2N) characteristic of the sporophyte phase in plants.

DNA: see *Deoxyribose nucleic acid*.

Dominant character (factor): (1) a gene that masks or hides the presence of its allele; (2) that characteristic which excludes the appearance of its contrasting character in a hybrid (the latter is the recessive character).

Dormancy: a period of greatly reduced physiological activity in various plant parts, especially seeds and buds, even though the environment may be suitable for growth.

Double fertilization: refers to the situation in flowering plants where one sperm fuses with the egg and the second sperm fuses with the two polar nuclei.

Drupe: a fruit in which the exocarp is a thin skin, the mesocarp is the fleshy pulp, and the endocarp is hard (the pit).

Ecology: the study of inter-relationships between organisms and their environment.

Egg: female gamete or sex cell.

Embryo: the rudimentary sporophytic plant developed from a zygote within an archegonium or an ovule.

Embryo sac: female gametophyte of flowering plants; it develops from a megaspore.

Endocarp: the inner layer of the pericarp or fruit wall (ovary wall).

Endodermis: a one-celled layer forming the innermost portion of the cortex; it is most obvious in roots.

Endoplasmic reticulum: the inter-connected network of membranes that constitute a part of the submicroscopic structure of the protoplasm.

Endosperm: in angiosperms, a triploid nutritive tissue surrounding the embryo; in gymnosperms, it is the haploid female gametophyte.

Energy: the ability to do work.

Energy-rich phosphate bond: a bond joining certain phosphate groups to an organic molecule; energy is made available when the bond is broken; see ADP and ATP.

Enzyme: a proteinaceous catalyst produced by living cells and which speeds up the rate of specific reactions.

Epicotyl: that part of the embryo above the point of attachment of the cotyledons; upon growth it forms the young stem of the plant.

Epidermis: the surface layer of cells before cork is formed.

Epigynous flower: a flower in which the ovary is embedded and the floral parts seem to arise from the top of the ovary.

Erosion: the removal of soil by natural agents, especially by water and wind.

Essential elements: elements required by plants for normal growth and development.

Etiolation: the condition of a plant grown in the absence of light; the plant typically lacks chlorophyll, has an abnormally elongated stem, and poorly developed leaves.

Evolution: the development of a group of organisms; descent with modification.

Exocarp: the outer layer of the pericarp or fruit wall (ovary wall).

Eye spot: a small, pigmented, light-sensitive structure present in certain algae.

F_1: the first generation of progeny following a cross or mating; later generations are known as the F_2, F_3, etc.

Family: a taxonomic grouping including one or more genera.

Fat: organic compound consisting of carbon, hydrogen, and oxygen, with the last in much smaller proportionate amounts than in carbohydrates; if liquid at room temperature, they are called oils.

Fermentation: a complex series of cellular oxidation-reduction reactions in which energy is made available to the cell in the absence of oxygen; the incomplete oxidation of substrate with various organic materials as end products.

Fertilization: the fusion of two gametes.

453

Fertilizer: material added to the soil to provide essential elements or to improve the physical condition of the soil.

Fiber: greatly elongated, tapering, thick-walled cell which serves to support and strengthen a structure.

Fibrous root system: see *Diffuse root system*.

Field capacity: the amount of water held in a soil against the forces of gravity.

Filament: (1) the stalk of a stamen; (2) a threadlike row of cells.

Fission: asexual reproduction of a unicellular organism in which the cell divides to form two organisms.

Flagellum: a rather long cytoplasmic projection which functions as an organ of motility.

Florigen: a hypothetical plant hormone which influences flower initiation.

Flower: the reproductive structure of angiosperms; consists of sepals, petals, stamens, and pistil if all of the parts are present.

Flower bud: a bud which develops into a flower.

Food: an organic substance which furnishes energy (in respiration or fermentation) or which is transformed into protoplasm and cell secretions.

Food chain: a group of plants and animals inter-related by their food dependencies.

Fossil: any evidence of a former living thing.

Frond: the leaf of a fern.

Fruit: a mature ovary or group of ovaries, usually containing seed.

Fucoxanthin: the brownish pigment of certain algae.

Funiculus: the stalk connecting the ovule to the ovary wall.

Gametangium: a structure in which gametes are produced.

Gamete: a sex cell.

Gametophyte: the haploid, gamete-producing phase of the plant life cycle.

Gene: one of the determiners of hereditary characteristics, located on chromosomes.

Genetics: the study of heredity and variation.

Genotype: the genetic composition of an organism.

Genus: a taxonomic grouping including one or more species; the official name of an organism consists of its genus and species categories.

Geotropism: a growth movement in response to the influence of gravity.

Germination: the resumption of growth by a seed, spore, or other reproductive structure.

Gills: in certain Basidiomycetes, the platelike structures beneath the cap and on which basidia are borne.

Girdling: the removal of a ring of tissue external to the cambium.

Glucose: a simple sugar, $C_6H_{12}O_6$.

Glycogen: a starchlike carbohydrate found in some plants, especially certain fungi and algae.

Glycolysis: that part of the respiratory process during which glucose is changed anaerobically to pyruvic acid with the production of a small amount of available energy.

Grafting: the joining of two plant parts so that their tissues unite; the joining of scion to stock.

Grain: a dry, one-seeded fruit in which the seed coat is fused with the ovary wall.

Granum: one of the disc-like bodies within the chloroplast; the chlorophyll and carotenoid pigments are located in the grana.

Growth regulator: organic compounds, other than nutrients, which influence growth and development in plants.

Growth ring: see *Annual ring*.

Guard cell: one of the two epidermal cells which enclose a stoma.

Guttation: the exudation of liquid water from plants.

Gymnosperm: a plant in which the seeds are not enclosed in an ovary.

Habitat: the natural environment of an organism; the area in which it is usually found.

Haploid: having one set of chromosomes; the situation (N) characteristic of the gametophyte phase in plants.

Head: a dense cluster of flowers crowded on a common receptacle.

Herb: a non-woody plant, usually with a succulent annual stem.

Herbivorous: plant-eating.

Heredity: the characteristics which are transmitted from parent to progeny.

Heterogamous: producing two kinds of gametes.

Heterosporous: producing two types of spores.

Heterothallic: a condition in which an individual produces only one kind of gamete, usually in reference to fungi and algae; two different types of individuals are necessary for sexual reproduction.

Heterotrophic: organisms which cannot manufacture their own food but must obtain it from some external source.

Heterozygous: when the members of a gene pair are not alike.

Hilum: a scar on the seed where the seed stalk had been attached.

Holdfast: the basal portion of an algal thallus which anchors it to a solid object.

Homologous chromosomes: chromosomes that associate in pairs during meiosis.

Homosporous: producing only one kind of spore.

Homothallic: a condition in which an individual produces two kinds of gametes, usually in reference to fungi and algae.

Homozygous: when the members of a gene pair are alike.

Hormone: an organic substance produced in one part of the plant and which influences reactions in other parts.

Humidity: water vapor content of the atmosphere; *Relative humidity* refers to the amount of water vapor present as a percentage of the amount which would be present if the atmosphere was saturated under similar conditions.

Humus: a complex colloidal mixture of partially decomposed organic matter in the soil.

Hybrid: (1) the progeny of a cross between parents differing in one or more genes; (2) the progeny resulting from a cross between two species.

Hybrid vigor: the increased vitality of progeny which frequently results when inbred lines are crossed.

Hydathode: a pore, usually in leaves at the end of a vein, out of which liquid water may exude slowly.

Hydrolysis: the conversion of a compound into simpler compounds involving the uptake of water; digestion is a hydrolytic reaction.

Hydrophyte: a plant that grows in water or in very wet soils.

Hydroponics: the growth of plants in solutions containing the essential mineral elements.

Hypha: the filament of a fungus.

Hypocotyl: that part of the embryo between the radicle and the point of attachment of the cotyledons.

Hypogynous flower: a flower in which the floral parts are attached below the ovary.

Imbibition: the uptake of water and the resultant swelling of a solid as a result of capillarity and the adsorption of water to the internal surfaces of the solid.

Immunity: resistance to a disease.

Imperfect flower: a flower which has stamens or pistils but not both.

Inbreeding: the breeding of closely related organisms; brings about the homozygous condition.

Inclusion: a non-living structure within the cell.

Incomplete dominance: the condition that results when the hybrid is intermediate in characteristics as compared with the homozygous parents.

Incomplete flower: a flower which lacks one or more of the floral parts.

Independent assortment: the random segregation of two or more pairs of genes to the gametes during meiosis; these gametes later combine at random.

Indusium: a covering over the sorus in ferns.

Inferior ovary: an ovary which has the floral parts arising at the top of the ovary.

Inflorescence: a cluster of flowers.

Inheritance: the transmission of characteristics from parents to progeny.

Integument: the outer layer (frequently two layers) of the ovule which develops into the seed coat.

Internode: the region of the stem between two successive nodes.

Interphase: the stage between mitotic divisions.

Ion: electrically charged atoms or groups of atoms formed by the dissociation (ionization) of a molecule.

Irritability: the ability to respond to a stimulus.

Isogametes: sex cells which are alike.

Isogamy: sexual reproduction in which there is a fusion of isogametes.

Isotope: a form of an element that has the same chemical properties but a different weight from other forms of the same element.

Karyolymph: the more liquid portion of the nucleus.

Kinetic energy: the energy that results from movement of a body; motion energy.

Knot: a portion of the base of a branch which is embedded in wood.

Krebs cycle: a complex, cyclic series of oxidation-reduction reactions during which pyruvic acid is oxidized to carbon dioxide as it loses hydrogens; these latter go through terminal oxidations yielding water; much energy results from these oxidations.

Lamella: see *Middle lamella.*

Lateral bud: a bud in the axil of a leaf; an axillary bud.

Leaf bud: a bud which develops into a stem with leaves.

Leaf gap: an interruption in the continuity of the vascular cylinder caused by the branching of the vascular tissue into the leaf; this area is filled with parenchyma tissue.

Leaf primordium: a small protuberance which develops from the growing point of a bud and which grows into a leaf.

Leaf scar: a scar left on a stem when the leaf falls.

Leaflet: one of the parts constituting the blade of a compound leaf.

Lenticel: a pore in corky tissues of the stem and root.

Leucoplast: a non-pigmented plastid, in which starch is usually formed.

Lignin: a complex organic compound frequently associated with the cellulose of cell walls.

Linkage: the tendency for two or more genes to be inherited together because they are on the same chromosome.

Loam: a type of soil whose excellent garden characteristics are the result of a mixture of sand, silt, clay, and organic matter.

Long-day plant: a plant which flowers only when the illumination exceeds the critical amount.

Macronutrient: a mineral element required in relatively large amounts.

Megagametophyte: the female gametophyte.

Megaphyllous: having large leaves.

Megasporangium: the structure in which megaspores are produced; in angiosperms, frequently called the nucellus.

Megaspore: a haploid spore which develops into a female gametophyte.

Megasporophyll: a modified leaf which bears a megasporangium.

Meiosis: the two divisions during which homologous chromosomes separate and the resultant cells have one-half the number of chromosomes that the original cell contained; there is a reduction from the diploid to the haploid number.

Meristem: a tissue composed of cells that are capable of further divisions.

Mesocarp: the middle layer of the pericarp or fruit wall (ovary wall).

Mesophyll: the parenchyma tissue between the upper and lower epidermis of a leaf; the cells usually contain chloroplasts.

Mesophyte: plant which grows in soils that contain moderate amounts of moisture.

Metabolism: the sum total of the chemical processes that occur in an organism.

Metaphase: the stage of mitosis or meiosis when the chromosomes are at the central region of the cell.

Microgametophyte: the male gametophyte.

Micronutrient: a mineral element required in very small amounts; sometimes called minor elements or trace elements.

Microphyllous: having small leaves.

Micropyle: the small opening in the integuments of an ovule.

Microsporangium: the structure in which microspores are produced.

Microspore: a haploid spore which develops into a male gametophyte.

Microsporophyll: a modified leaf which bears a microsporangium.

Middle lamella: a wall layer, primarily of pectic substances, which is common to two adjoining cells and serves to cement them together; it is located between the primary wall layers.

Mitochondrion: extremely small granular or rod-shaped cytoplasmic body which is the site of the enzymes responsible for the Krebs cycle and terminal oxidation portions of respiration.

Mitosis: nuclear division in which the resultant nuclei have the same number and kind of chromosomes as the original nucleus.

Mixed bud: a bud which develops into both flowers and a stem with leaves.

Monocotyledon: a flowering plant with one cotyledon or seed leaf in the embryo.

Monoecious: having male and female sex structures borne on the same plant.

Monohybrid cross: a cross between organisms differing in a single gene.

Multiple genes: two or more sets of alleles produce more or less equal and cumulative effects on the same characteristic, resulting in a quantitative gradation.

Mutation: a sudden unpredictable change in a gene.

Mycelium: the mass of hyphae which forms the body of a fungus.

Naked bud: a bud without bud scales.

Natural selection: agents other than man determine which individuals will survive; often termed "survival of the fittest."

Nectary: a glandular structure that secretes a sugary liquid.

Net venation: a type of vein arrangement in leaves in which the profusely branching veins form a network of vascular tissue.

Nitrification: the conversion of ammonia or ammonium compounds to nitrites and then to nitrates by the activity of certain soil bacteria.

Nitrogen fixation: the conversion of nitrogen gas into organic nitrogenous compounds by certain microorganisms.

Node: the region of the stem where one or more leaves are attached.

Nodule: enlargements on the roots of certain plants within which are found masses of nitrogen-fixing bacteria.

Nucellus: see *Megasporangium*.

Nucleic acid: the structural units of DNA and RNA.

Nucleolus: the small, spherical, deeply staining body located in the nucleus; probably the center of RNA synthesis.

Nucleoprotein: a substance formed by the combination of protein and nucleic acid.

Nucleus: the more or less spherical protoplasmic structure that contains the chromosomes; it also governs the activities of the cell.

Oögamous: producing a large, non-motile egg and a small sperm.

Oögonium: a one-celled structure in which one or more eggs are produced.

Operculum: in mosses, the lid or cover of the capsule (sporangium).

Order: a taxonomic group including one or more families.

Organic compound: a compound containing carbon.

Osmosis: the net movement of water through a differentially permeable membrane from a region of high diffusion pressure to a region of lower diffusion pressure of water.

Osmotic concentration: the total concentration of solutes.

Osmotic pressure: the maximum pressure which may develop in a solution separated from pure water by a rigid membrane permeable to water only.

Ovary: the enlarged, basal portion of a pistil in which ovules develop.

Ovule: in seed plants, a megasporangium surrounded by one or more integuments; it develops into a seed.

Oxidation: a loss of electrons; in biology, an energy-yielding process usually resulting from a loss of hydrogens or the addition of oxygen to a compound.

Palisade mesophyll: a leaf tissue composed of cylindrical cells containing chloroplasts.

Palmate venation: a type of net venation in which the main veins originate at the base of the leaf blade and radiate outwardly.

Palmately compound leaf: the leaflets are attached at the top of the petiole.

Parallel evolution: similar evolution in different groups of organisms.

Parallel venation: a type of venation in which the main veins of a leaf are parallel or nearly so.

Parasite: a heterotrophic organism that obtains its food from the living tissues of another organism.

Parenchyma: a tissue composed of cells which are thin-walled and basically isodiametric; it is typically a storage tissue which retains meristematic capabilities.

Parthenocarpy: the development of fruit without fertilization.

Parthenogenesis: the development of an embryo from an egg without fertilization.

Pasteurization: the treatment of materials for brief periods at temperatures high enough to kill certain bacteria; the temperatures are not sufficient to kill all bacteria.

Pathogen: a disease-producing organism.

Pedicel: the stalk of one flower in a cluster.

Peduncle: the main stalk of a flower cluster or the stalk of an individual flower.

Penicillin: an antibiotic produced by certain species of *Penicillium,* an Ascomycete.

Perennial: a plant which lives for more than two years; it usually flowers annually after a period of vegetative growth.

Perfect flower: having both stamens and pistil.

Perianth: collective term for the calyx and corolla.

Pericarp: the wall of a fruit (ovary wall).

Pericycle: a parenchyma tissue just outside of the vascular tissue and inside of the endodermis; the branch roots develop from this tissue.

Periderm: collective term for cork, cork cambium, and phelloderm.

Perigynous flower: a flower in which the floral parts are fused and surrounding the ovary but not fused with it.

Peristome: a ring of toothlike structures surrounding the opening of a moss capsule.

Perithecium: a flask-shaped structure with an opening and containing asci; it is composed of hyphae.

Petal: one of the units of the corolla of a flower; frequently showy and conspicuous.

Petiole: the stalk of a leaf.

Phellem: cork (which see).

Phelloderm: a secondary parenchyma tissue formed from the cork cambium on its inner surface.

Phellogen: cork cambium (which see).

Phenotype: the external appearance of an organism.

Phloem: one of the vascular tissues whose main function is the conduction of organic materials.

Phloem ray: that portion of the vascular ray which extends through the secondary phloem.

Photoperiodism: the influence of light exposures of different durations on plant growth and development.

Photosynthesis: the manufacture of food, mainly sugar, from carbon dioxide and water in the presence of chlorophyll utilizing light energy and releasing oxygen gas.

Phototropism: a growth movement in response to the influence of light.

Pileus: the gill-bearing cap of a mushroom (a Basidiomycete).

Pinnate venation: a type of net venation in which the secondary veins arise from each side of a single main vein.

Pinnately compound leaf: the leaflets are attached at intervals along the sides of a common axis.

Pistil: the central structure of the flower, composed of one or more carpels, and enclosing one or more ovules.

Pit: a thin area in the cell wall.

Pith: the parenchyma tissue in the center of a dicotyledonous stem.

Placenta: that portion of the ovary wall to which the ovules are attached.

Plankton: floating or free-swimming aquatic organisms.

Plasma membrane: the outermost layer of cytoplasm; it is differentially permeable.

Plasmodesmata: minute cytoplasmic strands that extend from cell to cell through pores in the cell walls.

Plasmolysis: shrinkage of protoplasm away from the cell wall as a result of water loss.

Plastid: specialized bodies in the cytoplasm; frequently involved in food manufacture and storage.

Plumule: another name for the epicotyl (which see).

Polar nuclei: in angiosperms, the two central nuclei of the female gametophyte; they unite with a sperm to form a triploid endosperm nucleus.

Pollen grain: in seed plants, the young male gametophyte.

Pollen tube: a tubular outgrowth of a pollen grain which carries sperms to the egg in the ovule.

Pollination: in angiosperms, the transfer of pollen from anther to stigma; in gymnosperms, the transfer of pollen from a microsporangium to an ovule.

Polyploid: having more than two sets of chromosomes.

Primary tissue: tissue which develops from an apical meristem.

Primordium: a rudimentary structure; the beginning of a structure.

Procambium: a strand of immature cells, derived from the apical meristem, which differentiates into the primary vascular tissue; also called provascular tissue.

Prophase: the beginning stage of mitosis or meiosis in which the chromosomes become distinct and in which their doubled condition is visible.

Protein: complex, nitrogenous, organic compounds built up from amino acids and composed of carbon, hydrogen, oxygen, and nitrogen, and frequently sulfur and phosphorus.

Prothallus: gametophyte of ferns and similar plants.

Protonema: in mosses and similar plants, the filamentous growth forming the early stage of the gametophyte.

Protoplasm: the living portion of the cell.

Pyrenoid: a proteinaceous body on the chloroplast of certain algae; it is a center for starch formation.

Rachis: the extension of the petiole which bears a leaflet.

Radial section: a longitudinal section cut along a radius.

Radicle: the lower part of an embryo axis; it develops into the primary root of the seedling.

Ray flower: in composites (sunflower family), the marginal flower of a head; it has a strap-shaped corolla.

461

Receptacle: (1) the apex of a flower stalk from which the floral parts arise; (2) the swollen tips of certain brown algae within which sporangia are borne.

Recessive character: (1) a gene whose presence is masked by the presence of its dominant allele; (2) that characteristic whose appearance is excluded by the presence of its contrasting character in a hybrid.

Reduction division: see *Meiosis*.

Respiration: a series of complex oxidation-reduction reactions whereby living cells obtain energy through the breakdown of organic material and in which some of the intermediate materials can be utilized for various syntheses.

Rhizoid: threadlike appendages in some of the lower plant forms which serve as absorbing and anchoring structures.

Rhizome: a horizontal, underground stem; frequently a storage organ.

Ribose nucleic acid (RNA): the nucleic acid found in the nucleolus and cytoplasm; it carries genetic information to the ribosomes where it becomes involved in protein synthesis.

Ribosome: submicroscopic granules located on the endoplasmic reticulum; they are rich in RNA and are the main site for the synthesis of proteins.

RNA: see *Ribose nucleic acid*.

Root cap: a thimblelike, protective mass of cells over the root apex; it develops from the apical meristem of the root.

Root hair: long, tubular outgrowth from an epidermal cell in the lower portion of the region of maturation; it tremendously increases the absorbing surface of the cell.

Saprophyte: a heterotrophic organism which obtains its food from non-living organic matter.

Scion: the shoot which is grafted to a stock.

Sclerenchyma: strengthening tissue composed of thick-walled cells.

Secondary tissue: tissue which develops from a cambium.

Seed: the characteristic reproductive structure of seed plants which is formed from the ovule and the embryo contained therein.

Seed coat: the outer layer of the seed which develops from the integuments of the ovule.

Segregation: the separation of alleles during meiosis.

Self-pollination: the transfer of pollen from an anther to a stigma on the same plant.

Sepal: one of the units of the calyx of a flower, the outermost whorl of flower parts; frequently green and leaflike.

Sessile: lacking a stalk.

Sexual reproduction: involves the fusion of gametes, which is followed eventually by meiosis.

Shoot: collective term for a stem and its leaves.

Short-day plant: a plant which flowers only when the illumination is shorter than the critical amount; the continuous dark period must exceed a critical amount.

Sieve tube: in the phloem, a series of sieve tube elements arranged end to end; functions in conducting organic materials.

Sieve tube element: an elongated phloem cell having perforated end walls (sieve plates).

Silt: mineral particles of the soil which vary in diameter from 0.02 to 0.002 mm.

Simple leaf: a leaf in which the blade is not divided.

Solute: a substance dissolved in a solvent.

Solvent: a liquid in which other substances are dissolved.

Sorus: in ferns, a cluster of sporangia.

Species: the smallest taxonomic grouping of organisms.

Sperm: male gamete.

Spirillum: a curved bacterium.

Spongy mesophyll: a leaf tissue composed of loosely packed, irregular cells containing chloroplasts.

Sporangiophore: the stalk that bears a sporangium.

Sporangium: a structure in which spores are produced.

Spore: an asexual reproductive structure, usually unicellular; in bacteria, it is a resistant structure but not a reproductive body.

Spore mother cell: see *Sporocyte*.

Sporocyte: a diploid (2N) cell which produces four haploid (N) spores as a result of meiosis.

Sporophore: a spore-bearing structure, especially in Basidiomycetes.

Sporophyll: a modified leaf which bears sporangia.

Sporophyte: the diploid, spore-producing phase of the plant life cycle.

Stamen: the pollen-producing structure of the flower, consisting of an anther and a filament.

Staminate cone: in gymnosperms, a cone which produces pollen; more correctly, a microsporangiate or microsporophyllous cone.

Staminate flower: a flower having stamens but no pistil.

Starch: a complex, insoluble carbohydrate built up from many molecules of glucose (sugar), and which is a common storage product in plants.

Stigma: the part of the pistil, usually the apex, which receives pollen.

Stipe: a supporting stalk, as in the brown algae or the Basidiomycetes.

Stipule: an appendage, usually green and leaflike, located near the base of a petiole.

Stock: the stem or root to which a scion is grafted; the basal portion of a graft-union.

Stolon: (1) a slender, horizontal stem which often develops new plants at its nodes; (2) horizontal, surface hypha of certain fungi.

Stoma: the pore or opening between two guard cells in the epidermis.

Strobilus: a cone-shaped aggregation of sporophylls.

Style: that part of the pistil between the stigma and ovary, usually elongated.

Suberin: a waxy substance deposited in certain cell walls, particularly cork cells.

Succession: an orderly sequence of one plant community replacing another until the climax is obtained.

Superior ovary: an ovary situated above the point of attachment of the floral parts.

Symbiosis: an intimate living together of dissimilar organisms.

Synapsis: the pairing of homologous chromosomes during meiosis; since the chromosomes have doubled and four chromatids are present, this pairing represents a tetrad stage.

Synergid: in angiosperms, one of the small cells lying near the egg in the megagametophyte.

Tangential section: a longitudinal section cut at right angles to a radius.

Tap-root system: a root system in which the primary root is larger and more conspicuous than the others.

Teleology: the assigning of a purpose to natural processes.

Telophase: the final stage of mitosis or meiosis during which the chromosomes become organized into two new nuclei; the new cell wall begins forming at this time also.

Tendril: a slender, coiling, supporting structure; usually a modified leaf or stem.

Testa: the seed coat (which see).

Thallus: an undifferentiated plant body without true roots, stems, or leaves.

Tissue: a group of cells, generally of similar structure, which perform a common function.

Toxin: a poisonous substance produced by an organism, stimulates the production of antibodies.

Toxoid: toxin treated to make it non-poisonous but still capable of stimulating the formation of antibodies.

Trace element: see *Micronutrient*.

Tracheid: a conducting and strengthening cell of the xylem; it is elongated, tapering, thick-walled, pitted, and contains no protoplasm.

Translocation: the movement of organic material through the phloem.

Transpiration: the loss of water in vapor form from a plant.

Transverse section: a section cut at right angles to the long axis; a cross section.

Triploid: having three sets of chromosomes.

Tropism: a growth response resulting from an external stimulus.

Tube cell: the elongated cell of the germinating pollen grain.

Tuber: an enlarged portion of a rhizome (underground stem).

Turgid: the plump, swollen condition of a cell resulting from the osmotic uptake of water.

Turgor movement: movements resulting from changes in the turgidity of cells rather than from growth.

Turgor pressure: the actual pressure that develops in a cell as a result of the osmotic uptake of water; this pressure is exerted against the cell wall.

Unicellular: an organism consisting of one cell.

Vaccine: dead or weakened pathogens (bacteria or viruses), or their treated toxins, which are injected into the body to induce active acquired immunity.

Vacuolar membrane: the layer of cytoplasm which borders a vacuole.

Vacuole: a cavity within the cytoplasm containing a solution of various substances.

Vascular bundle: a strand of xylem and phloem, the conducting tissues.

Vascular cambium: a meristematic tissue which produces secondary xylem and secondary phloem.

Vascular ray: ribbonlike mass of parenchyma-type cells extending radially (horizontally) through the secondary xylem and secondary phloem; produced by the vascular cambium.

Vascular tissue: conducting tissue; the xylem and phloem.

Vegetative: concerned with growth, development, and maintenance, rather than with sexual reproduction.

Vegetative reproduction: reproduction by a primarily vegetative part of the plant; not involving fusion of gametes.

Vein: a vascular bundle; usually used in reference to a leaf.

Venation: the arrangement of the vascular bundles in a leaf.

Vessel: a tubelike structure in the xylem composed of a vertical series of cells whose end walls are gone; it conducts water and minerals.

Vessel element: one of the cells of a vessel; somewhat elongated, pitted, thick-walled cell in which the end walls are gone.

Virus: a submicroscopic pathogen that can reproduce only in living host cells; it consists of protein and nucleic acid, a nucleoprotein.

Vitamin: an organic substance which is essential for normal growth and development but is not a food or a source of energy; green plants synthesize their own vitamins.

Wall pressure: the pressure exerted by a cell wall upon the cell contents; it is equal and opposite to the turgor pressure.

Water table: the upper limit of the standing water in a completely saturated soil.

Wilt: a limp or flaccid condition resulting from a deficiency of water and a low turgor pressure within the cells of a structure.

Whorl: a circle of three or more parts.

Wood: the xylem.

Xanthophylls: yellow to orange carotenoid pigments associated with chlorophyll in chloroplasts; also found in some chromoplasts.

Xerophyte: a plant which grows in soils with a scanty water supply.

Glossary   **Xylem:** that component of the vascular tissue which functions primarily to conduct water and minerals.

Xylem ray: that portion of the vascular ray which extends through the secondary xylem.

Zoosporangium: a structure in which zoospores are produced.

Zoospore: a motile spore; in algae and fungi.

Zygote: a diploid cell resulting from the fusion of two gametes; a fertilized egg.

Units of Measurement

Length

1 kilometer = 1,000 meters = km.
1 meter = 10 decimeters = 100 centimeters = 1,000 millimeters = 39.37 inches = m.
1 inch = 2.54 centimeters.
1 decimeter = 10 centimeters = one-tenth of a meter = dm.
1 centimeter = 10 millimeters = one-hundredth of a meter = cm.
1 millimeter = one-tenth of a centimeter = one thousandth of a meter = mm.
1 micron = one-thousandth of a millimeter = one millionth of a meter = μ.

Volume

1 kiloliter = 1,000 liters = kl.
1 liter = 1,000 milliliters = 1000.27 cubic centimeters = 1.056 quarts = l.
1 cubic foot = 7.48 gallons = 28.32 liters.
1 milliliter = one-thousandth of a liter = ml.
   Because the difference between the milliliter (ml) and cubic centimeter (cc) is negligible, no distinction is made between them; therefore, 1 ml = 1 cc.
1 microliter = one-thousandth of a milliliter = one-millionth of a liter = μl.

Weight

1 kilogram = 1,000 grams = kg = kgm = 2.205 pounds avoirdupois.
1 gram = the weight of 1 milliliter of water at 4 degrees centigrade = g = gm.
1 gram = 10 decigrams = 100 centigrams = 1,000 milligrams.
1 pound = 453.6 grams.
1 ounce = 28.35 grams.
1 milligram = one-thousandth of a gram = mg.
1 microgram = one-thousandth of a milligram = one-millionth of a gram = μg = μgm.

Units of Measurement

Temperature

Centigrade = °C. Melting point of ice = 0 degrees at one atmosphere pressure.

Boiling point of water = 100 degrees at one atmosphere pressure.

Fahrenheit = °F. Melting point of ice = 32 degrees at one atmosphere pressure.

Boiling point of water = 212 degrees at one atmosphere pressure.

To convert Centigrade to Fahrenheit degrees: $(°C \times \frac{9}{5}) + 32 = °F$.

To convert Fahrenheit to Centigrade degrees: $(°F - 32) \times \frac{5}{9} = °C$.

General Topics

and Questions

1. Discuss the following statement by Louis Pasteur: "In the realm of observation chance favors only the prepared mind."
2. Discuss the following statement: "Science cannot concern itself with moral issues."
3. Discuss the danger inherent to any insistence that only applied research (i.e., research for practical applications) should be supported.
4. Consider the possibilities of the following statement: "In some areas corn production has been doubled by the practices of soil and water conservation; it has been doubled again by the development and use of improved fertilizers; and it has been doubled a third time by the breeding of superior strains of corn. By these improved farming methods, by the exploitation of atomic energy, and by tapping the productive potential of the sea, we can increase indefinitely the capacity of the world to sustain a high standard of living for an increasing population."

   Present a discussion agreeing or disagreeing with the above statement and including explanations of the biological facts you cite.
5. Groups of similar potato plants of uniform quality were grown in a series of carefully controlled growth chambers as follows:

   (a) Ten plants grown in sand, irrigated with tap water, and held at day temperatures of 25°C. and night temperatures of 15°C.
   (b) Ten plants grown in sand, irrigated with a balanced mineral nutrient solution, and held at day temperatures of 40°C. and night temperatures of 35°C.
   (c) Ten plants grown in sand, irrigated with a balanced mineral nutrient solution, and held at day temperatures of 25°C. and night temperatures of 15°C.
   (d) Ten plants grown in sand, irrigated with a balanced mineral nutrient solution, and held at day temperatures of 40°C. and night temperatures of 15°C.

(e) Ten plants grown in sand, irrigated with tap water, and held at day temperatures of 40°C. and night temperatures of 15°C.

At the end of the growing season the plants were harvested and their tubers weighed with the following results:

(a) = three pounds   (c) = twelve pounds
(b) = two pounds   (d) = ten pounds
(e) = two pounds.

Draw all the logical conclusions from these experiments and in each case describe your reasoning.

6. Biologists have noted that several disease-producing bacteria, formerly controllable by treatment with penicillin, can no longer be checked completely with that antibiotic. A magazine article on this subject quoted a biologist as stating that this fact was not due to a directed adaptation on the part of the bacteria, but was a result of evolution on a small scale.
    Elaborate further upon this explanation.

7. Select one of the topics listed below and discuss in detail the experimental procedure required to solve the problem. The discussion should include methods of obtaining data and the various interpretations that are possible.

(a) The effect of mercury salts on lipase (a fat-digesting enzyme) activity.
(b) The effect of light intensity on the germination of tomato seed.
(c) The effect of temperature on the germination of fern spores.
(d) The presence or absence of auxin in the endosperm of a castor bean.
(e) The factor which is limiting or retarding photosynthesis of a young tobacco plant growing in the greenhouse.

8. Critically discuss the following statement: "Mutations arise so that an organism, or its progeny, may survive adverse environmental conditions."

9. Explain the reasoning behind the following statement: "Most of our machines and engines are powered by photosynthesis."

10. A person who has two kinds of apple trees in his yard (*Delicious* and *Pippin*) was heard to remark: "These *Delicious* apples certainly taste differently since that *Pippin* tree began to flower and bear fruit."
    Explain whether or not there is any basis for the person's statement.

Index

Page numbers in boldface refer to illustrations, graphs, or tables.

471 ⧸❧

473 ଓ